Exam :

D - K    H,

Tues 8:30

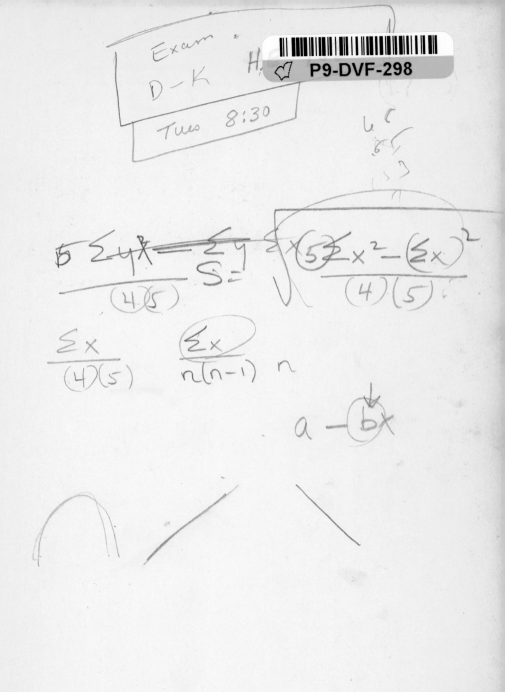

$$5 \frac{\Sigma y \bar{x} - \frac{\Sigma y}{S}}{(4)(5)} \quad S = \sqrt{\frac{(5 \Sigma x^2 - (\Sigma x)^2}{(4)(5)}}$$

$$\frac{\Sigma x}{(4)(5)} \qquad \frac{\Sigma x}{n(n-1)} \quad n$$

$$a - bx$$

MODERN
# ELEMENTARY STATISTICS

PRENTICE-HALL MATHEMATICS SERIES

*Dr. Albert A. Bennett, Editor*

**JOHN E. FREUND**

*Professor of Mathematics*
*Arizona State University*

MODERN

## ELEMENTARY STATISTICS

second edition

**PRENTICE-HALL, INC.** Englewood Cliffs, N. J.

*Library of Congress Catalog Card Number: 60-13107*

*First printing............June, 1960*
*Second printing.......January, 1961*
*Third printing..........June, 1961*
*Fourth printing.........April, 1962*

PRINTED IN THE UNITED STATES OF AMERICA

59342-C

# Preface

Although *Modern Elementary Statistics* has been rewritten almost completely in this edition, its objectives have remained the same: to acquaint beginning students in the natural and social sciences with the fundamentals of modern statistics. Most of the illustrations and exercises are new, distributed as impartially as possible among the various fields of application.

The emphasis and order of some of the material has been changed in line with recent developments in the field of statistics. There is increased emphasis on statistical inference, with three chapters on tests on hypotheses, including one on nonparametric tests; there is also a brief and informal introduction to the subject of decision-making in the face of uncertainty. So far as changes in order are concerned, the introduction to theoretical distributions is delayed until after the chapter on probability, index numbers are included in the part on descriptive statistics as an optional chapter, and the chapter on time series immediately follows those on regression and correlation, consisting at least in part of an application of the material on regression.

Mathematical proofs and derivations are still keyed to the lowest level at which, in the opinion of the author, modern statistics can effectively be taught. Since the mathematical training assumed of the reader is a knowledge of arithmetic and some algebra, many theorems (for example, those relating to sampling distributions) are given without proof but with suitable references in annotated bibliographies.

There have been some changes in symbolism in accordance with developments in the field. Population means are given throughout as $\mu$ instead of $m$ and regression equations are given as $y' = a + bx$ instead of $y' = mx + b$. Another noteworthy change is that $n - 1$ has taken the place of $n$ in the denominator of $s$, the sample standard

v

deviation. This change was suggested, indeed, insisted upon, by many colleagues and most users of the first edition of this text.

The author would like to express his appreciation to his many colleagues and students whose helpful suggestions and criticisms contributed so greatly to the original text as well as this revised edition. The author also would like to express his appreciation to the editorial staff of Prentice-Hall, Inc., for their courteous cooperation in the production of this book and, above all, to his wife, for her cheerful encouragement in spite of the demands made by the revision of this book on her husband's time.

Finally, the author would like to express his appreciation and indebtedness to Professor R. A. Fisher and Messrs. Oliver and Boyd, Ltd., Edinburg, for permission to reprint in Tables II and III parts of Tables III and IV from their book *Statistical Methods for Research Workers;* to Professor E. S. Pearson and the Biometrika trustees for permission to reproduce the material in Tables IV and V; to Henry Holt and Company for permission to reprint Table I; to Professor E. S. Pearson and the Cambridge University Press for permission to reproduce the random numbers of Table VII; and to the Macmillan Company for permission to reprint Table VIII.

JOHN E. FREUND

# Contents

## PART TWO.   PROBABILITY, ESTIMATION, AND TESTS OF HYPOTHESES

PART THREE.  REGRESSION, CORRELATION, AND TIME SERIES

PART ONE

# Descriptive Methods

# Chapter 1

# Introduction

## 1.1 / Introduction

Beginning students in the natural and social sciences, for whom this
book is written, often face the study of statistics with mixed emo-
tions. They know, or at least they are told, that they cannot
proceed to advanced studies in their fields without an understanding
of statistics, but they also remember some of the difficulties which
they experienced in previous contacts with the subject of mathematics. The statement that an understanding of statistics is needed
in the study of science is not an exaggeration; the growth of statistical ideas has been such in recent years that it has made itself felt in
almost every phase of human activity. Statistics no longer consists
merely of the collection and presentation of data in tables and charts;
it encompasses, in fact, *it constitutes the science of decision-making in
the face of uncertainty.* We meet uncertainty when we toss a coin,
when we experiment with a new drug, when we try to decide which
of two production processes is more efficient, when we try to predict
an election, when we market a new product, when we dig for oil, even
when we decide whether to take a trip to the mountains or a seaside
resort. It would be presumptuous to say that statistics, in its present
state of development, can handle *all* situations involving uncertainties, but new methods are being developed all the time and modern
statistics, at least, provides the framework for looking at these
situations in a logical and systematic way.

There can be no doubt that it is practically impossible to understand the meaning and implications of work done in the natural and social sciences without having at least a speaking acquaintance with the subject of statistics. Numerical data derived from surveys, experiments, and other sources form the raw material on which interpretations, analyses, and decisions are based, and it is essential to know how to squeeze usable information from such data. This, in fact, is the major objective of statistics.

Numerous textbooks have been written on business statistics, psychological statistics, educational statistics, medical statistics, agricultural statistics, and so forth. It is true, of course, that these diversified fields of scientific inquiry demand somewhat different and specialized techniques to handle particular problems, but the fundamental principles underlying the various methods are identical regardless of the field of application. It is hoped that this will become evident to the reader once he realizes that *statistical concepts and statistical methods are nothing but a refinement of everyday thinking.*

The approach we shall use in this elementary treatment of statistics is, indeed, keynoted by the above statement. It is our goal to introduce the beginning student in the natural and social sciences to the ideas and concepts that are basic to modern statistics. This in turn — it is hoped — will enable him to gain a better understanding of scientific principles and the scope and limitations of empirical (scientific) knowledge.

As we said before, the study of statistics may be directed toward applications in particular fields of inquiry. Furthermore, the subject may be presented in varying degrees of mathematical refinement and in almost any balance between theory and application. As it is much more important, in our opinion, to understand the meaning and implications of basic ideas than it is to memorize an impressive assortment of formulas, we shall have to sacrifice some of the mathematical detail that is sometimes included in introductory courses in statistics. This is unfortunate in some respects, but it will prevent us from getting lost in an excessive amount of detail which might easily obscure the most important issues. It is hoped that this will avoid the dangerous effect that often results from the indiscriminate application of so-called standard techniques without a thorough understanding of the fundamental ideas that are involved.

It is true, of course, that a limited amount of mathematics is a prerequisite for any statistics course on the college level. Indeed, a thorough study of the theoretical principles of statistics would require a knowledge of mathematical subjects covered ordinarily only on the graduate level. Since this book is intended for students with relatively little background in mathematics, our aims and, therefore, also our prerequisites are considerably more modest.

Actually, the mathematics needed for this study of elementary statistics is amply covered in college algebra or any equivalent course on the freshman level; even a good knowledge of high school algebra provides a sufficient foundation. Besides having a reasonable skill in arithmetic, it will help the reader to have some familiarity with substituting numbers into formulas, representing numbers with symbols such as $x$, $y$, and $z$, solving simple equations, using the functional notation, and using simple mathematical tables. To help the reader in connection with this, the use of square root tables is explained in Appendix III and calculations with rounded numbers are discussed in Appendix II.

## 1.2 / Descriptive and Inductive Statistics

Everything dealing even remotely with the collection, processing, analysis, interpretation, and presentation of numerical data may be classified as belonging to the domain of statistics. It includes such diversified tasks as calculating a baseball player's batting average, the collection and presentation of data on births and deaths, the evaluation of the reliability of missiles, and even the study of laws governing the behavior of atomic particles in what is called statistical mechanics.

The word *statistics* itself is used in a variety of ways. In the plural it denotes a collection of numerical data such as those found in the financial pages of newspapers or, say, the *Statistics Abstract of the United States*. A second meaning of *statistics*, also in the plural, is that of the totality of methods employed in the collection and analysis of numerical data or as we said before, more broadly, that of the science of decision-making in the face of uncertainty. In this sense, statistics is a branch of applied mathematics and it is this field of mathematics which is the subject matter of this book. In order to complete this linguistic analysis of the word *statistics*, let us also mention that *statistic*, in the singular, is used to denote a particular measure or formula such as an average, an index number, or a coefficient of correlation, calculated on the basis of given data.

It has been the custom to divide statistics into the fields of *descriptive* and *inductive* statistics, although this division is becoming less and less distinct. By *descriptive statistics*, or better, *descriptive statistical methods*, we shall understand any treatment of numerical data that does not involve generalizations. In contrast, we shall speak of *inductive statistics* or *statistical inference* the very moment we make generalizations, predictions, estimations, or more generally decisions in the face of uncertainty. (The distinction between descriptive and inductive statistics is becoming less pronounced because the ultimate, though perhaps not the immediate, purpose of collecting and presenting data is to make some sort of decision.)

To clarify the distinction between descriptive and inductive methods with an example, let us suppose that two students, Smith and Jones, have taken three tests in a certain subject and that Smith received grades of 63, 41, and 55, while Jones received 60, 58, and 59. On the basis of this information we can say that Smith had an *average* of

$$\frac{63 + 41 + 55}{3} = 53$$

and that Jones had an *average* of

$$\frac{60 + 58 + 59}{3} = 59$$

What we have done with these numbers belongs to the domain of *descriptive statistics:* we followed simple arithmetical rules in calculating the two averages which are, indeed, descriptive of the two sets of grades. However, if we now conclude on the basis of these averages that Jones is the better student, we are making a generalization, a *statistical inference*, and we find ourselves in the domain of *inductive statistics*. So long as we restricted ourselves to the calculation of the two averages, we did not add anything to the given information, we merely rearranged it in a different and possibly more useful form. This is characteristic of descriptive statistics. As soon as we generalized by saying that Jones is the better student, we said more than we were given in the original data and this, in turn, is characteristic of inductive statistics. It does not follow by any means that Jones is necessarily the better student. Smith might have had an off day when he took the second test, he might have been ill, or Jones might have been plain lucky in studying the right material for the tests or in guessing some of the answers. We thus face uncertainties, and if we say that Jones is the better student we may or may not be correct. *The careful evaluation, analysis, and control of the chances that must be taken when making such generalizations (or decisions) is one of the main tasks of inductive statistics.*

When thinking about the above example, there are many questions that immediately come to one's mind. For instance, if the difference between the two averages had been very large, say, if Smith had averaged 23 and Jones 95, we might have been inclined to say that Jones is the better student without going through much of a statistical analysis. Similarly, if the difference had been very small, say, if Smith had averaged 58 and Jones 59, we probably would have been extremely reluctant to say that Jones is actually a better student. *But what if the difference on which the decision has to be based is neither "very large" nor "very small" — where do we draw the line?* Also, how do we know that 3 test scores for each student provide enough information to reach any conclusion whatsoever? Would it not have been better, or necessary, to give them 5 tests or, perhaps, 10? These are important questions, the kind we shall be able to answer with the methods of inductive statistics.

*WHAT SIZE OF DIFFERENCE*

*How many Samples*

There is another point which is extremely important whenever we want to make generalizations like the one concerning the ability of the two students; *we must ask ourselves whether the data were obtained in such a way (the survey or experiment conducted in such a way) that generalizations are at all possible.* For instance, if Jones had been told what chapters to study for the tests and Smith had not, it is obvious that no reasonable, or meaningful, comparison is possible.

*How was data obtained*

We made the last point to stress the fact that in statistics we do not merely concern ourselves with looking at sets of data, performing certain calculations, and arriving at conclusions. The questions *how the data were collected* and *how the whole experiment or survey was planned* are of major importance. Unless proper care is taken in the planning of experiments, surveys, or other kinds of investigations, it may be impossible to arrive at any valid results whatsoever.

Generally speaking, we shall use the terms *descriptive statistics* and *inductive statistics* with reference to the kinds of problems we wish to solve, not with reference to particular formulas. Thus, Part One of this book is titled "Descriptive Methods" although, we must admit, even here we shall frequently allude to problems of inference.

As we pointed out earlier, the distinction is becoming less pronounced, and in most recently published texts the emphasis is shifting more and more to problems of inductive statistics.

### 1.3 / Subscripts and Summations

Since the formulas which we shall study in subsequent chapters must be applicable to different kinds of data, we shall have to represent the figures (measurements or observations) to which the formulas are to be applied with some general symbols such as $x$, $y$, and $z$. However, unless we modify this symbolism slightly, there will be immediate complications; for example, if we tried to assign a different letter to the age of each person living in New York City, we would use up the English, Greek, Russian, and Hebrew alphabets, accommodating only a minute fraction of these data. This is why we shall follow the practice of using *subscripts*, writing, for example, $x_1$, $x_2$, and $x_3$ for the three grades obtained by Jones in the illustration of the preceding section. Similarly, we could use $y_1$, $y_2$, and $y_3$ for the grades obtained by Smith, using different letters to distinguish between the grades obtained by these individuals. If we want to refer to these grades in general we can, so to speak, use variable subscripts and write $x_i$ or $y_j$, where $i$ and $j$ can both equal 1, 2, or 3.

Instead of writing the subscripts as $i$ and $j$ we could just as well have used other letters such as $k$, $l$, $m$, $\ldots$, and instead of $x$ and $y$ we could also have used other letters or symbols. Generally speaking, *it is customary to use different letters for different kinds of measurements and different subscripts for measurements of the same kind.* Thus, we might write $x_{31}$ and $x_{57}$ for the weights of the thirty-first and fifty-seventh persons on a list, and we might write $x_{15}$, $y_{15}$, and $z_{15}$ for, say, the intelligence quotient, age, and income of the fifteenth person in a certain sample.

To simplify formulas which will be applied to large sets of data, let us also introduce the symbol $\sum$ (capital Greek *sigma*, standing for the letter S) which is merely a mathematical shorthand notation. By definition

$$\sum_{i=1}^{n} x_i = x_1 + x_2 + x_3 + \ldots + x_n$$

and it reads "the summation of the $x$'s with $i$ going from 1 to $n$."

In other words, $\sum_{i=1}^{n} x_i$ stands for the *sum* of the $x$'s having the subscripts 1, 2, 3, ..., and $n$. We can thus also write

$$\sum_{i=1}^{4} x_i^2 = x_1^2 + x_2^2 + x_3^2 + x_4^2$$

$$\sum_{i=2}^{6} x_i y_i = x_2 y_2 + x_3 y_3 + x_4 y_4 + x_5 y_5 + x_6 y_6$$

To simplify the appearance of formulas which would otherwise seem rather unwieldy, we sometimes omit the subscripts and write the sum of the $x$'s simply as $\sum x$. In this abbreviated notation it must be understood, of course, what $x$'s we are referring to, how many there are, etc.

Since summations will appear in many formulas, it should be helpful to the reader to study some of their fundamental arithmetical rules. Three of these, with proofs, are given in Appendix I. Later, we shall also have the occasion to use *double subscripts* and *double summations;* these will be explained as soon as the need for their use arises in Chapter 12.

## EXERCISES

**1.** Write each of the following in full, that is, without summation signs:

(a) $\sum_{i=1}^{6} x_i = x_1 + x_2 + x_3 + x_4 + x_5 + x_6$    (d) $\sum_{i=1}^{4} (x_i - 3) = (x_1 - 3) + (x_2 - 3) + (x_3 - 3) + (x_4 - 3)$

(b) $\sum_{i=2}^{4} x_i^2 = (x_2)^2 + (x_3)^2 + (x_4)^2$    (e) $\sum_{j=3}^{7} x_j y_j z_j = (x_3 y_3 z_3) + (x_4 y_4 z_4) + (x_5 y_5 z_5) + (x_6 y_6 z_6) + (x_7 y_7 z_7)$

(c) $\sum_{j=1}^{3} (x_j + y_j) = (x_1 + y_1) + (x_2 + y_2) + (x_3 + y_3)$    (f) $\sum_{i=1}^{5} x_i^2 f_i = (x_1^2 f_1) + (x_2^2 f_2) + (x_3^2 f_3) + (x_4^2 f_4) + (x_5^2 f_5)$

**2.** Write each of the following as summations:

(a) $x_3 + x_4 + x_5 + x_6 + x_7 + x_8 + x_9 + x_{10}$ $= \sum_{i=3}^{10} x_i$

(b) $x_1 f_1 + x_2 f_2 + \ldots + x_8 f_8$ $= \sum_{i=1}^{8} x_i f_i$

(c) $(x_1 - z_1) + (x_2 - z_2) + \ldots + (x_m - z_m) = \sum_{i=1}^{m} (x_i - z_i)$

(d) $x_2^3 y_2 + x_3^3 y_3 + x_4^3 y_4 + \ldots x_9^3 y_9 = \sum_{i=2}^{9} x_i^3 y_i$

**3.** Given $x_1 = 4$, $x_2 = -2$, $x_3 = 2$, $x_4 = 1$, $x_5 = 3$, $y_1 = 5$, $y_2 = -3$,

$y_3 = 8, y_4 = 10, y_5 = -5, f_1 = 1, f_2 = 6, f_3 = 18, f_4 = 10$, and $f_5 = 3$, evaluate each of the following:

(a) $\sum_{i=1}^{5} x_i$ $= 8$

(b) $\sum_{i=1}^{3} y_i$ $= 10$

(c) $\sum_{i=1}^{5} x_i f_i$ $= 47$

(d) $\sum_{i=2}^{3} x_i^2$ $= 8$

(e) $\sum_{i=1}^{5} (x_i + y_i)$ $= 23$

(f) $\sum_{i=3}^{5} x_i^2 y_i$ $-3$

**4.** Check whether it is true in general that $\left[\sum_{i=1}^{n} x_i\right]^2 = \sum_{i=1}^{n} x_i^2$. (*Hint:* try $n = 2$.)    NO

(a) $\sum_{i=1}^{5} x_i = x_1 + x_2 + x_3 + x_4 + x_5$

$(4) + (-2) + (2) + (1) + (3) = 8$

#4 When $n = 2$

$\left[\sum_{i=1}^{2} x_i\right]^2 = (x_1 + x_2)^2 = x_1^2 + 2x_1 x_2 + x_2^2$

$\sum_{i=1}^{2} x_i^2 = x_1^2 + x_2^2$

$x_1^2 + 2x_1 x_2 + x_2^2 \neq x_1^2 + x_2^2$

Chapter **2**

# Frequency Distributions

## 2.1 / Introduction

Grouping, classifying, and thus describing measurements and observations is as basic in statistics as it is in science and in many activities of everyday life. To illustrate its importance in statistics, let us consider the problem of an economist who wants to study personal income of families in the United States. Not giving a thought to the possibility of conducting a survey of his own — the expense would be staggering assuming even that it would yield the information he needs — he immediately turns to one of the many organizations that specialize in the gathering of statistical data, namely, the U. S. Department of Commerce. This department not only provides government agencies with statistical data needed for over-all planning and day-by-day operations, but it also makes this information available to businessmen and research workers in various fields. Like other organizations engaged in gathering statistical data, it thus faces the problem of *how to present* the results of its surveys in the most effective and the most usable form. With reference to the information needed by the above-mentioned economist, the Department of Commerce *could* print sheets containing millions of numbers, the actual personal incomes reported by individual families; it is needless to say, however, that this would not be very effective and, directly, not very "usable."

When dealing with large sets of numbers, a good over-all picture and sufficient information can often be conveyed by grouping the data into a number of classes, and the Department of Commerce could, and in fact does, publish its data on personal income in tables like the following for the year 1953:

| Personal Income (dollars) | Number of Families (thousands) |
|---|---|
| under 1,000 | 2,866 |
| 1,000 – 1,999 | 5,433 |
| 2,000 – 2,999 | 6,488 |
| 3,000 – 3,999 | 7,399 |
| 4,000 – 4,999 | 7,247 |
| 5,000 – 5,999 | 6,276 |
| 6,000 – 7,499 | 6,240 |
| 7,500 – 9,999 | 4,834 |
| 10,000 – 14,999 | 2,273 |
| 15,000 and over | 1,494 |

This kind of table is called a *frequency distribution;* it shows how the 1953 family incomes are distributed among the various income groups. (Omitting the word "frequency," frequency distributions are often referred to simply as distributions.)

Although frequency distributions present data in a relatively compact form, give a good over-all picture, and contain information that is adequate for many purposes, they do omit some of the facts. For example, by looking at the above distribution one cannot tell whether any of the families had incomes over $50,000, whether there was a family with an income of exactly $4,375.28, or how many families had incomes, say, between $6,250 and $6,499. In order to recover any such information, it would be necessary to go back to the *raw data* ("raw" in the sense that they have not yet been subjected to any kind of statistical treatment) in the files of the Department of Commerce.

In the study of frequency distributions it is customary to distinguish between *numerical* and *categorical* distributions. A distribution is said to be *numerical* if the data are grouped according to numerical size. The personal income distribution given above is a numerical distribution, where the family incomes are classified according to size, and so is the following distribution obtained in a study in which it was pertinent to measure the widths of female crabs:

| Widths (millimeters) | Number of Female Crabs |
|---|---|
| 10.0 – 29.9 | 43 |
| 30.0 – 49.9 | 69 |
| 50.0 – 69.9 | 186 |
| 70.0 – 89.9 | 144 |
| 90.0 – 109.9 | 96 |
| 110.0 – 129.9 | 66 |
| 130.0 – 149.9 | 46 |
| 150.0 – 169.9 | 73 |
| 170.0 – 189.9 | 34 |

A distribution is said to be _categorical_ if the data are sorted into categories according to some qualitative description rather than numerical size. (Categorical distributions are also called _qualitative_ distributions and, correspondingly, numerical distributions are also called _quantitative_ distributions.) Categorical distributions can be obtained by classifying individuals according to occupation, cars according to make or color, dogs according to breed, TV shows according to type, and so on. The following is a categorical distribution pertaining to the 1955 immigration to the United States from other American countries:

| Last Permanent Residence | Number of Immigrants |
|---|---|
| Canada | 32,435 |
| Mexico | 43,702 |
| Central America | 3,667 |
| South America | 7,654 |
| West Indies | 12,876 |
| Others | 10,102 |

SOURCE: _Statistical Abstract of the United States 1956_

In Sections 2.2 and 2.3 we shall discuss some general problems connected with the construction of numerical distributions, various modifications, and the presentation of numerical distributions in graphical form. In Section 2.4 we shall study categorical distributions and, later, in Section 15.4 we shall go into the problem of grouping _paired_ data into _two-way_ frequency distributions. By paired data we mean, for example, the heights and weights of a number of guinea pigs, the ages and pulse rates of a number of persons, the production costs and sales prices of a number of manufactured products, and so forth.

Although frequency distributions serve primarily to present large sets of data in a relatively compact form, making it possible to include information about basic data in reports, theses, and other kinds of publications, numbers are sometimes grouped solely to simplify the calculation of further statistical descriptions. We shall go into this in Sections 3.3, 3.4, 4.4, and 15.4, but it is worth noting that this function of frequency distributions is becoming less important in view of the increasing availability of high-speed computing equipment.

## 2.2 / Numerical Distributions

The process of constructing a frequency distribution consists essentially of three steps: we must choose the classes into which the data are to be grouped, sort the data by putting a check for each item into the appropriate class, and finally count the number of items in each class. (If the data are recorded on punch-cards, a method that is nowadays widely used for the handling of mass data, the sorting and counting can be done automatically in a single step.) Since the last two steps are purely mechanical, let us concentrate on the first, namely, that of choosing appropriate classifications.

One thing which should always be remembered is that the selection of a grouping or classification is essentially arbitrary, and that it will have to depend largely on the ultimate purpose the distribution is supposed to serve. Hence, it is difficult to provide general instructions that should invariably be followed, and most of the rules that we shall mention merely reflect what is considered to be sound practice.

In the construction of a numerical distribution we will always have to decide first into *how many classes* the data are to be grouped and from *where to where each class is to go*, that is, the range of values each class is to contain. The first of these decisions is partly a matter of judgment, the choice of 3, 5, 10, or 20 classes will have to depend to some extent on what we intend to do with the grouped data, but it also depends on the total range of values to be covered and, above all, on the actual number of items that are to be grouped. Clearly, if a set of data contains only 12 numbers, there is nothing to be gained by grouping them into 20 classes, many of which would have to be empty. On the other hand, we might be losing too much information if we grouped these 12 numbers into as few as 2 classes. In actual practice we would ordinarily not even think of grouping 12 numbers, and we only meant to illustrate that too many classes can make a distribution unwieldy, thus defeating its purpose, while too few classes may lead to too great a loss of information.

Referring again to the income distribution on page 12, we could have grouped the data into intervals of $10, but we would then have needed hundreds of classes, and the resulting distribution could hardly be described as providing an easy-to-use picture of the over-all situation. We could also have grouped them as follows:

| Personal Income (dollars) | Number of Families (thousands) |
|---|---|
| under 1,000 | 2,866 |
| 1,000 – 14,999 | 46,190 |
| 15,000 and over | 1,494 |

but it must be apparent that (for many practical purposes) this does not give much relevant information. To state some general rule, we might say that _there are few occasions requiring the use of fewer than 6 classes or more than 15,_ but it must be understood that this merely comes under the heading of "sound practice based on experience."

*usually from 6 – 15 Classes*

To consider a concrete example, let us take the following data representing the speeds (in miles per hour) with which 200 west-bound cars passed a checkpoint on U. S. 66 in Arizona between the hours of 8 A.M. and 2 P.M. (based on data provided by the Arizona State Highway Department):

| | | | | | | | | | |
|---|---|---|---|---|---|---|---|---|---|
| 52 | 47 | 50 | 54 | 59 | 63 | 67 | 57 | 55 | 48 |
| 54 | 35 | 53 | 58 | 47 | 53 | 52 | 61 | 54 | 53 |
| 49 | 46 | 56 | 43 | 57 | 45 | 53 | 28 | 42 | 55 |
| 60 | 56 | 61 | 55 | 55 | 51 | 56 | 37 | 53 | 51 |
| 55 | 47 | 51 | 52 | 48 | 60 | 44 | 49 | 57 | 62 |
| 40 | 53 | 57 | 46 | 57 | 62 | 53 | 57 | 47 | 45 |
| 58 | 48 | 50 | 53 | 54 | 44 | 52 | 50 | 55 | 50 |
| 55 | 61 | 47 | 63 | 49 | 59 | 54 | 59 | 46 | 56 |
| 51 | 54 | 63 | 53 | 53 | 47 | 54 | 38 | 41 | 49 |
| 57 | 48 | 30 | 42 | 56 | 49 | 46 | 56 | 60 | 55 |
| 45 | 47 | 44 | 52 | 54 | 59 | 56 | 49 | 58 | 43 |
| 60 | 52 | 58 | 55 | 61 | 51 | 50 | 48 | 50 | 54 |
| 56 | 51 | 46 | 46 | 58 | 38 | 52 | 55 | 51 | 52 |
| 52 | 42 | 53 | 60 | 45 | 48 | 56 | 50 | 46 | 53 |
| 54 | 51 | 47 | 56 | 54 | 54 | 52 | 57 | 53 | 43 |
| 59 | 55 | 62 | 50 | 47 | 59 | 66 | 53 | 49 | 74 |
| 53 | 53 | 56 | 51 | 49 | 53 | 58 | 44 | 55 | 64 |
| 65 | 65 | 45 | 57 | 52 | 46 | 52 | 57 | 48 | 58 |
| 56 | 55 | 48 | 53 | 54 | 51 | 56 | 64 | 68 | 54 |
| 44 | 53 | 54 | 58 | 49 | 61 | 55 | 50 | 47 | 55 |

Before making a decision about the number of classes into which these speeds are to be grouped, let us briefly consider some of the factors that must always be taken into account. It surely would be embarassing if after selecting a classification we were to discover that it does not accommodate all of our data. To avoid this, we usually begin by looking for the smallest and largest values, which in our example are 28 and 74 mph, respectively. At the same time we note that the entire classification will have to cover an interval of $74 - 28 = 46$ units. This indicates that if we were to use *five* classes, each would have to cover an interval close to 10 and we might choose classes going from 25 to 34, 35 to 44, 45 to 54, 55 to 64, and 65 to 74. If we used *eight* classes, each would have to cover an interval close to 6 and we might choose classes going from 28 to 33, 34 to 39, 40 to 45, 46 to 51, 52 to 57, 58 to 63, 64 to 69, and 70 to 75. Also, if we used *ten* classes, each would have to cover an interval of close to 5 and we could choose classes going from 25 to 29, 30 to 34, 35 to 39, 40 to 44, 45 to 49, 50 to 54, 55 to 59, 60 to 64, 65 to 69, and 70 to 74.

Actually, it is not absolutely necessary that the classes we choose have all equal lengths; they need not cover equal ranges of values and those of the income distribution on page 12 do not. However, there are several reasons why it is desirable that *equal class intervals (classes of equal length) be used whenever feasible.* Frequency distributions with equal classes are not only easier to read and sometimes easier to construct, but as we shall see in Sections 2.3 and 3.3, they also lend themselves more readily to graphical presentations and the calculation of further statistical descriptions.

If in our example we used the five classes going from 25 to 34, 35 to 44, . . ., we would find that all but 25 (or 87.5 per cent) of the values fall into two classes, the ones from 45 to 54 and 55 to 64, and it would seem that we might thus be losing too much information about the bulk of our data. Choosing instead the ten classes mentioned above, the ones going from 25 to 29, 30 to 34, . . ., let us now perform the tally, showing our work in the table on page 17. The tally shown in the middle of this table helps in the construction of the frequency distribution, but it is generally omitted in the final presentation of the distribution. The numbers shown in the right-hand column are called the *class frequencies;* they give the number of cases falling into each class.

When we decided to use ten classes, we might have been tempted

| Speed (miles per hour) | Tally | Number of Cars |
|---|---|---|
| 25 – 29 | / | 1 |
| 30 – 34 | / | 1 |
| 35 – 39 | //// | 4 |
| 40 – 44 | //// //// /// | 13 |
| 45 – 49 | //// //// //// //// //// //// //// //// | 40 |
| 50 – 54 | //// //// //// //// //// //// //// //// //// //// //// //// //// | 65 |
| 55 – 59 | //// //// //// //// //// //// //// //// //// //// // | 52 |
| 60 – 64 | //// //// //// /// | 18 |
| 65 – 69 | //// | 5 |
| 70 – 74 | / | 1 |

to choose classes ranging from 25 to 30, 30 to 35, 35 to 40, . . ., but
it would immediately have become apparent that this causes
difficulties in classifying such values as 30, 35, 40, etc. Each of these
values could rightfully be placed into either of two classes, and in
order to eliminate ambiguities of this kind let us state, specifically,
that *overlapping classes must always be avoided*. By overlapping
classes we mean classes having one or more values in common. This
rule was followed in the construction of the distribution on page 12,
and had the classes been

Personal Income
(dollars)

under 1,000
1,000 – 2,000
2,000 – 3,000
3,000 – 4,000
. . .

there would have been ambiguities about values equalling exactly
$2,000, $3,000, $4,000, etc.

As we mentioned earlier, it would be embarassing to construct
a classification that does not accommodate all of our data. Although
it is necessary to make sure that the smallest and largest items are
covered, this by itself is not enough. We must also make sure that
there are no *gaps* between the classes into which one or more values
might conceivably fall. Had the speeds in our illustration been

measured to the nearest *tenth* of a mile, there would have been no place in our classification for such values as 29.6, 44.5, 64.3, to mention but a few. An appropriate modification would have been to write

*Speed*
(miles per hour)

| |
| --- |
| 25.0 – 29.9 |
| 30.0 – 34.9 |
| 35.0 – 39.9 |
| 40.0 – 44.9 |
| . . . |

Similarly, if the personal incomes of the distribution on page 12 had been given to the nearest cent, there would have been no place to put values such as $1,999.27 and $4,999.52, and it would have been necessary to adjust the classes to read

*Personal Income*
(dollars)

| |
| --- |
| under 1,000.00 |
| 1,000.00 – 1,999.99 |
| 2,000.00 – 2,999.99 |
| 3,000.00 – 3,999.99 |
| . . . |

In this modified classification there is a unique class to accommodate each figure given to the nearest cent.

Since the choice of a classification is arbitrary to some extent, there is really nothing to prevent us from using an alternate classification in the speed-check example in which there are *eight* classes going from 27 to 32, 33 to 38, 39 to 44, 45 to 50, 51 to 56, 57 to 62, 63 to 68, and 69 to 74. These classes are all equal, they do not overlap, and they accommodate all of the data. Nevertheless, this alternate classification has the undesirable features that the tally would be more tedious and the resulting table more difficult to read. (The first of these disadvantages is of special importance if the work is done with automatic equipment where the sorting is done on one or more suitable columns of digits.) Generally speaking, *it is desirable to use classifications with equal classes that are, from this point of view, easy to construct and easy to use.*

We could have phrased the last sentence to say that the *class limits* should be such that the tally is easy to perform and the resulting table easy to read. By definition, the smallest and largest values falling into a class are referred to as its class limits or, more specifically, as its *lower* and *upper class limits*. In the speed-check distribution on page 17 the limits of the first class are 25 and 29, those of the second class are 30 and 34, ..., and those of the last class are 70 and 74. Similarly, the lower class limits of the width-of-crabs distribution on page 13 are 10.0, 30.0, 50.0, ..., while the upper class limits are 29.9, 49.9, 69.9, ...

If we plotted the class limits which were actually used in the speed-check example on a scale, we would discover (see Figure 2.1)

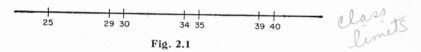

Fig. 2.1

that there are gaps between the successive classes. In Figure 2.1 there is a gap between 29 and 30, another between 34 and 35, a third between 39 and 40, and so forth. From a practical point of view this really does not matter since the speeds are given to the nearest mile and cannot possibly fall into the gaps. However, since there are some problems in which it will be preferable to eliminate these gaps (see page 31, Section 3.4, and Section 8.1), let us use the artificial device of "splitting the difference" and incorporating half of each gap into each of the two adjacent classes. Spreading, in this fashion, the classes of the speed-check example over a *continuous*

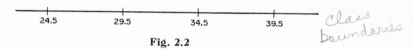

Fig. 2.2

scale, we shall say that the first class goes from 24.5 to 29.5, the second from 29.5 to 34.5, ..., and the last from 69.5 to 74.5 (see Figure 2.2.).

The dividing lines between successive classes thus spread over a continuous scale are referred to as their *class boundaries* or sometimes as their *"true" class limits*. In the speed-check example the *lower* boundary of the first class is 24.5 and its *upper* boundary is 29.5. Similarly, the lower boundary of the fourth class of this distribution is 39.5 and the upper boundary of the eight class is 64.5.

In the width-of-crabs example on page 13 the midpoints of the gaps between successive classes are 29.95, 49.95, 69.95, ..., and the class boundaries are 9.95, 29.95, 49.95, ..., and 189.95. It should be noted that the first and last values were obtained by proceeding as if there were additional classes preceding the first and following the last. Incidentally, if the classification used in the width-of-crab example had been

| Width (millimeters) |
| --- |
| 0.0 – 19.9 |
| 20.0 – 39.9 |
| 40.0 – 59.9 |
| . . . |

the boundaries of the first class would have been −0.05 and 19.95. Of course, the width of a crab cannot be negative and it must be remembered that class boundaries are used as an artificial device to spread classes over continuous scales.

The length of a class interval, or simply the *class interval*, is by definition the difference between the upper and lower boundaries of a class. In the speed-check example the class interval is 5, the same for each class, and in the width-of-crab example it is 20, again the same for each class. In the personal income distribution on page 12 the second, third, fourth, fifth, and sixth classes have intervals of $1,000, the seventh class has an interval of $1,500, the eighth an interval of $2,500, and the ninth an interval of $5,000. As can be seen from the various examples, the lengths of class intervals are also given by the differences between successive upper (or lower) class limits.

*Class marks* are by definition the midpoints between the boundaries (or limits) of the various classes belonging to a classification. They are obtained by averaging the respective boundaries or limits, that is, by adding them and then dividing by 2. In the speed-check example the class marks are $\frac{25 + 29}{2} = 27, \frac{30 + 34}{2} = 32,$ $\frac{35 + 39}{2} = 37$, etc., and in the width-of-crabs example the class marks are $\frac{10.0 + 29.9}{2} = 19.95, \frac{30.0 + 49.9}{2} = 39.95$, etc.

When distributions contain a few values that are much greater (or much smaller) than the rest, the number of classes needed can often be reduced and the over-all picture simplified by the use of so-called *open classes*. This was done in the personal income distribution on page 12, where the first class read "under $1,000" and the last read "$15,000 and over." Generally speaking, a class is said to be open if, instead of having definite class limits or boundaries, it reads "... or more," "... or less," "greater than ...," or "less than ..."

To consider an example where an open class might profitably be used, let us suppose that in the speed-check example the highest speed had been 98 instead of 74, all other values remaining unchanged. Using the same kind of classification as on page 17, we would have to add classes going from 75 to 79, 80 to 84, 85 to 89, 90 to 94, 95 to 99, and all but the last would have a frequency of zero. In order to avoid having so many *empty* classes, we could change the entire classification using, say, classes going from 20 to 29, 30 to 39, ..., and 90 to 99, but we would then find that the majority of our data falls into two classes and this could very well hide too much relevant information. To avoid this, we could change the last class of the original distribution to read "70 or more," and this would accommodate the one high value without requiring further modifications. (Incidentally, if one or very few values fall into an open class, it is advisable to list the exact values in a footnote. This will often add to the usefulness of a distribution.)

Beside their obvious advantages, open classes unfortunately have also some definite disadvantages. As we illustrated above, their main advantage lies in the fact that they can accommodate a wide range of values without requiring too many classes, or classes that hide too much relevant information. Their worst feature is that they do not tell us how much "greater than" or "less than" a given value might be. In the speed-check example, a speed of "70 miles or more" could be 70, 82, 94, or, for all we know, even over 100. Classifications with open classes have the additional disadvantage that they do not lend themselves to the most common types of graphical presentations (see page 29), and that they cannot be used to calculate certain kinds of statistical descriptions (see page 52). While on the subject of open classes, we might add that a distribution can have an open class at either end or, for that matter, at both ends.

Since speed checks are made by highway departments to provide bases for decisions concerning the widening of pavements, banking of curves, posting of limits, or perhaps to support legislation, it may be more relevant to know how many cars went above or below certain speeds than how many cars are in each class of the distribution on page 17. To accommodate these and similar needs, the speed-check distribution (or any distribution) can readily be *cumulative*

converted into a *cumulative "less than"* or a *cumulative "or more"*
*distribution.*

To illustrate the meaning of these terms, let us first construct a
cumulative "less than" distribution for the speed-check data.
Using the distribution on page 17, this will not require very much
work: as can be seen by inspection, *none* of the cars went under 25,
*one* traveled at less than 30 mph, while $1 + 1 = 2$ went under 35.
Adding, thus, the class frequencies, we find that $1 + 1 + 4 = 6$
cars went under 40 mph, $1 + 1 + 4 + 13 = 19$ went under 45 mph,
$1 + 1 + 4 + 13 + 40 = 59$ went under 50 mph, and so on. The
resulting cumulative "less than" distribution looks as follows:

| Speed (miles per hour) | Number of Cars |
|---|---|
| less than 25 | 0 |
| less than 30 | 1 |
| less than 35 | 2 |
| less than 40 | 6 |
| less than 45 | 19 |
| less than 50 | 59 |
| less than 55 | 124 |
| less than 60 | 176 |
| less than 65 | 194 |
| less than 70 | 199 |
| less than 75 | 200 |

Had we wanted to show how many cars went *above* or, better,
*not below* certain speeds, we could have added the frequencies
beginning at the other end of the distribution, and we would have
obtained the following "or more" distribution:

| Speed (miles per hour) | Number of Cars |
|---|---|
| 25 or more | 200 |
| 30 or more | 199 |
| 35 or more | 198 |
| 40 or more | 194 |
| 45 or more | 181 |
| 50 or more | 141 |
| 55 or more | 76 |
| 60 or more | 24 |
| 65 or more | 6 |
| 70 or more | 1 |
| 75 or more | 0 |

Instead of "25 or more," "30 or more," ..., we could also have said
"more than 24," "more than 29," ..., and we would then have
referred to this distribution as a *cumulative "more than" distribution*.

It is important to know that if we had wanted a distribution showing how many cars went "more than 25," "more than 30," ..., we would not have been able to use the distribution on page 17; it would have been necessary in that case to refer back to the original raw data.

The same applies also to the "less than" distribution on page 22. Instead of "less than 25," "less than 30," ..., we could have said "24 or less," "29 or less," ..., and we would then have called it a *cumulative "or less" distribution*. Had we wanted to know how many cars went "25 or less," "30 or less," ..., it would again have been necessary to refer to the raw data.

If a highway engineer has to decide whether to post additional speed limit signs near the check-point referred to in our example, it would probably not be enough for him to know that 5 cars traveled at speeds falling into the interval from 65 to 69, or that only one car traveled at 70 or more; he would also have to know the total number of cars included in the count or be given equivalent information of some sort. Since one purpose of frequency distributions is to provide relevant information at a glance, without requiring further information or calculations, it would be appropriate in our example and in similar situations to convert the various distributions into *percentage distributions*. Any distribution can be made into a percentage distribution by dividing the class frequencies (or cumulative frequencies) by the total number of cases, the *total frequency*, and then multiplying by 100. (If the last step is omitted and the figures are not multiplied by 100, the resulting distribution would be a *distribution of proportions*.)

Dividing each class frequency by 200, the total number of cars included in the speed-check illustration, and then multiplying by 100, the distribution on page 17 reduces to the following *percentage distribution*:

| Speed (miles per hour) | Percentage of Cars |
|---|---|
| 25 – 29 | 0.5 |
| 30 – 34 | 0.5 |
| 35 – 39 | 2.0 |
| 40 – 44 | 6.5 |
| 45 – 49 | 20.0 |
| 50 – 54 | 32.5 |
| 55 – 59 | 26.0 |
| 60 – 64 | 9.0 |
| 65 – 69 | 2.5 |
| 70 – 74 | 0.5 |

Converting in an identical manner the "or more" distribution on page 22 into an *"or more" percentage distribution*, we get

| Speed<br>(miles per hour) | Percentage<br>of Cars |
|---|---|
| 25 or more | 100.0 |
| 30 or more | 99.5 |
| 35 or more | 99.0 |
| 40 or more | 97.0 |
| 45 or more | 90.5 |
| 50 or more | 70.5 |
| 55 or more | 38.0 |
| 60 or more | 12.0 |
| 65 or more | 3.0 |
| 70 or more | 0.5 |
| 75 or more | 0.0 |

We obtained these percentages by dividing the cumulative frequencies on page 22 by 200 and then multiplying by 100 (or simply dividing them by 2), but they could just as well have been obtained by directly adding the percentages of the percentage distribution given above.

## EXERCISES

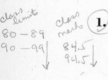

1. The weights of a number of school children are measured to the nearest pound, the smallest and largest being 87 and 174 pounds, respectively. Construct a table with 10 classes into which these weights might be grouped. Give the class limits as well as the class marks.

2. If the prices of a number of items sold at a department store varied from $21.45 to $78.25, construct a table with 12 classes into which these prices might be grouped. Give the class limits, class boundaries, and class marks.

3. A set of prices given to the nearest dollar are grouped into a classification with class limits $10–$19, $20–$29, $30–$39, $40–$49. Find (a) the corresponding class boundaries, (b) the class marks, and (c) the class interval.

4. Modify the classes of Exercise 3 so that the classification can accommodate prices from $10.00 to $49.99 in dollars and cents. Give (a) the new class limits, (b) the new class boundaries, and (c) the new class marks.

**5.** A set of measurements given to the nearest centimeter is grouped into a table having the class boundaries 4.5, 9.5, 14.5, 19.5, 24.5, 29.5, and 34.5. Find (a) the class limits of these six classes, (b) their class marks, and (c) the class interval.

**6.** The weights of all patients in a certain hospital (rounded to the nearest pound) are grouped into a distribution with class limits 0–39, 40–79, 80–119, 120–159, 160–199, 200–239. Find (a) the corresponding class boundaries, (b) the class marks, and (c) the class interval.

**7.** The class marks of a distribution of retail food prices (in cents) are 17, 32, 47, 62, 77, and 92. Find the corresponding class limits.

**8.** The methods discussed in this section lead to some complications when applied to distributions of *ages*. For example, a person is considered to belong to the age group from 5 to 9 if he has passed his fifth birthday and has not yet reached his tenth. Taking this into account, what are the class boundaries and the class marks of the following distribution: 10–19, 20–29, 30–39, 40–49, and 50–59 years?

**9.** The following are the L (linguistic) scores obtained by 183 students, who transferred in the spring of 1958 to a southwestern state college, in the ACE Psychological Examination:

| | | | | | | | | | | | |
|---|---|---|---|---|---|---|---|---|---|---|---|
| 65 | 41 | 54 | 54 | 63 | 86 | 67 | 93 | 71 | 63 | 57 | 77 |
| 45 | 59 | 69 | 65 | 44 | 53 | 66 | 74 | 56 | 74 | 61 | 95 |
| 44 | 59 | 79 | 77 | 58 | 54 | 65 | 76 | 52 | 99 | 84 | 78 |
| 79 | 99 | 25 | 72 | 45 | 59 | 63 | 69 | 114 | 44 | 73 | 84 |
| 74 | 79 | 75 | 53 | 65 | 71 | 36 | 61 | 62 | 49 | 54 | 58 |
| 52 | 65 | 63 | 97 | 79 | 52 | 64 | 38 | 77 | 70 | 63 | 51 |
| 48 | 68 | 79 | 62 | 52 | 57 | 81 | 82 | 49 | 70 | 50 | 81 |
| 93 | 63 | 58 | 71 | 35 | 53 | 58 | 56 | 74 | 81 | 49 | 75 |
| 73 | 73 | 81 | 58 | 57 | 68 | 53 | 79 | 114 | 50 | 64 | 67 |
| 41 | 56 | 90 | 84 | 70 | 57 | 71 | 85 | 90 | 39 | 81 | 63 |
| 44 | 68 | 60 | 88 | 65 | 47 | 67 | 47 | 87 | 77 | 61 | 64 |
| 77 | 83 | 92 | 62 | 94 | 88 | 77 | 61 | 71 | 78 | 69 | 61 |
| 66 | 52 | 66 | 74 | 58 | 73 | 99 | 41 | 70 | 57 | 68 | 59 |
| 42 | 71 | 41 | 83 | 69 | 48 | 52 | 77 | 51 | 44 | 62 | 64 |
| 75 | 41 | 57 | 48 | 82 | 68 | 99 | 83 | 80 | 81 | 75 | 52 |
| 67 | 71 | 14 | | | | | | | | | |

Group these scores into a table with class intervals of 10.

**10.** Convert the distribution obtained in Exercise 1 into a cumulative "less than" distribution.

**11.** The following are the lengths of root penetration (in feet) of 120 crested wheatgrass seedlings one month after planting:

| | | | | | | | | | |
|---|---|---|---|---|---|---|---|---|---|
| .81 | 1.01 | 1.04 | 1.41 | .67 | .83 | 1.23 | .90 | .88 | .95 |
| .78 | 1.21 | .80 | 1.43 | 1.27 | 1.16 | 1.06 | .86 | .70 | .80 |
| 1.15 | .86 | 1.25 | .75 | .81 | .80 | .62 | 1.00 | .93 | .71 |
| .91 | .62 | .84 | 1.08 | .99 | 1.38 | .98 | .93 | .80 | 1.25 |
| .60 | .83 | .83 | .53 | .84 | .90 | .79 | .85 | .97 | .82 |
| .95 | .68 | 1.27 | .97 | .80 | 1.13 | .89 | .83 | 1.47 | .96 |
| 1.36 | .73 | 1.00 | .85 | .95 | 1.13 | .95 | .75 | .87 | 1.34 |
| .94 | .80 | 1.33 | .91 | 1.03 | .93 | 1.34 | .82 | .82 | .95 |
| 1.00 | .85 | 1.17 | 1.06 | .92 | .80 | .90 | 1.21 | 1.02 | 1.11 |
| .88 | .86 | .64 | .96 | .88 | .95 | .74 | .57 | .96 | .78 |
| .84 | 1.19 | .83 | .87 | 1.08 | .73 | .88 | .89 | .81 | .89 |
| .94 | .70 | .76 | .85 | .97 | .86 | .94 | 1.06 | 1.27 | 1.09 |

Group these measurements into a table having the classes .50–.59, .60–.69, .70–.79, ... Also construct a cumulative "less than" distribution.

**12.** Convert the cumulative distribution obtained in Exercise 11 into a cumulative percentage distribution. Round to the nearest tenth of a per cent.

**13.** The following are the scores obtained by 150 college students aged 16 to 20 in a religious literacy test in which the maximum score is 50:

| | | | | | | | | | | | | | | |
|---|---|---|---|---|---|---|---|---|---|---|---|---|---|---|
| 14 | 25 | 34 | 27 | 12 | 40 | 19 | 23 | 20 | 39 | 16 | 28 | 30 | 15 | 26 |
| 38 | 21 | 23 | 37 | 22 | 21 | 32 | 31 | 33 | 34 | 26 | 43 | 27 | 29 | 34 |
| 33 | 44 | 29 | 35 | 29 | 26 | 30 | 18 | 26 | 25 | 20 | 29 | 22 | 38 | 18 |
| 19 | 24 | 26 | 30 | 20 | 24 | 37 | 29 | 14 | 27 | 33 | 24 | 33 | 27 | 28 |
| 24 | 31 | 28 | 17 | 26 | 34 | 29 | 35 | 27 | 44 | 26 | 34 | 37 | 19 | 33 |
| 43 | 20 | 11 | 32 | 40 | 25 | 19 | 22 | 24 | 29 | 12 | 25 | 24 | 21 | 24 |
| 26 | 28 | 22 | 19 | 28 | 39 | 26 | 28 | 36 | 19 | 30 | 27 | 23 | 28 | 41 |
| 23 | 26 | 38 | 24 | 3 | 33 | 16 | 22 | 20 | 13 | 22 | 11 | 22 | 20 | 21 |
| 17 | 33 | 29 | 28 | 35 | 29 | 23 | 34 | 32 | 27 | 41 | 37 | 26 | 33 | 26 |
| 29 | 30 | 26 | 33 | 27 | 16 | 21 | 42 | 25 | 28 | 29 | 33 | 19 | 35 | 32 |

Group these scores into a distribution having the classes 0–4, 5–9, 10–14, 15–19, ... Also construct a cumulative "or more" percentage distribution, rounding to the nearest tenth of a per cent. (The author is indebted to Professor J. D. Haggard for supplying the data on which this exercise is based.)

**14.** The following are the amounts (in dollars) that 80 engineering freshmen spent on textbooks in the spring semester, 1958:

| 30.25 | 24.10 | 22.50 | 32.40 | 20.15 | 28.50 | 38.85 | 43.80 |
|-------|-------|-------|-------|-------|-------|-------|-------|
| 42.60 | 23.50 | 12.25 | 21.80 | 33.50 | 22.15 | 31.25 | 13.50 |
| 31.70 | 36.65 | 37.40 | 19.20 | 29.75 | 27.10 | 33.60 | 33.00 |
| 39.25 | 26.10 | 33.80 | 30.50 | 32.70 | 29.35 | 35.45 | 22.75 |
| 25.15 | 31.95 | 28.60 | 32.50 | 42.80 | 17.90 | 34.25 | 38.25 |
| 35.20 | 38.15 | 25.75 | 44.60 | 34.45 | 33.40 | 36.90 | 40.10 |
| 25.00 | 27.50 | 36.80 | 23.80 | 32.75 | 27.00 | 43.80 | 35.00 |
| 35.75 | 27.35 | 29.75 | 32.45 | 25.40 | 33.05 | 37.55 | 37.15 |
| 30.25 | 31.25 | 24.80 | 26.70 | 35.50 | 34.95 | 29.30 | 41.75 |
| 26.25 | 46.20 | 24.50 | 33.40 | 12.75 | 33.95 | 26.20 | 31.50 |

Group these figures (given to the nearest 5 cents) into a distribution having the classes $10.00–$14.95, $15.00–$19.95, $20.00–$24.95, etc. What are the class boundaries of this distribution? Also construct a cumulative "or more" distribution.

**15.** The following are the lengths (in centimeters) of 100 sea trouts caught by a commercial trawler in Delaware Bay:

| 19.5 | 19.8 | 18.9 | 20.4 | 20.2 | 21.5 | 19.9 | 21.7 | 19.5 | 20.9 |
|------|------|------|------|------|------|------|------|------|------|
| 18.1 | 20.5 | 18.3 | 19.5 | 18.3 | 19.0 | 18.2 | 23.9 | 17.0 | 19.7 |
| 20.7 | 23.1 | 20.6 | 16.6 | 19.4 | 18.6 | 22.7 | 18.5 | 20.1 | 18.6 |
| 20.3 | 19.7 | 19.5 | 22.9 | 20.7 | 20.3 | 20.8 | 19.8 | 19.4 | 19.3 |
| 19.4 | 21.8 | 20.4 | 21.0 | 21.4 | 19.8 | 19.6 | 21.5 | 20.2 | 20.1 |
| 19.2 | 19.6 | 17.3 | 19.3 | 19.5 | 20.4 | 23.5 | 19.0 | 19.4 | 18.4 |
| 20.1 | 19.3 | 18.2 | 20.9 | 20.6 | 22.4 | 19.0 | 20.5 | 19.6 | 25.8 |
| 22.0 | 20.0 | 20.8 | 18.9 | 19.9 | 19.3 | 21.4 | 19.6 | 20.3 | 19.9 |
| 19.5 | 18.5 | 19.5 | 19.6 | 18.7 | 19.2 | 20.7 | 19.0 | 18.4 | 21.7 |
| 19.6 | 20.9 | 21.3 | 20.5 | 19.8 | 18.5 | 19.1 | 22.6 | 19.8 | 20.4 |

Group these measurements into a distribution having a class interval of 1 centimeter. Also construct a cumulative "less than" distribution. (The author is indebted to Dr. F. C. Daiber, Department of Biology, University of Delaware, for supplying the data on which this exercise is based.)

**16.** The following are 60 measurements (in 0.0001 inch) of the thickness of an aluminum alloy plating obtained in an operation analysis of an anodizing process:

| 2.5 | 3.9 | 3.4 | 2.2 | 3.3 | 3.2 | 3.6 | 4.1 | 2.4 | 2.4 |
|-----|-----|-----|-----|-----|-----|-----|-----|-----|-----|
| 2.1 | 3.2 | 3.6 | 2.6 | 4.3 | 2.8 | 3.0 | 2.7 | 3.8 | 2.5 |
| 3.3 | 4.2 | 3.0 | 3.2 | 3.1 | 3.4 | 2.1 | 2.7 | 3.5 | 4.8 |
| 3.5 | 2.6 | 2.1 | 3.0 | 3.7 | 3.9 | 2.5 | 3.3 | 3.6 | 2.7 |
| 2.9 | 2.8 | 2.6 | 2.2 | 2.3 | 3.0 | 4.3 | 2.0 | 3.1 | 2.2 |
| 2.4 | 2.0 | 3.8 | 3.6 | 2.8 | 3.1 | 2.9 | 3.0 | 2.3 | 3.7 |

Group these thicknesses into a distribution having a class interval of 0.5 ten thousandth of an inch. Also construct a cumulative "or more" percentage distribution, rounding the percentages to the nearest tenth of a per cent.

17. The following are 106 time lapses (in minutes) between eruptions of Old Faithful Geyser in Yellowstone National Park (recorded between the hours of 8 A.M. and 10 P.M. on July 6 to July 14, 1955, and measured from the beginning of one eruption to the beginning of the next):

| | | | | | | | | | | | | |
|---|---|---|---|---|---|---|---|---|---|---|---|---|
| 68 | 62 | 68 | 72 | 50 | 76 | 59 | 69 | 62 | 70 | 67 | 44 | 71 |
| 63 | 62 | 65 | 69 | 62 | 70 | 40 | 62 | 74 | 59 | 68 | 66 | 68 |
| 66 | 55 | 60 | 65 | 63 | 57 | 66 | 68 | 67 | 58 | 74 | 74 | 66 |
| 63 | 62 | 61 | 66 | 67 | 67 | 74 | 76 | 63 | 70 | 65 | 71 | 67 |
| 61 | 67 | 71 | 64 | 52 | 76 | 63 | 71 | 76 | 60 | 74 | 41 | 72 |
| 44 | 73 | 60 | 69 | 55 | 81 | 55 | 68 | 51 | 67 | 62 | 66 | 66 |
| 60 | 72 | 68 | 59 | 69 | 55 | 58 | 60 | 69 | 58 | 66 | 63 | 68 |
| 62 | 55 | 67 | 67 | 64 | 45 | 65 | 60 | 64 | 67 | 71 | 72 | 72 |
| 71 | 67 | | | | | | | | | | | |

Group these data into a table having the class limits 40–44, 45–49, 50–54, etc. Also construct a cumulative "or less" distribution. (The author is indebted to Mr. David de L. Condon, Chief Park Naturalist of Yellowstone National Park, for supplying these data.)

18. In order to show how the choice of different classifications can alter the over-all shape of a distribution (see also Exercise 7 on page 37), regroup the data of Exercise 17 into tables having (a) the class limits 31–40, 41–50, 51–60, etc., and (b) the class limits 33–42, 43–52, 53–62, etc.

## 2.3 / Graphical Presentations

Whenever frequency distributions are constructed primarily to condense large sets of data and display them in an "easy to digest" form, it is advisable to present them graphically, that is, in a form that lends itself readily to the human power of visualization. The most widely used form of graphical presentation of numerical distributions is the *histogram*, an example of which is shown in Figure 2.3. Histograms are constructed by representing the measurements or observations that are grouped (in Figure 2.3 the speeds in miles per hour) on a *horizontal* scale, the class frequencies on a *vertical* scale, and drawing rectangles, whose bases are given by the

class intervals and whose heights are determined by the corresponding class frequencies. The markings on the horizontal scale can be
the class boundaries, the class limits as in Figure 2.3, or for that

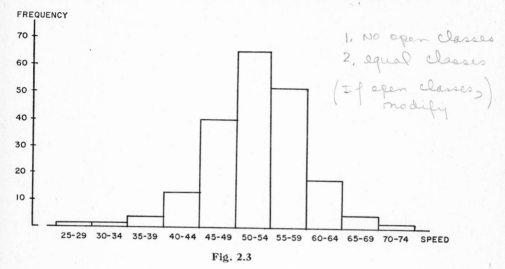

Fig. 2.3

*1. No open classes*
*2. equal classes*
*(If open classes,)*
*   modify*

matter arbitrary key values. For easy readability, it is generally
best to indicate the class limits, although the bases of the rectangles
actually go from one class boundary to the next.

There are several points that must be watched in the construction of histograms. First, it must be remembered that this kind of
figure cannot be used for distributions with *open classes*. Second,
it should be noted that the picture presented by a histogram can be
very misleading if a distribution has *unequal classes* and no suitable
adjustments are made. To illustrate this point, let us regroup the
speed-check data by combining all speeds from 55 to 64 mph into
one class. The distribution on page 17 thus becomes

| *Speed* (miles per hour) | *Number of Cars* |
|---|---|
| 25 – 29 | 1 |
| 30 – 34 | 1 |
| 35 – 39 | 4 |
| 40 – 44 | 13 |
| 45 – 49 | 40 |
| 50 – 54 | 65 |
| 55 – 64 | 70 |
| 65 – 69 | 5 |
| 70 – 74 | 1 |

and its histogram, with the class frequencies, as before, given by the heights of the rectangles, is shown in Figure 2.4.

Figure 2.4 gives the immediate impression that over half (about

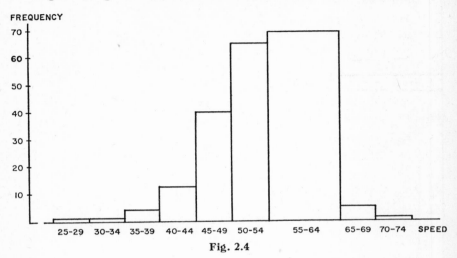

Fig. 2.4

two thirds) of the speeds fall between 55 and 64, and this error is due to the fact that we intuitively compare the *areas* of the rectangles instead of their heights. In order to adjust for this peculiarity of perception, it is necessary to make the following adjustment: *if a class interval is twice as long as the others, we divide the height of its*

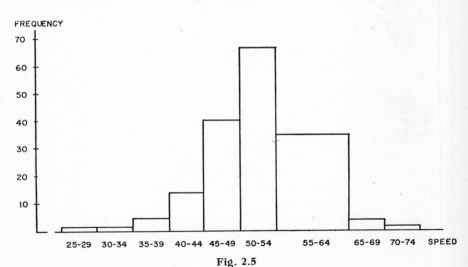

Fig. 2.5

*rectangle by two; if a class interval is three times as long as the others,* height
*we divide the height of its rectangle by three, and so on.* By following length
this practice, we actually represent the class frequencies by means
of the *areas* of the rectangles, and it is better in that case to omit
the vertical scale, indicating instead the frequencies as we have
done in the adjusted histogram of Figure 2.5.

The practice of representing class frequencies by means of areas
is specially important if histograms are to be approximated with
smooth curves. For instance, if we wanted to approximate the
histogram of Figure 2.3 with a smooth curve, we could say that the
number of cars traveling at speeds of 60 mph or more is given by the

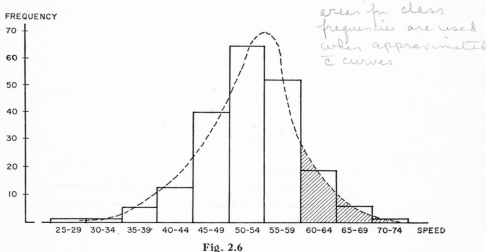

areas for class
frequencies are used
when approximated
c curves.

Fig. 2.6

shaded area of Figure 2.6. Clearly, this area is approximately equal
to the sum of the areas of the corresponding three rectangles.

An alternate, though less frequently used, way of presenting
distributions in graphical form is what is called a *frequency polygon*. frequency
Frequency polygons are constructed by plotting the class frequencies polygon
at the corresponding class marks (see Figure 2.7) and connecting the
points thus obtained by means of straight lines. In order to complete
the picture, one extra class is usually added at each end of the
distribution, and since these classes have zero frequencies, both ends
of the figure will come down to the horizontal axis.

When there are open or unequal classes, frequency polygons pose
the same difficulties as histograms. They cannot be used for distributions with open classes and an appropriate adjustment, the

same as in the case of histograms, must be made to account for unequal classes. (If a class interval is twice as long as the others, we divide the class frequency by two before plotting it at the class mark, and so on.)

If the technique of constructing a frequency polygon is applied

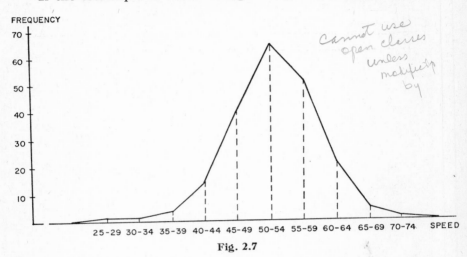

Fig. 2.7

to a cumulative distribution, we obtain a figure that goes under the name of "ogive." One difference between a frequency polygon and an ogive is that in an ogive the cumulative frequencies are not

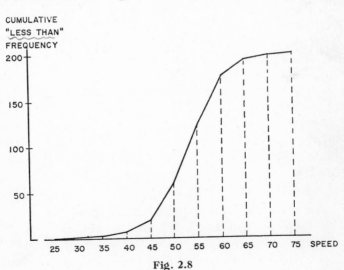

Fig. 2.8

plotted at the class marks.  Clearly, it would only be reasonable to plot the cumulative frequency corresponding to "less than 40" at 40 (see Figure 2.8). Since "less than 40" and "40 or less," *which do not mean the same*, could both rightfully be plotted at 40, it is desirable always to indicate whether an ogive represents a "less than" or an "or less" distribution. Incidentally, this difficulty can be avoided by plotting the cumulative frequencies at the *class boundaries* instead of the class limits.  With reference to the speed-check example, we would then plot the cumulative frequency corresponding to "less than 40" at 39.5, and that corresponding to "40 or less" at 40.5.  What we have said here applies, of course, equally well to "or more" and "more than" distributions.

Figure 2.8 presents the ogive of the "less than" distribution of the speed-check data.  To make it more useful and more meaningful at a glance, we could change the frequency scale to a percentage

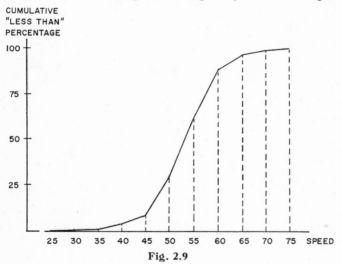

CUMULATIVE "LESS THAN" PERCENTAGE

Fig. 2.9

scale (see Figure 2.9), and it would then be possible to read off directly what percentage of the cars went under 40 mph, under 50, under 60, . . .

Although the visual appeal of histograms, frequency polygons, and ogives is an improvement over that of frequency tables, there are ways in which distributions can be presented more dramatically and probably more effectively.  We are referring here to various kinds of pictorial presentations (see, for example, Figure 2.10), with which the reader must surely be familiar through newspapers, magazines, advertizing, and other sources. The number of ways in which distributions (and other statistical data) can be displayed pictorially is almost unlimited, depending only on the imagination and artistic talent of the individual engaged in their presentation.

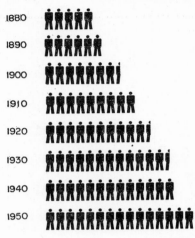

EACH SYMBOL = 10 MILLION PEOPLE

**Fig. 2.10.** United States population (Source: 1956 Statistical Abstract of the United States).

If the reader is interested in a detailed treatment of this subject, he will find suitable references in the bibliography on page 41.

Although frequency distributions, or better their histograms, can have almost any shape or form, there are certain standard types that fit most distributions met in actual practice. Foremost, there is the _bell-shaped_ distribution illustrated by the histogram of Figure 2.11. Many of the distributions met earlier in this chapter,

symmetrical bell curve

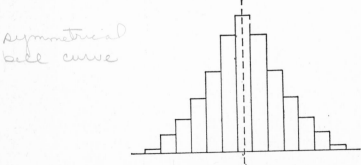

**Fig. 2.11.** A bell-shaped distribution.

for example, the speed-check distribution, the distribution of the time lapses between eruptions of Old Faithful (Exercise 17 on page 28), and the distribution of the lengths of root penetration (Exercise 11 on page 26), may very well be described as bell-shaped. Indeed, there are theoretical reasons why, in problems to be discussed later, we can actually *expect* to get bell-shaped distributions.

The distribution of the lengths of sea trouts (Exercise 15 on page 27) may also be described as bell-shaped, but it is apparent from Figure 2.12 that it presents the picture of a somewhat "lopsided bell." In order to distinguish between distributions like those of Figures 2.11 and 2.12, it is customary to refer to the first as *symmetrical* and the second as *skewed*.

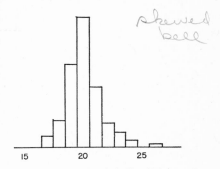

Fig. 2.12. A skewed distribution

A distribution is said to be symmetrical if one can, figuratively, fold its histogram along some dotted line (for example, that of Figure 2.11) and have the two halves more or less coincide. If a distribution has a "tail" at one end or the other, such as the distribution of Figure 2.12, it is said to be skewed. Among the distributions we have already met, the personal income distribution on page 12 and the width-of-crab distribution on page 13 are both skewed. The problem of how to measure or describe the extent to which a distribution is skewed will be taken up in Section 5.2.

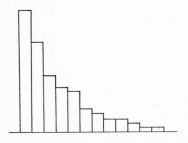

Fig. 2.13. A J-shaped distribution.

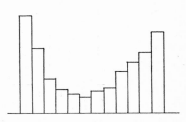

Fig. 2.14. A U-shaped distribution.

Two other kinds of distributions, called *J-shaped* and *U-shaped*, are sometimes, though less frequently, met in actual practice. As is illustrated in Figures 2.13 and 2.14, their names literally describe their shapes. To give an example of a J-shaped distribution, we could cite the distribution of the number of claims filed each year against holders of automobile liability insurance policies. Against most there are none, against some there is one, against fewer there are two, and so on. Another example of a J-shaped distribution is that of the number of station wagons owned by individual families. Most families have no station wagon, some have one, fewer have two, and so forth.

To give an example of a U-shaped distribution, let us refer to a game of chance, the game of *head or tails*, and let us suppose that after each flip of the coin we check whether we are *ahead, even*, or *behind*. Letting W and L stand for "win" and "loss," let us suppose, furthermore, that a series of 6 flips produced the following results:

W    L    W    W    L    L

From this it may be seen that after the first flip we were *ahead* one, after the second flip we were *even*, after the third flip we were *ahead one*, after the fourth flip we were *ahead two*, after the fifth flip we were *ahead one*, and after the sixth flip we were again *even*. In this series of 6 flips we were, thus, ahead exactly 4 times out of 6.

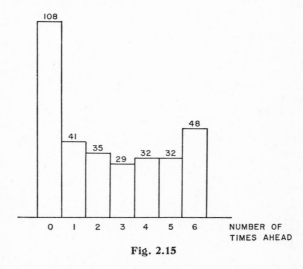

Fig. 2.15

In an actual experiment consisting of 320 such series of 6 flips of a coin there were 108 series in which we were *never ahead*, 41 in which we were *ahead exactly once*, 35 in which we were *ahead twice*, 29 in which we were *ahead three times*, 32 in which we were *ahead four times,* 32 in which we were *ahead five times,* and 48 in which we were *always ahead.* The results of this experiment are shown graphically by means of the U-shaped histogram of Figure 2.15, and it is apparent that we are more apt to be *ahead all the time* or *ahead none of the time* than, say, half the time. This illustrates the fact that once we get ahead (in business, games of chance, sports, etc.) we are apt to stay ahead for a while, and once we get behind we are apt to stay behind for some time.

## EXERCISES

1. Construct a histogram of the width-of-crab distribution on page 13.

2. Convert the width-of-crab distribution on page 13 into a "less than" percentage distribution and draw its ogive.

3. Construct a histogram and a frequency polygon for whichever data you grouped among those of Exercises 9, 11, 13, 14, 15, 16, and 17 on pages 25 through 28.

4. Construct an ogive of the cumulative distribution of Exercise 10 on page 25.

5. Construct an ogive of the cumulative percentage distribution obtained in Exercise 12 on page 25.

6. Construct an ogive for whichever data you constructed a cumulative distribution among those of Exercises 13, 14, 15, 16, and 17 on pages 25 through 28.

7. Draw histograms of the two distributions obtained in Exercise 18 on page 28.

8. The following is a distribution of the number of defective pieces found in 100 fifty-piece samples taken from very large shipments of a certain kind of shaft:

| Number of Defective Pieces | Frequency |
|:---:|:---:|
| 0 – 4 | 48 |
| 5 – 9 | 20 |
| 10 – 14 | 12 |
| 15 – 19 | 10 |
| 20 – 24 | 5 |
| 25 – 29 | 3 |
| 30 – 34 | 0 |
| 35 – 39 | 1 |
| 40 – 44 | 1 |

Draw a histogram of this distribution and also an ogive of the corresponding "or more" cumulative percentage distribution.

**9.** The following is a distribution of the scores obtained by 143 high school seniors in a mathematics contest given in 1957 by the Arizona Association of Teachers of Mathematics:

| Scores | | Number of Pupils |
|---|---|---|
| 10 – 24.5 | | 10 |
| 25 – 39.5 | | 14 |
| 40 – 54.5 | | 23 |
| 55 – 69.5 | | 29 |
| 70 – 84 | | 26 |
| 85 – 99 | | 16 |
| 100 – 114 | | 13 |
| 115 – 129 | | 7 |
| 130 – 144 | | 1 |
| 145 – 159 | | 4 |

Construct (a) a histogram and (b) an "or more" percentage ogive of this distribution. Also draw a histogram of the modified distribution obtained by combining all scores from 70 through 114 into one class.

**10.** Indicate one example each of data (other than those used as illustrations in the text) that can reasonably be expected to have (a) a symmetrical bell-shaped distribution, (b) a skewed bell-shaped distribution, and (c) a J-shaped distribution.

## 2.4 / Categorical Distributions

Many of the observations made in Section 2.2 in connection with numerical distribution apply equally well to categorical (or qualitative) distributions. Again, we must decide how many categories (classes) to use, what each category is to contain, and we must make sure that all the data will be accommodated and that there are no ambiguities.

Any decision about the number of categories will have to be dictated partly by the nature of the data and partly by the objective for which the data are to be grouped. For instance, if we wanted to construct a table showing the 1954 fall-term enrollment at the University of Washington, we could choose three categories and arrive at the following distribution

| Category | Number of Students |
|---|---|
| Undergraduate | 10,942 |
| Graduate | 18,44 |
| Professional | 889 |

If, for some reason, a finer classification were needed, we could subdivide undergraduates into freshmen, sophomores, juniors, seniors, and special students, and we would get

| Category | Number of Students |
|---|---|
| Freshman | 3,458 |
| Sophomores | 2,612 |
| Juniors | 2,237 |
| Seniors | 2,509 |
| Special students | 126 |
| Graduate students | 1,844 |
| Professional | 889 |

This break-down could lead to ambiguities if there were, say, special graduate students, but it seems that no such students existed at the University of Washington in 1954. Also, if necessary, the category "professional" could be subdivided further into students attending Law School, the School of Dentistry, and the School of Medicine. Clearly, it would be silly in a problem like this to decide more or less arbitrarily to use 8, 10, or 15 classes without giving due consideration to the nature of the data.

Since categories must often be chosen *before* any data are actually collected, it can be difficult to foresee all eventualities and it is, therefore, sound practice to add a category labeled "others." This was done, for example, in the categorical distribution on page 13. Sometimes categories are combined later under the heading of "others" in order to cut down the size of a table or to combine categories with very small frequencies.

One reason why great care must be taken in the selection of categories is that it is easy to make the mistake of choosing overlapping classes. For example, if we tried to classify items sold at a supermarket into "meats," "frozen foods," "baked goods," and so on, it would be difficult to decide where to put, for instance, frozen hamburger steaks. Similarly, if we wanted to classify occupations, it would be difficult to decide where to put a farm manager, if our table contained (without qualifications) the two categories "farmers" and "managers."

When constructing categorical distributions we do not have to worry about such mathematical details as class limits, class boundaries, and class marks, but the tally can be much more difficult than in the case of a numerical distribution. The problem here is a question of *definition*, that is, the question of being very explicit as to what each category is to contain. For example, if we tried to classify industries into manufacturers of (a) luggage, (b) handbags and small leather goods, and (c) gloves and miscellaneous leather goods, it might turn out to be rather difficult to know where a particular industry belongs *unless these categories are accompanied by very specific definitions*. For this reason it is often advisable to use standard categories developed by the Bureau of the Census and other government agencies. (For references to such lists see P. M. Hauser and W. R. Leonard, *Government Statistics for Business Use.* New York: John Wiley, 1956.)

Categorical distributions, particularly categorical percentage distributions, are often presented pictorially as *pie charts*, like the one shown in Figure 2.16. Their construction is easy; since the sum

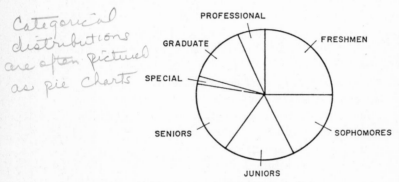

*Categorical distributions are often pictured as pie charts*

**Fig. 2.16.** 1954 fall-term enrollment at the University of Washington.

of the central angles of all the sectors is 360 degrees and the entire circle represents 100 per cent, 1 per cent is represented by a central angle of 360/100 = 3.6 degrees. For example, in the distribution on page 39 the proportion of freshmen is 3,458/13,675 = 0.253 or 25.3 per cent, and this "slice" is represented in Figure 2.16 by a sector having a central angle of 25.3 *times* 3.6 or 91 degrees.

## EXERCISES

1. Use a university or college catalogue to construct a table showing how its teaching staff is distributed among the ranks of Professor, Associate Professor, Assistant Professor, etc.

**2.** In the decoding of secret messages it is sometimes useful to check the frequencies with which each letter or symbol occurs. To get a rough idea about the frequencies with which some letters of the alphabet occur, construct a distribution showing how often the vowels a, e, i, o, u appeared in the text on page 20.

**3.** Take that part of the classified ads of a large daily newspaper in which individuals (not dealers) advertize cars for sale, and construct a distribution showing how many of these cars were made by General Motors, Ford, Chrysler, and others.

**4.** Use a daily newspaper giving New York Stock Exchange prices and construct a categorical distribution showing how many stocks traded on a certain day had a net increase, a net decrease, or no change in price.

## BIBLIOGRAPHY

Further material on the construction and use of frequency distributions may be found in

Croxton, F. E., and Cowden, D. J., *Applied General Statistics*, 2nd ed. Englewood Cliffs, N. J.: Prentice-Hall, 1955, Chap. 8.

Simpson, G., and Kafka, F., *Basic Statistics*, rev. ed. New York: W. W. Norton, 1957, Chap. 8.

The subject of graphical (pictorial) presentation of statistical data is treated in detail in

Modley, R., and Lowenstein, D., *Pictographs and Graphs*. New York: Harper Brothers, 1952.

Smart, L. E., and Arnold, S., *Practical Rules for Graphic Presentation of Business Statistics*. Columbus, Ohio: Bureau of Business Research, Ohio State University, 1951.

Spear, M. E., *Charting Statistics*. New York: McGraw-Hill, 1952.

The question of *what not to do* in the presentation of statistical data is discussed in an amusing fashion in

Huff, D., *How to Lie with Statistics*. New York: W. W. Norton, 1954.

Chapter  *3*

# Measures of Location

### 3.1 / Introduction

When describing a chair, a flower, a dog, or a car, one's description
will have to depend partly on the nature of the object itself and
partly on the reason for giving the description. Thus, an official
issuing dog licenses may want to know that a certain dog is healthy,
male, and black, whereas a dog show official may want to know that
this dog is a poodle, his age, and his ancestry. The same argument
also applies to the description of statistical data. The type of
description we may choose or the statistical technique we may
employ will have to depend partly on the nature of the data themselves and partly on the purpose that we have in mind.

In this and the next two chapters we shall study four basic kinds
of descriptions of statistical data called *measures of location, measures
of variation, measures of symmetry and skewness,* and *measures of
peakedness.* The first of these, which we shall study in this chapter,
are also referred to as "measures of central tendencies," "measures
of central values," and "measures of position."

The measures of location which will be discussed in Sections 3.3
through 3.7 may be referred to crudely as "averages" in the sense
that they provide numbers that are indicative of the "center,"
"middle," or the "most typical" of a set of data. In Section 3.8 we
shall treat some other kinds of "locations," for example, the location
of a value which is such that it is exceeded only by 25 per cent of
the data.

## 3.2 / Samples and Populations

When we said in the preceding section that the choice of a statistical description will have to depend on the nature of the data themselves, we were referring among other things to the following distinction: sometimes a set of data consists of all conceivably (or hypothetically) possible observations of a certain phenomenon and sometimes it contains only part, that is, a sample of these observations. We shall refer to the first as a *population* and the second as a *sample*.

If we are given complete records of the I.Q.'s of all seniors attending a certain high school, these figures may be looked upon as a population. Similarly, if we are given complete figures on the ages of all persons who immigrated to the United States in 1958, these ages may be looked upon as a population. In each case we are given *all the facts* about a certain situation; in the first case it is the I.Q.'s of the seniors at the particular high school and in the second case it is the ages of the particular group of immigrants.

It may have occurred to the reader while reading the preceding paragraph that *whether a set of data is to be considered a population or a sample will have to depend to some extent on how we look at it.* After all, if we were interested in the I.Q.'s of all high school seniors in the United States, data on the students in one school would only be a sample. Similarly, if we were interested in the ages of persons who immigrated to the United States over the past 50 years, information on the ages of the persons immigrating in 1958 would only be a sample.

Whether a set of data is to be referred to as a population or a sample depends, thus, on how we look at it and what we intend to do with it. If we are not interested in making generalizations about the I.Q.'s of high school seniors at other schools, and if we are not interested in making generalizations about the ages of immigrants in years other than 1958, we can in each case look upon the data as populations. However, the moment that we want to infer something about a larger group of high school students or the ages of a larger group of immigrants, these data must be looked upon as samples and we shall have to worry about the question of whether or not it is at all possible to make generalizations.

In statistics, the word "sample" is used very much in its every-day connotation. If we interview 50 out of a total of 800 employees working at a certain plant, the opinions they express constitute a sample of the opinions of all employees. Similarly, if we measure the number of miles that 4 tires made by a certain company will last before showing appreciable damage, these measurements constitute a sample of the corresponding performance of all tires made by this firm. This last illustration also shows why we must often be satisfied with samples. Clearly, complete information about these tires could be obtained only by testing them all, and the company would then have none left to sell.

In some texts the word "universe" is used instead of "population," and the very fact that in statistics these terms are synonymous indicates that neither is used in its colloquial sense. As we said above, both terms, in their technical sense, refer to sets of data consisting of all possible or all *hypothetically possible* observations of a given phenomenon. We added the word "hypothetical" because later on we shall want to consider, for example, 5 flips of a coin as a sample from the population consisting of all hypothetically possible flips of the coin. Similarly, we shall want to consider the weights of 10 twenty-day-old white mice as a sample of *all* (past, present, and future) twenty-day-old white mice, and we shall want to look, more generally, upon the results obtained in an experiment as a sample of what we might obtain if we repeated the experiment over and over again.

In the next few chapters we shall limit ourselves to methods of description without making generalizations, but it is important even here to distinguish between samples and populations. As we have said before, the kind of description we may want to use will have to depend on what we intend to do later on, whether we merely want to present facts about populations or whether we want to generalize from samples. We shall, thus, begin in this chapter with the practice of using *different symbols* depending on whether we are dealing with samples or populations; in Chapter 4 we shall carry this distinction one step further by even suggesting the use of different formulas.

## EXERCISES

1. Suppose we are given the College Board scores of all male freshmen entering a certain university in the fall of 1958. Give one example each of problems in which we would consider these scores to constitute (a) a sample and (b) a population.

2. Suppose that the final election returns from a certain county show that Candidate A received 2,498 votes while his opponent, Candidate B, received the remaining 679 votes. What offices might these candidates

be running for so that we could look upon these figures as (a) a sample and (b) a population?

3. Suppose we are given complete information about the salaries paid to elevator operators in New York City in April 1958. Give one example each of situations in which we would consider this information to constitute (a) a sample and (b) a population.

## 3.3 / The Mean

There are many problems in which it is important to represent a set of numbers by means of a single number that is, so to speak, descriptive of the entire set. The most popular measure used for this purpose is what laymen call an *average* and what statisticians call an *arithmetic mean* or simply a *mean*. (Statisticians do not like the word "average" because it has too many different connotations in everyday language. It has different meanings, for instance, when we refer to an *average person*, a *batting average*, or an *average taste*.) By the "average" of $n$ numbers most people understand *their sum divided by n* and this is, indeed, how we shall define their arithmetic mean. Given $n$ numbers $x_1$, $x_2$, $x_3$, ..., and $x_n$, their arithmetic mean is*

$$\text{arithmetic mean} = \frac{\sum_{i=1}^{n} x_i}{n} \qquad (3.3.1)\blacktriangle$$

or literally *the sum of the x's divided by n*. To illustrate the calculation of an arithmetic mean (which the reader must surely have done before although he may not have called it by this name), let us suppose that we are given the following figures representing the pulse rates (beats per minute) of 5 babies at birth

$$130 \quad 132 \quad 127 \quad 129 \quad 132$$

Substituting into (3.3.1) we find that the "average" pulse rate of these babies, namely, the arithmetic mean, is

$$\frac{130 + 132 + 127 + 129 + 132}{5} = \frac{650}{5} = 130$$

Most of the time arithmetic means are referred to simply as "means," and we shall follow this practice from now on. Since there also exist *geometric means* and *harmonic means* (see Section 3.6), it

---

*Formulas marked ▲ are actually used for practical computations. This will make it easier for the reader to distinguish between formulas needed for calculations and formulas given primarily for purposes of definition or as part of derivations.

should be understood that the abbreviated term "mean" stands for "arithmetic mean" and not for the others.

Since the mean is undoubtedly the most widely used statistical description, it will be profitable to represent it with a special symbol, and it is here that we shall distinguish first between descriptions of samples and populations. If a set of numbers $x_1$, $x_2$, $x_3$, ..., and $x_n$ constitute a sample, we shall write the mean as $\bar{x}$ ($x$-bar); similarly, the mean of $n$ sample values $y_1$, $y_2$, $y_3$, ..., and $y_n$ will be written as $\bar{y}$, and the mean of $n$ sample values $z_1$, $z_2$, $z_3$, ..., and $z_n$ as $\bar{z}$. If a set of numbers constitutes a population, its mean will be represented by the symbol $\mu$ (the Greek letter *mu*). The importance of this distinction will become apparent in later chapters where we shall have the occasion to use the mean of a sample as an estimate of the mean of a population. Clearly, it would sound very confusing if we said that we use a mean to estimate a mean. Instead, we shall say that we use an $\bar{x}$ to estimate a $\mu$. If we wanted to generalize from the information given above about babies' pulse rates at birth, we could say that our sample value of $\bar{x} = 130$ is an estimate of $\mu$, the *true* (but unknown) average pulse rate of babies at birth.

Among the noteworthy properties of the mean we find that (1) most people understand (or can easily be made to understand) what is meant by a mean, although they may not actually call it by that name; (2) the mean *always exists*, it can be calculated for any kind of numerical data; (3) it is *always unique*, or, in other words, a given set of data has one and only one mean; and (4) it takes into account *each individual item*.

Whether this fourth property is really desirable is open to question, as is shown by the following example: suppose that the total annual incomes of 8 families living in a small apartment house are \$3,200, \$4,000, \$3,500, \$4,500, \$3,800, \$4,200, \$3,600, and \$53,200, the latter being the income of the owner of the building who has a penthouse on the top floor. Calculating the mean of these numbers we get

$$\frac{3,200 + 4,000 + 3,500 + 4,500 + 3,800 + 4,200 + 3,600 + 53,200}{8} = \$10,000$$

and the existing situation would probably be grossly misunderstood if we merely stated that the average income of families living in this building is \$10,000 a year.

The fact that the mean is easily affected by one very large (or very small) item can lead to serious consequences in problems where sample means are used for purposes of estimation. To illustrate, let us suppose that a technician is testing the "lifetimes" of five electronic tubes made by a certain firm, namely, the number of hours they will last in continuous use, and that in writing down his results, which were 942, 820, 981, 929, and 703 hours, he makes the mistake of recording the last figure as 203 instead of 703. He thus gets a sample mean of

$$\frac{942 + 820 + 981 + 929 + 203}{5} = 775 \text{ hours}$$

instead of the correct value of 875 hours.

This shows how one careless mistake can have a pronounced effect on a mean. It would certainly be serious if, on the basis of this experiment and the technician's mistake, we estimated $\mu$, the average (mean) lifetime of all similar tubes made by this firm, as 775 hours instead of 875. In Section 3.4 we shall meet another kind of average, called the *median*, which has the important feature that it is not so readily affected by a very large or very small value.

To add two more properties of the mean to the list which we began on page 46, let us also say that (5) it is possible to combine the means of several sets of data into an over-all mean without having to go back to the original raw data, and that (6) the mean is relatively *reliable* in problems of estimation and in tests of hypotheses. The property listed as (5) ties in closely with the concept of a *weighted mean*, and we shall take it up under this heading in Section 3.7. The question of *reliability* will be touched upon in Section 3.4. Roughly, it refers to the fact that means generally do not vary so much from sample to sample as some other kinds of statistical descriptions.

Since the computation of means is quite easy, involving only addition and one division, there is usually no need to look for shortcuts or simplification. However, if the numbers are unwieldy, that is, if each number has many digits, or if there are very many numbers, it may be advantageous to group the data first and then compute the mean from the resulting distribution. Another reason why we shall have to investigate the problem of obtaining means from grouped data is that *statistical information is often made available only in the form of distributions*. For instance, if we wanted to determine the mean of the contest scores of Exercise 9 on page 38, we would have to base it on the given distribution or go to the trouble of writing to the Arizona Association of Teachers of Mathematics for more detailed information.

On page 12 we observed that the grouping of a set of data entails some loss of information and that in a distribution each measurement, so to speak, loses its identity. It would thus seem that it is impossible to get the mean of a set of numbers once they have been grouped, and this is true *unless we are willing to make some assumption about the distribution of the items within each class* and to settle, thus, for an approximation. The assumption we shall make is that *all measurements falling into a class are located at its class mark*, namely, at the midpoint of its class interval. This assumption is not as unreasonable as it may seem; we cannot really expect all numbers within a class to be located at the class mark, some will fall above the class mark and some will fall below, but the error introduced by this assumption into the calculation of the mean will generally (more or less) average out.

To illustrate the calculation of a mean of grouped data, let us refer again to the speed-check distribution on page 17. Writing the class marks in the middle column, we have

| Speed (miles per hour) | Class mark | Number of Cars |
|---|---|---|
| 25 – 29 | 27 | 1 |
| 30 – 34 | 32 | 1 |
| 35 – 39 | 37 | 4 |
| 40 – 44 | 42 | 13 |
| 45 – 49 | 47 | 40 |
| 50 – 54 | 52 | 65 |
| 55 – 59 | 57 | 52 |
| 60 – 64 | 62 | 18 |
| 65 – 69 | 67 | 5 |
| 70 – 74 | 72 | 1 |

and according to the assumption made above, these speeds will be treated as if *one* had been 27, *one* had been 32, *four* had been 37, *thirteen* had been 42, *forty* had been 47, and so on. To find the sum needed in the numerator of the formula for the mean, we shall, thus, have to add 27 to 32 to *four* times 37 to *thirteen* times 42 to *forty* times 47, etc., and we can write

$$\bar{x} = \frac{27 + 32 + 4(37) + 13(42) + 40(47) + 65(52) + 52(57) + 18(62) + 5(67) + 72}{200}$$

$$= \frac{10,500}{200} = 52.5 \text{ mph}$$

It is interesting to note that if we had calculated the mean of the 200 ungrouped speeds with formula (3.3.1), we would have obtained 52.525 mph. The small difference between these two values is due to the error introduced by the assumption that all measurements belonging in a class are located at its class mark.

To state more formally what we have done in calculating the mean of the speed-check distribution, let us suppose that we are given a distribution having the *class marks* $x_1$, $x_2$, $x_3$, ..., $x_k$ and the class frequencies $f_1, f_2, f_3, ..., f_k$. Proceeding as before, we shall assume that the $f_1$ values in the first class are all equal to $x_1$, the $f_2$ values in the second class are all equal to $x_2$, the $f_3$ values in the third class are all equal to $x_3$, ..., and the $f_k$ values in the $k$th class are all equal to $x_k$. The mean of this distribution can then be written as

$$\bar{x} = \frac{x_1 f_1 + x_2 f_2 + x_3 f_3 + \ldots + x_k f_k}{f_1 + f_2 + f_3 + \ldots + f_k}$$

where the numerator stands for the sum of all the numbers and the denominator stands for the total number of items, that is, the total frequency. Simplifying this expression with the use of summation signs, let us finally write the formula for the *mean of a distribution with k classes* as

$$\bar{x} = \frac{\sum_{i=1}^{k} x_i f_i}{\sum_{i=1}^{k} f_i} \qquad (3.3.2) \blacktriangle$$

In words, we divide the sum of the products $x \cdot f$ by the sum of the $f$'s. Incidentally, if the data were looked upon as a population, we would write $\mu$ instead of $\bar{x}$, but otherwise the formula would remain unchanged.

The calculation of the mean of the speed-check distribution was very easy, due mainly to the fact that the frequencies were small and the class marks were easy-to-work-with two-digit numbers. If we tried to calculate the mean of the width-of-crab distribution on page 13 with formula (3.3.2), we would find that the class marks are 19.95, 39.95, ..., 179.95 and the arithmetic much more involved. To reduce the amount of work required in problems like this, let us demonstrate a short-cut technique based on what is called a *change of scale*. In Figure 3.1 we have drawn a histogram of the width-of-crab distribution with the class marks (in millimeters) indicated on the scale labeled $x$. To simplify the numbers with which we have to work in the calculation of the mean, let us imagine that we remove the *x*-scale without changing the remainder of the diagram, and that in its place we substitute a new scale which, in Figure 3.1, is labeled the *u-scale*. This new scale is chosen in such a way that

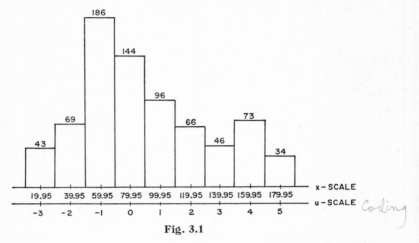

**Fig. 3.1**

*its units coincide with the class marks of the distribution*, making the new class marks −3, −2, −1, 0, 1, 2, 3, 4, and 5.

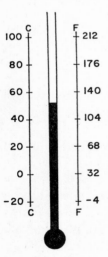

**Fig. 3.2**

The process of changing a scale — mathematicians also refer to it as *performing a transformation* and some statisticians call it *coding* — is not as far-fetched as it might seem. It is used, for instance, when we measure length in inches and feet or in centimeters and meters, and then change from one scale to the other, depending on the scale in which we want to perform the calculations and the scale in which we want to present the result. Another well-known example pertains to the measurement of temperature, which is sometimes measured in the Fahrenheit scale and sometimes in the centigrade scale. Figure 3.2 shows a thermometer with both scales, and the reader is probably familiar with the formula

$$F = \frac{9}{5}C + 32 \tag{3.3.3}$$

which makes it possible to convert temperature readings from centigrade to Fahrenheit and vice versa.

What we intend to do in the calculation of the mean of a distribution is very much the same. *We shall first calculate the mean in the u-scale, and then find $\bar{x}$ by converting the result to the x-scale with a formula analogous to* (3.3.3). It is easy to see that in the width-of-crab example (see Figure 3.1) this formula must be

$$x = 20u + 79.95$$

A value in the $u$-scale will first have to be multiplied by 20 since 1 unit in the $u$-scale corresponds to 20 units in the $x$-scale, and then 79.95 has to be added to account for the fact that this is the value which we chose for the zero point of the new scale.

More generally, if we introduce a new scale by assigning the values ..., $-4, -3, -2, -1, 0, 1, 2, 3, 4, \ldots$ to the class marks of a distribution, the formula which will enable us to change from one scale to the other is

$$x = c \cdot u + x_0 \tag{3.3.4}$$

where $c$ stands for the length of the class interval (as measured in the original $x$-scale) and $x_0$ stands for the class mark which is chosen as the zero of the new scale.

Substituting $u$'s for $x$'s in (3.3.2), and writing $n$ for the total frequency, we get

$$\bar{u} = \frac{\sum_{i=1}^{k} u_i f_i}{n} \tag{3.3.5}$$

and this gives the mean of a distribution in the new scale. To find $\bar{x}$, we have only to convert this value to the $x$-scale with the use of (3.3.4). Substituting into this equation we get

$$\bar{x} = \frac{c \cdot \sum_{i=1}^{k} u_i f_i}{n} + x_0 \tag{3.3.6} \blacktriangle$$

and this is the so-called *short-cut formula for calculating the mean of a distribution.* In words, $c$, the class interval, is multiplied by the sum of the products $u \cdot f$ and divided by the total frequency; then $x_0$, the class mark which was chosen as the zero of the new scale, is added to this result. (Incidentally, if we wanted to look upon a set of data as a population instead of a sample, we would write $\mu$ instead of $\bar{x}$, but otherwise the short-cut formula would remain unchanged.)

To illustrate the ease with which the mean of a distribution can be found with the short-cut formula, let us refer to the width-of-crab distribution on page 13. Arranging the work as follows:

| *Width* (millimeters) | $u$ | $f$ | $u \cdot f$ |
|---|---|---|---|
| 10.0 – 29.9 | −3 | 43 | −129 |
| 30.0 – 49.9 | −2 | 69 | −138 |
| 50.0 – 69.9 | −1 | 186 | −186 |
| 70.0 – 89.9 | 0 | 144 | 0 |
| 90.0 – 109.9 | 1 | 96 | 96 |
| 110.0 – 129.9 | 2 | 66 | 132 |
| 130.0 – 149.9 | 3 | 46 | 138 |
| 150.0 – 169.9 | 4 | 73 | 292 |
| 170.0 – 189.9 | 5 | 34 | 170 |
| | | 757 | 375 |

we find that the sum of the products $u \cdot f$ is 375, the total frequency is 757, and substitution into (3.3.6) yields

$$\bar{x} = \frac{20(375)}{757} + 79.95$$

$$= 89.86 \text{ millimeters}$$

It should be noted that, save for errors in arithmetic, *formulas (3.3.2) and (3.3.6) will always give identical results.* Had we used the short-cut formula to calculate the mean of the speed-check distribution, we would also have obtained 52.5 mph (see Exercise 8 on page 54).

The short-cut method is so simple and can save so much time that it should always be used for the calculation of means from grouped data. About the only time that the short-cut method does not provide appreciable savings in time and energy is when the original class marks are already easy-to-use numbers like, for example, those of the speed-check distribution. In order to reduce the work to a minimum, it is generally advisable to put the zero of the $u$-scale near the middle of the distribution, preferable at a class mark having one of the highest frequencies.

A fact worth noting is that the short-cut method cannot be used for distributions with *unequal classes*, although there exists a modification which makes it applicable also in that case. Of course, formula (3.3.2) *can* be used for distributions with unequal classes. Neither the short-cut formula nor (3.3.2) are applicable to distributions with *open classes*. Means of such distributions cannot be found without going back to the raw data or making special assumptions about the values that fall into an open class.

## EXERCISES

1. The daily high and low temperatures recorded at Sky Harbor Airport, Phoenix, during February 1958 were:

   *High:* 74, 76, 66, 61, 61, 65, 70, 65, 68, 67, 70, 68, 68, 69, 71, 74, 79,
   80, 79, 65, 74, 76, 75, 76, 65, 65, 62, 63

   *Low:* 46, 43, 54, 53, 43, 42, 47, 46, 46, 45, 43, 39, 51, 40, 42, 43, 45,
   46, 54, 53, 49, 51, 52, 51, 51, 49, 39, 35

   Find the mean of the daily high temperature readings and also that of the daily lows.

2. Find the mean of the following grades obtained by 20 students in a short quiz: 7, 10, 10, 5, 8, 4, 6, 9, 10, 3, 9, 9, 10, 8, 6, 7, 9, 6, 10, and 4.

3. Find the mean of the following weights of the football players on the Ohio State 1958 Rose Bowl squad:

   216, 208, 215, 189, 204, 215, 165, 193, 181, 172, 203, 202, 234, 195, 207, 258, 234, 212, 196, 184, 194, 209, 207, 217, 222, 192, 192, 180, 269, 206, 178, 168, 176, 168, 182, 204, 188, 198, 206, 191, 206, 178, 192, and 174.

4. The monthly values of the *Wholesale Price Index* (all commodities other than farm products and foods) as reported for 1954 and 1955 in the *Monthly Labor Review* were:

   *1954:* 114.6, 114.4, 114.2, 114.5, 114.5, 114.2, 114.3, 114.4, 114.4, 114.5, 114.8, 114.9

   *1955:* 115.2, 115.7, 115.6, 115.7, 115.5, 115.6, 116.5, 117.5, 118.5, 119.0, 119.4, 119.8

   Find the mean of this index (a) for 1954 and (b) for 1955. Also find the mean for the two years combined and compare this result with the mean of the values obtained separately for 1954 and 1955.

5. The following are a family's monthly electricity bills in 1957:

   | | | | | | |
   |---|---|---|---|---|---|
   | $14.02, | $13.05, | $10.34, | $13.33, | $13.90, | $11.99, |
   | $10.56, | $10.54, | $12.87, | $11.37, | $22.47, | $20.72 |

   Find the mean, that is, the average amount this family spent on electricity per month in 1957.

6. Find the mean of the following measurements of the thickness of a grease coating (in microns) produced on 20 steel rods by a certain machine: 39, 49, 61, 55, 55, 64, 61, 58, 42, 39, 44, 41, 51, 53, 46, 47, 63, 59, 56, 64.

7. Use formula (3.3.2) to find the mean of the contest scores of Exercise 9 on page 38.

8. Use the short-cut formula to find the mean of the speed-check distribution on page 17 and compare your result with the value obtained by the long method on page 48.

9. Use formula (3.3.2) to find the mean of the *modified* speed-check distribution, the one with unequal classes, on page 29.

10. Find the mean of the ACE linguistic scores of Exercise 9 on page 25 (a) on the basis of the ungrouped data, and (b) on the basis of the distribution constructed in that exercise.

11. Calculate the mean of the lengths of root penetration of Exercise 11 on page 26 (a) on the basis of the ungrouped data, and (b) on the basis of the distribution obtained in that exercise.

12. Find the mean of the religious literacy scores of Exercise 13 on page 26 (a) on the basis of the ungrouped data, and (b) on the basis of the distribution obtained in that exercise.

13. Calculate the mean of the amounts of Exercise 14 on page 26 (a) on the basis of the ungrouped data, and (b) on the basis of the distribution constructed in that exercise.

14. Find the mean of the lengths of the sea trouts of Exercise 15 on page 27 (a) on the basis of the ungrouped data, and (b) on the basis of the distribution obtained in that exercise.

15. Find the mean of the plating thicknesses of Exercise 16 on page 27 (a) on the basis of the ungrouped data, and (b) on the basis of the distribution constructed in that exercise.

16. Find the mean of the time lapses between eruptions of Old Faithful given in Exercise 17 on page 28 (a) on the basis of the ungrouped data, and (b) on the basis of the distribution constructed in that exercise.

17. Calculate the means of *both* distributions constructed in Exercise 18 on page 28.

## 3.4 / The Median

The *median* is a measure of location that is sometimes used instead of the mean to describe the "center," "middle," or "average" of a set of data. It is defined simply as *the value of the middle item (or the mean of the values of the two middle items) when the items are arranged in an increasing or decreasing order of magnitude.*

Given an *odd* number of measurements, there is always a middle item whose value, by definition, is the median. For instance, the median of

13   16   18   20   10

is 16 and the median of

6   8   13   13   13   13   19

is 13. In the first example it is easy to make the mistake of saying, without thinking, that the median is 18. Remembering that the numbers must first be arranged according to size, we get 10, 13, 16, 18, 20, and it is apparent that the median is 16. In the second example the numbers are already arranged according to size and it can be seen by inspection that the middle (or fourth) item has a value of 13.

Generally speaking, if $n$ is *odd*, the median of $n$ numbers is given by the value of the $\frac{n+1}{2}$th counting from either end, provided, of course, that the numbers are arranged according to size.* Among 35 numbers the median is the $\frac{35+1}{2}$th or 18th, among 63 numbers the median is the $\frac{63+1}{2}$th or 32nd, and among 215 numbers the median is the $\frac{215+1}{2}$th or 108th.

If several values are equal (for instance, the four 13's in our second example), the order in which they are written does not matter at all. Given the numbers 2, 2, 3, 5, 5, 5, 5, 5, and 9, it would be meaningless to ask which particular 5 is the median. The median is a number, the value of the middle item, and in this example it is equal to 5.

Given an *even* number of measurements, there never is a middle item and according to our definition the median is the mean of the values of the middle two. For instance, the median of

8   11   13   15   17   25

---

*Beginning students often commit the error of mistaking $\frac{n+1}{2}$ for a formula that actually *gives* the median. This is incorrect. The formula merely tells us how many of the ordered items one has to count to reach the particular number (or midpoint between numbers, see page 56) whose value is the median.

is the mean of the 3rd and 4th, namely, $\dfrac{13 + 15}{2} = 14$. The median of an even number of measurements is, thus, halfway between the two middle values and, interpreted correctly, the formula $\dfrac{n + 1}{2}$ will again give the position of the median. If there are six numbers, $\dfrac{n + 1}{2} = \dfrac{6 + 1}{2} = 3\frac{1}{2}$ and we interpret this as meaning "halfway between the 3rd and 4th." Similarly, for $n = 60$, $\dfrac{n + 1}{2} = \dfrac{60 + 1}{2} = 30\frac{1}{2}$ and the median is the mean of the 30th number and the 31st (provided that the numbers are first ordered according to size).

In order to find the median of the ungrouped speed-check data on page 15, we first have to arrange the 200 numbers according to size and then calculate the mean of the 100th and 101st.* Finding, thus, that the 100th and 101st are both 53, it follows that the median, itself, is 53.

It should not be surprising that this value does not coincide with the mean, which, as we saw on page 49, was 52.525. *The median and the mean describe the center of a set of data in different ways*, and the very fact that they differ here by as little as 0.475 will later, in Chapter 5, be interpreted as indicating a further property of the given data, namely, their *symmetry*.

There are some problems in which it is necessary to determine the median (that is, a value which–except for ties–is exceeded by as many values as it exceeds) directly from grouped data. This can happen, for example, when data needed in a study are supplied by an *external source*, say, a government agency, and available only in the form of a distribution. At other times, it may simply be too much work to arrange the data, perhaps thousands of numbers, according to size.

As we pointed out earlier in this chapter, the grouping of a set of data makes it impossible to calculate the mean unless we make some assumption about the distribution of the measurements within each class. This argument applies also to the median, and we shall take care of it by making a slight modification in its definition. The

---

*Actually, this work can be simplified by noting that in the distribution on page 17 there are 59 values less than 50 and 124 less than 55. Counting the 50's, 51's, 52's, 53's, and 54's among the raw data on page 15, we find that these numbers occur, respectively, with frequencies of 9, 10, 12, 19, and 15. It follows from this that the 91st to 109th values are all 53's and, hence, that the 100th and 101st values are both 53's.

definition of the median of grouped data is most easily understood with the aid of a diagram like that of Figure 3.3, showing again the histogram of the speed-check distribution. With reference to this figure, *the median of a distribution is defined as a number, a point, which is such that half of the total area of the rectangles of the histogram*

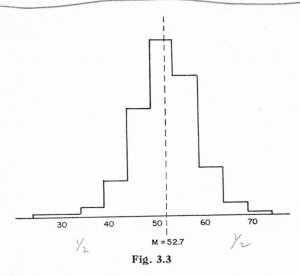

**Fig. 3.3**

*lies to its left and half to its right.* This means that the sum of the areas of the rectangles (or parts of rectangles) to the left of the dotted line in Figure 3.3 must equal the sum of the areas to its right.

This definition of the median of a distribution really agrees quite closely with the one given earlier for the median of ungrouped data. As we pointed out on page 31, the areas of the rectangles represent, or are proportional to, the class frequencies. Hence, if the total area to the left of the median equals that to its right, there is the implication that there are as many items to the left of the median (below the median) as there are to its right (or above). Actually, this is not *quite* correct, as it would have to depend on the distribution of the items within the class into which the median falls. The definition given with the aid of Figure 3.3 assumes that the items are distributed, or spread out, evenly throughout the interval of this class.

In contrast to finding the median of ungrouped data, where we looked for the middle item (or items) and counted off $\dfrac{n+1}{2}$, we are now looking for a number, a dividing line, that divides the total area of the histogram into two equal parts, each representing a frequency of $n/2$. *Hence, to find the median of a distribution with a total frequency of n, we must, so to speak, count n/2 items starting at either end.*

To illustrate this procedure, let us again refer to the speed-check distribution on page 17. Since $n$ equals 200, we will have to count $200/2 = 100$ items from either end. Beginning at the bottom of the distribution and using class boundaries, it can be seen that *one* value was less than 29.5, *two* were less than 34.5, *six* were less than 39.5, *nineteen* were less than 44.5, *fifty-nine* were less than 49.5, and *hundred twenty-four* were less than 54.5. It follows that the median will have to lie somewhere in the interval from 49.5 to 54.5, and that we shall have to count another $100 - 59 = 41$ items in addition to the 59 falling below 49.5. Using the assumption made above, namely, that the 65 items in the class going from 49.5 to 54.5 are *evenly distributed* throughout this class, we reach the median by adding 41/65 of this interval to the lower class boundary of 49.5. We thus get

$$\text{median} = 49.5 + 5 \cdot \frac{41}{65} = 52.7 \text{ mph}$$

rounded to the nearest tenth of a mile.

What we have done here is shown geometrically in **Figure 3.4.**

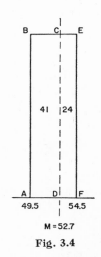

Fig. 3.4

Since 41 of the 65 cases falling into the interval from 49.5 to 54.5 must be *to the left of the median*, the area of rectangle $ABCD$ must be 41/65 of the area of rectangle $ABEF$. Hence $AD$ must be 41/65 of $AF$, or 41/65 *times* 5, and the median is finally obtained by adding this quantity to the lower class boundary of 49.5.

Generally speaking, if $L$ is the lower boundary of the class into which the median must fall, $f_M$ the frequency of this class, $c$ the class interval, and $j$ the number of items we still lack when reaching $L$, then *the median, $M$, is given by the formula*

$$M = L + c \cdot \frac{j}{f_M}$$    (3.4.1)▲

If, in the speed-check example, we had begun counting at the other end, namely, with the highest speeds, we would have had to modify formula (3.4.1) by substituting $U$, the upper class boundary, for $L$, and changing the $+$ to $-$. Since 76 of the speeds exceed 54.5 and 141 exceed 49.5, we get

$$M = 54.5 - 5 \cdot \frac{24}{65} = 52.7 \text{ mph}$$

and this is identical, as it should be, with the result obtained before. Figure 3.4 shows why we had to subtract 24/65 of 5 from the upper class boundary 54.5.

In general, if the median of a distribution is to be obtained by counting $n/2$ items starting *at the top* of the distribution, that is, starting with the largest values, we can write analogous to (3.4.1)

$$M = U - c \cdot \frac{j'}{f_M}$$    (3.4.2)▲

where $j'$ is the number of items we still lack when reaching $U$, the upper boundary of the class into which the median must fall.

In (3.4.1) and (3.4.2) we wrote the median as $M$, but there is no general agreement in this respect. In some texts the word "median" is simply spelled out in full, in some it is abbreviated to Med, Md, or M, and in some it is given as $\tilde{x}$. Also, since in practical applications medians are used mainly to estimate (or test hypotheses about) population means, that is, $\mu$'s, there is really no need to introduce different symbols for medians of samples and medians of populations.

To list some of the advantageous properties of the median, let us point out that (1) it always exists, it can be determined for any set of numerical data; (2) it is always unique; and (3) it can be found with a minimum of arithmetic. Unfortunately, the last advantage is offset by the disadvantage that the numbers must first be arranged according to size, and this can be a very tedious job. Two other desirable properties of the median which, incidentally, it does not share with the mean, are that (4) it is not easily affected by extreme values (a very large or very small value), and (5) it can be found even for distribution with *open classes* at either end. The only exception to this is when the median, itself, falls into an open class, but for this to happen the distribution would have to be strange indeed.

To illustrate the fact that the median is not so easily affected by an extreme value as is the mean, let us refer again to the example on page 47, where a technician made the mistake of writing down 203 instead of 703. His measurements of the "lifetimes" of the five tubes were 942, 820, 981, 929, 703, whose median is 929, and as can easily be verified, the median will still be 929 if the fifth reading is changed from 703 to 203. (Had the technician made the mistake of recording 981 incorrectly as 681, the median would have been affected. Nevertheless we can say that *in general* the median is not so easily affected by extreme values as is the mean.)

Another point worth mentioning about the median is that it can serve to define the *middle* of a set of objects, properties, or attributes that do not permit a quantitative description. For instance, we could rank samples of different kinds of chocolate sirup and then choose the middle one as having "average" consistency or "average" flavor. It is needless to say that the mean could not have been used in this situation.

Among the *disadvantages* of the median, we already mentioned that it can be a very tedious job to arrange a set of data according to size. Let us now add that given the medians of two or more sets of data, we generally cannot find the over-all median without going back to the raw data. For example, the median of 24, 27, and 30 is 27, the median of 25, 49, and 52 is 49, and knowing only these two medians we would never be able to arrive at the result that the over-all median of the six numbers is 28.5.

A further disadvantage of the median, *perhaps the most important one*, is that in problems of estimation and tests of hypotheses it is generally not very *reliable*, at least, not as reliable as the mean. To explain what this means, let us suppose that three biologists undertake to determine the true average length of full-grown scorpions of a newly discovered variety, and that they decide that each is to base his estimate on a sample of 3 scorpions. Let us suppose, furthermore, that the results they obtain are:

| | |
|---|---|
| Biologist A: | 1.4, 2.1, 2.2 inches |
| Biologist B: | 1.6, 1.6, 2.2 inches |
| Biologist C: | 1.5, 1.9, 2.0 inches |

If all three of them used the *mean* to estimate the true average length of this kind of scorpion, they would get 1.9, 1.8, and 1.8 inches, respectively. On the other hand, if they used the *median*, their estimates would be 2.1, 1.6, and 1.9 inches. These results show that whereas the means are relatively close together, varying only from 1.8 to 1.9, the medians are scattered over the much wider interval from 1.6 to 2.1. *It is in this sense that we say that the mean is more reliable than the median; the mean is subject to less chance variation.*

Since the last illustration was artificial and somewhat exaggerated to prove our point, let us consider another example, one referring to a game of chance. Rolling 3 dice *six times* and recording in each case the numbers obtained as well as their mean and median, an actual experiment yielded the following results:

| Rolls of 3 Dice | Mean | Median |
|:---:|:---:|:---:|
| 6, 2, 5 | $4\frac{1}{3}$ | 5 |
| 4, 3, 3 | $3\frac{1}{3}$ | 3 |
| 6, 1, 5 | 4 | 5 |
| 1, 5, 2 | $2\frac{2}{3}$ | 2 |
| 2, 6, 4 | 4 | 4 |
| 2, 2, 5 | 3 | 2 |

Studying these results we find that there is, indeed, a greater variation between the medians than there is between the means (see

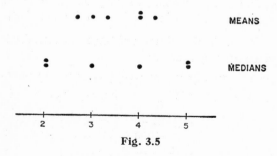

**Fig. 3.5**

Figure 3.5). Incidentally, if a die is rolled a great number of times, its points will average 3.5, and this is the mean $\mu$ about which the sample values are scattered in Figure 3.5. In case the reader is not convinced by this example, he is welcome to duplicate the experiment for himself. Although we cannot *guarantee* results, he should usually find that the medians are scattered somewhat more widely than the means. This problem will be discussed further in Chapter 9.

### EXERCISES

1. Find the median of the following grades obtained by 25 students in a history examination: 67, 98, 72, 63, 59, 71, 58, 50, 93, 68, 49, 57, 77, 89, 76, 84, 70, 21, 64, 35, 54, 73, 84, 46, 80.     68

2. Find the median of the following numbers of defective machine parts observed in lots of 400 each: 3, 7, 10, 8, 1, 6, 8, 0, 12, 5, 4, 9, 5, 6, 2, 8, 28, 3.

3. Find the median of the grades given in Exercise 2 on page 53.

4. Find the median of the daily low temperatures given in Exercise 1 on page 53 and also that of the daily high temperatures.

5. Find the median of the weights of the football players given in Exercise 3 on page 53.

6. Find the median of the thicknesses of grease films given in Exercise 6 on page 53.

7. Find the median of the width-of-crab distribution given in the text on page 13.

8. Find the median of the ACE linguistic scores of Exercise 9 on page 25 (a) on the basis of the ungrouped data, and (b) on the basis of the distribution obtained in that exercise.

9. Find the median of the lengths of root penetration of Exercise 11 on page 26 on the basis of the distribution obtained in that exercise.

10. Find the median of the distribution obtained in Exercise 13 on page 26 for the religious literacy scores.

11. Determine the median of the distribution obtained in Exercise 14 on page 26. Check your result by using both (3.4.1) and (3.4.2).

12. Find the median of the plating thicknesses of Exercise 16 on page 27 (a) on the basis of the ungrouped data, and (b) on the basis of the distribution obtained in that exercise.

13. Use the distribution obtained in Exercise 17 on page 28 to find the median of the time lapses between eruptions of Old Faithful.

**14.** In order to compare two brands of tires, a research organization tested
5 tires of each kind, measuring the mileage for which each tire gave
adequate service. The results of this test were: The tires made by
Firm A lasted 26,800, 22,300, 27,400, 24,000, and 23,500 miles, while
those made by Firm B lasted 25,600, 23,400, 21,000, 26,000, and
25,000 miles. Comment on the claims made by *both* firms that "on
the average" their tires showed up better in this test.

## 3.5 / The Mode    — highest frequency

The mode is a third measure of location that is sometimes used and
it is defined simply as *the value, class, or category which occurs the
most often, that is, with the highest frequency*. It applies to numerical
as well as categorical data as is illustrated by the following examples:
If more students attending a certain college are 18 years old than
any other age, we say that 18 is the *modal age;* if, in a weight distribution, the class going from 140 through 149 has the highest frequency,
we say that it is the *modal class;* and if, among the members of a
certain sorority, blond is the most prevalent hair color, we say that
blond is the *modal color* of these girls' hair.

An obvious advantage of the mode is that it requires no calculations at all. We merely select the value, class, or category that
appears the most often; it is in this sense that the mode is *most
typical* of a set of data. Unfortunately, the mode also has some very
definite disadvantages. If in a set of measurements no two values
are alike, it would be rather trivial to say that each value is a mode,
namely, that each value occurs with the highest frequency. Actually,
we shall say in a situation like this that the mode *does not exist*.
Furthermore, the mode may *not be unique;* given the numbers 80,
82, 82, 82, 87, 89, 91, 96, 96, 96, 99, 99, and 102, for example, we
find that 82 and 96 *both* occur with the maximum frequency of 3 and
we can, thus, say that there are two modes or that the data is
*bimodal.*　　　　　　　　　　　　　　　　　　　　　　　　　bimodal

The mode's principal value lies in the fact that it can be used
with qualitative data. For instance, if we wanted to study consumers' preferences for different kinds of food, different kinds of
packaging, or different kinds of advertizing, we could in each case
determine the preference that is the mode and in some problems,
perhaps, compare the modal preferences expressed by several groups
of individuals. In a situation like this we could not have used either
the median or the mean. (As we pointed out on page 60, the median

can sometimes be used to describe the "middle" of qualitative data, but it is inapplicable unless the objects or items can be *ordered* in some way.)

When dealing with quantitative data, the disadvantages of the mode outweigh its desirable features and it is, in fact, rarely used. As we said before, it can easily happen that the mode does not exist or that it is not unique. Moreover, the mode is generally a very *unreliable* measure of central location in problems of estimation or tests of hypotheses (see page 75). Finally, like the median, it does not readily lend itself to further manipulations; for example, it is generally impossible to find the mode of combined data on the basis of their individual modes.

So far as the mode of grouped data is concerned, it is customary to refer to the class having the highest frequency as the *modal class*. In our speed-check example the modal class is the one containing speeds from 50 mph through 54 mph (see page 17), and in the width-of-crab example it is the one going from 50.0 to 69.9 millimeters (see page 13).

Although it is sometimes convenient to define the mode of a distribution as the *class mark of the modal class*, there are more

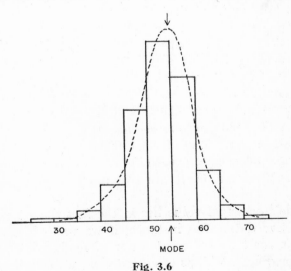

Fig. 3.6

sophisticated ways in which this may be done. One possibility is to approximate the histogram of the distribution with a smooth curve (see Figure 3.6) and then define the mode as the values that corresponds to its highest point. We shall not go into this any further since there are very few occasions where it is necessary, or desirable, to use the mode of a distribution. Suitable references to various definitions of the mode of distributions may be found in the Bibliography on page 76.

## EXERCISES

**1.** Find the mode of the ungrouped speeds on page 15.

**2.** Find the mode of each of the following sets of numbers (if it exists):

(a) 11, 15, 12, 13, 15, 13, 14, 14, 16, 14, 13, 14, 12 = 14
(b) 54, 38, 62, 47, 65, 31, 39, 35, 43, 56, 30 = does not exist.
(c) 27, 31, 31, 34, 32, 30, 31, 28, 34, 31, 34, 26　31 + 34 bimodal

**3.** Find the modes of the high and low temperatures of Exercise 1 on page 53. high = 65
Low = 46 43 51　Tri-modal

**4.** Find the modal classes and their class marks for the two distributions constructed in Exercise 18 on page 28.

**5.** When asking 30 college students for the dessert they like best, an interviewer obtained the following replies: ice cream, pudding, apple pie, chocolate cake, cherry pie, apple pie, ice cream, crepes suzette, strawberry shortcake, ice cream, apple pie, chocolate cake, pudding, rice pudding, ice cream, Napoleons, cherry pie, peach pie, apple pie, chocolate cake, chocolate cake, ice cream, apple pie, pumpkin pie, marble cake, cheese cake, apple pie, cherry pie, chocolate cake, and apple pie. Find the modal choice of this group of students.

## 3.6 / The Geometric and Harmonic Means

In our discussion of the mean we mentioned that, technically speaking, its full name is "arithmetic mean," in order to distinguish it from two other statistical measures called the *geometric* and *harmonic means*. The first of these rarely used measures of central location is defined as follows: given a set of numbers $x_1$, $x_2$, $x_3$, ..., $x_n$, the *geometric mean* is the $n$th root of their product or, symbolically,

$$\text{geometric mean} = \sqrt[n]{x_1 \cdot x_2 \cdot x_3 \cdot \ldots \cdot x_n} \qquad (3.6.1) \blacktriangle$$

Since this formula quite evidently involves a good deal of work, it would seem only reasonable to ask why and under what circumstances this kind of average should be used. To give an example in which its use would be appropriate, let us suppose that census counts show that in 1930 the population of a certain community was 3000, in 1940 it was 6000, and in 1950 it was 48,000. Let us suppose, furthermore, that on the basis of this information we are asked to determine the average *ten-year rate of change* in the size of this community. Clearly, from 1930 to 1940 the size of the population was multiplied by 2 and from 1940 to 1950 it was multiplied by 8. Calculating the (arithmetic) mean of these two numbers we find that *on the average* the population multiplied by $\dfrac{2+8}{2} = 5$ every ten years, but this result can easily be misunderstood. If we were told that in 1930 the population was 3000 and that on the average it multiplied by 5 every ten years, we might be led to believe that in 1940 the size of the population was 5(3000) = 15,000, and that in 1950 it was 5(15,000) = 75,000. Evidently, both of these figures are much too high. If we calculated the geometric mean of 2 and 8, we would get

$$\text{geometric mean} = \sqrt[2]{2 \cdot 8} = \sqrt[2]{16} = 4$$

and if we applied this "average rate of increase" to the 1930 figure of 3000, we might surmise that the 1940 and 1950 populations had been 4(3000) = 12,000 and 4(12,000) = 48,000, respectively. Although the 1940 figure is still too high, the 1950 figure is now correct.

The above illustrates in what kind of problem geometric means might profitably be used. In actual practice, geometric means are used mainly in problems in which we are interested in averaging ratios or rates of change, particularly index numbers, which we shall treat separately in Chapter 6.

Among the interesting aspects of the geometric mean we find that it must never be used if one of the numbers we wish to average is *zero* or *negative*. If one of the numbers is zero, the geometric mean is zero; and if one or more are negative, the geometric mean may turn out to be an imaginary number. Otherwise, the geometric mean is always uniquely defined and it takes into account each individual item. In contrast to the mean, it is not so readily affected by a very small or very large value (see page 47) and this is a major reason why it is sometimes preferred to the mean. If, for some reason, a geometric mean *has* to be found, its calculation can be simplified considerably by using logarithms and writing its formula as

$$\log G = \frac{\sum_{i=1}^{n} \log x_i}{n} \tag{3.6.2}$$ ▲

where $G$ stands for geometric mean. With this formula we can find $G$ by adding the logarithms of the $x$'s, dividing by $n$, and then taking the antilog. We shall not illustrate the use of (3.6.2), since, as we pointed out earlier, geometric means are very rarely used.

The same is true also for the *harmonic mean*, which is defined as *n divided by the sum of the reciprocals of the x's*, or, symbolically, as

$$\text{harmonic mean} = \frac{n}{\sum_{i=1}^{n} \frac{1}{x_i}} \qquad (3.6.3) \blacktriangle$$

To give an example in which the harmonic mean provides an appropriate average, let us suppose that we have spent \$24 on eggs costing 40 cents a dozen and \$24 on eggs costing 60 cents a dozen. To determine the average price per dozen, we might be tempted to calculate the mean of 40 and 60, but it is easy to demonstrate that $\frac{40+60}{2} = 50$ cents is incorrect. For the first \$24 we got 60 dozen eggs at 40 cents a dozen and for the second \$24 we got 40 dozen eggs at 60 cents a dozen. Hence, we bought a total of 100 dozen eggs for \$48 and the correct average price is 48 cents per dozen. Had we calculated the harmonic mean of 40 and 60 we would have obtained

$$\text{harmonic mean} = \frac{2}{\frac{1}{40} + \frac{1}{60}} = 48$$

and this is the correct average price per dozen.

Since the harmonic mean is used only in very special kinds of problems, we shall not discuss it any further. In case the reader is curious to learn more about these special means, he will find suitable references in the Bibliography on page 76.

### 3.7 / The Weighted Mean

There are some problems in which it is impossible to average quantities without accounting in some way for their relative importance in the over-all situation we are trying to describe. For instance, if a butcher sells three grades of sirloin steak at \$1.19, \$1.29, and \$1.49 a pound, it is impossible to determine the over-all price he receives per pound unless we also know the number of pounds sold of each grade. If most people buy the cheapest grade, the average price will be close to \$1.19, and if most of them buy the expensive grade, the average will be closer to $1.49. This illustrates how in some instances we cannot calculate a meaningful average without knowing the weight (the relative importance) of each of the numbers we wish to average. To give other examples, we cannot combine (or average) the batting averages of several baseball players without knowing their respective times at bat, and we would probably get a very misleading picture if we averaged changes in the values of certain stocks without paying due respect to the number of shares sold of each.

To return to the first example, let us suppose that in a certain week the butcher sells 800 pounds of the cheapest grade, 600 pounds of the medium priced grade, and 100 pounds of the most expensive grade. Simple arithmetic shows that he, thus, received a total of

$$800(1.19) + 600(1.29) + 100(1.49) = \$1875.00$$

for $800 + 600 + 100 = 1500$ pounds of steak and an average of $1875/1500 = \$1.25$ per pound. The average we have calculated in this example is called a *weighted mean;* we averaged the prices giving due weight to the relative importance of each, namely, to the number of pounds sold of each grade.

In general, the *weighted mean* of a set of numbers $x_1, x_2, x_3, \ldots, x_n$ whose relative importance is expressed numerically by some numbers $w_1, w_2, w_3, \ldots, w_n$ called the *weights,* is defined as

*weighted mean*

$$\bar{x}_w = \frac{\sum_{i=1}^{n} w_i x_i}{\sum_{i=1}^{n} w_i} \qquad (3.7.1)\blacktriangle$$

To give another example, let us suppose that Mr. Brown invests $4,000 at 5 per cent, $10,000 at 6 per cent, and that we are interested in determining the average interest rate on his total investments. Using the amounts invested at each rate as weights, namely, letting $w_1 = 4000$ and $w_2 = 10,000$, we find upon substituting into (3.7.1) that

$$\bar{x}_w = \frac{4000 \cdot 5 + 10,000 \cdot 6}{4000 + 10,000} = \frac{80,000}{14,000} = 5\tfrac{5}{7} \text{ per cent}$$

The choice of the weights did not pose any particular problems in our two numerical examples, but there are situations in which their selection is not quite so obvious. For instance, if we wanted to construct a *cost-of-living index,* we would have to worry about the relative importance of such things as food, rent, entertainment, medical care, and so on, in the average person's budget. To give one *Rule* general rule, the weights that are commonly used to average prices *wgts = quantit* are, as in the example of the steaks, the corresponding *quantities* sold, consumed, or produced.

A special form of the weighted mean arises when we want to determine the <u>*over-all mean*</u> <u>of several sets of data on the basis of</u> <u>their individual means and the number of items in each.</u> Given $n_1$ numbers whose mean is $\bar{x}_1$, $n_2$ numbers whose mean is $\bar{x}_2$, $n_3$ numbers whose mean is $\bar{x}_3$, ..., and $n_k$ numbers whose mean is $\bar{x}_k$, the over-all mean of all these numbers is

$$\bar{x} = \frac{\displaystyle\sum_{i=1}^{k} n_i \bar{x}_i}{\displaystyle\sum_{i=1}^{k} n_i} \qquad \text{over-all mean}$$

(3.7.2)▲

In this formula the over-all mean, $\bar{x}$, is obtained by weighting the individual means with the number of items on which they are based. To give an example, let us suppose that in a final examination in European History *twenty-eight* students in Section 1 had an average (mean) grade of 64.2, *twenty-four* students in Section 2 had a mean grade of 71.5, *thirty-five* students in Section 3 had a mean grade of 67.3, whereas *eighteen* students in Section 4 had a mean grade of 70.6. Substituting $n_1 = 28$, $n_2 = 24$, $n_3 = 35$, $n_4 = 18$, and $\bar{x}_1 = 64.2$, $\bar{x}_2 = 71.5$, $\bar{x}_3 = 67.3$, $\bar{x}_4 = 70.6$ into (3.7.2), we obtain

$$\bar{x} = \frac{28(64.2) + 24(71.5) + 35(67.3) + 18(70.6)}{28 + 24 + 35 + 18}$$

$$= \frac{7139.9}{105} = 68.0$$

for the over-all mean of these 105 students' grades.

This example explains what we meant on page 47 when we said that it is possible to combine the means of several sets of data into an over-all mean without having to go back to the raw data. It is fairly easy to see that formula (3.7.2) actually gives the *exact* value of the over-all mean. Since we originally defined $\bar{x}$ as *the sum of the x's divided by n*, it follows that *n times* $\bar{x}$ equals *the sum of the x's*, and each term in the numerator of (3.7.2) equals the sum of all numbers in the corresponding set of data. Hence, the numerator of (3.7.2) equals the sum of *all* the numbers, its denominator equals the total number of items, and the formula gives the exact over-all mean.

## EXERCISES

1. Find the geometric mean of (a) 4 and 16; (b) 4, 10, and 25; and (c) 1, 1, 2, and 8.

2. In a French vocabulary test a student answered 81 of 300 questions correctly on the first try, 108 of 300 on the second try a week later, and 256 of 300 on the third try a week after that. Thus, on the second try he did $108/81 = 4/3$ as well as on the first, and on the third he did $256/108 = 64/27$ as well as on the second. Use formula (3.6.1) to find the "average improvement ratio" between successive tries.

3. Find the harmonic mean of (a) 120 and 180, and (b) 3, 4, and 6.

4. If a motorist travels the first 20 miles of a trip at 30 mph and the second 20 miles at 60 mph, what is his average speed for this 40-mile trip? Would the harmonic mean give the correct answer?

5. In 1945 there were 0.42 fatalities per 1,000,000 revenue miles flown by commercial air carriers in the United States, in 1950 there were 0.28, and in 1953 there were 0.19. Given that the total number of revenue miles flown by these carriers in 1945, 1950, and 1953 were approximately 209 million, 364 million, and 519 million, respectively, find the weighted mean of the fatality rates for these three years.

6. The average price paid for a pound of copper in 1948, 1950, 1952, and 1954 was 22.2, 21.5, 24.4, and 29.8 cents. If in these same years the production of copper was 103, 106, 99, and 109 thousands of short tons, what is the average price paid for a pound of copper in these four years?

7. The average (mean) weight of the 4 backs who started the 1958 Rose Bowl game for Ohio State University was $187\frac{1}{4}$ pounds, and the mean weight of the 7 starting linemen was 202 pounds. Find the over-all mean of the weights of this starting eleven.

8. Given that the average (mean) age of the 36 members of one fraternity is 19.5 years, whereas that of the 39 members of a second fraternity is 20.1 years, and that of the 25 members of a third fraternity is 19.8 years, find the over-all mean of the ages of these fraternity men.

9. In an experiment to test a new reducing diet, 5 persons in the age group from 20 to 29 lost on the average 8.4 pounds, 8 persons in the age group from 30 to 39 lost on the average 9 pounds, 12 persons in the age group from 40 to 49 lost on the average 9.5 pounds, 6 persons in the age group from 50 to 59 lost on the average 14 pounds, while 5 persons in the age group from 60 to 69 lost on the average 6.6 pounds. Combine these five means into an over-all mean.

## 3.8 / Quartiles, Deciles, and Percentiles

The measures of location which we studied in the preceding sections belong under the heading of "measures of central location," providing numbers that are in some sense representative of the center or middle of a set of data. In this section we shall indicate methods of describing other kinds of locations; for example, we shall see how to obtain values that are exceeded by 25 per cent, 10 per cent, or 3 per cent of a set of data, and values that exceed, say, 5 per cent, 25 per cent, or 40 per cent of our data. Since there is really no sense in dividing small sets of data into 10 or even 100 equal parts, we shall discuss these measures only with reference to grouped data. However, as can be seen from Exercise 5 on page 74, it is possible to define analogous measures for ungrouped data.

The *quartiles* of a distribution are values which divide it into four parts so that *one fourth* of the data fall below the *first quartile*, $Q_1$, *half* of the data fall below the *second quartile*, $Q_2$, and *three fourths* of the data fall below the *third quartile*, $Q_3$. (By the same token, *one fourth* of the data fall above $Q_3$, *half* the data fall above $Q_2$, and

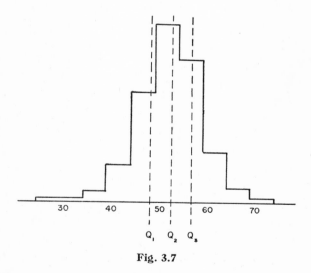

**Fig. 3.7**

*three fourths* of the data fall above $Q_1$.) Making the same assumption as in the case of the median, which, incidentally, coincides with $Q_2$, we shall say that by definition *the quartiles of a distribution divide the total area of the rectangles of its histogram into four equal parts* (see Figure 3.7). As on page 57, the assumption which we shall make is that within the classes into which the quartiles will fall, the respective items are evenly distributed throughout the class interval.

The steps needed to calculate $Q_1$ and $Q_3$ are, for all practical purposes, identical with those needed to find a median. The only difference is that starting at the bottom of the distribution, that is, starting with the smallest values, we must count $n/4$ cases to reach $Q_1$ and $3n/4$ cases to reach $Q_3$. Starting at the other end, we correspondingly have to count $3n/4$ cases to reach $Q_1$ and $n/4$ cases to reach $Q_3$.

To illustrate the calculation of $Q_1$ and $Q_3$, let us again refer to the speed-check distribution, for which we already found the median (or $Q_2$) on page 58. Since the total frequency is 200, we will have to count $200/4 = 50$ cases starting at the bottom of the distribution to reach $Q_1$ and $3 \cdot 200/4 = 150$ to reach $Q_3$. As in the calculation of the median (see page 59), we first will have to find the classes into which the quartiles will fall, and then we have to add fractions of the class interval to the lower class boundaries in order to account for the items we still lack. Since on page 17 there are 19 speeds below 44.5, we need $50 - 19 = 31$ of the speeds falling into the next class in order to reach $Q_1$. Hence, using a formula analogous to (3.4.1), we get

$$Q_1 = 44.5 + 5 \cdot \frac{31}{40} = 48.4 \text{ mph}$$

rounded to the nearest tenth. Similarly, since 124 of the speeds were below 54.5, we need $150 - 124 = 26$ of the 52 items falling into the next class in order to reach $Q_3$. Again using a formula analogous to (3.4.1), we obtain

$$Q_3 = 54.5 + 5 \cdot \frac{26}{52} = 57.0 \text{ mph}$$

If we wanted to calculate $Q_3$ by counting 50 cases from the other end of the distribution, we would get

$$Q_3 = 59.5 - 5 \cdot \frac{26}{52} = 57.0 \text{ mph}$$

using in this case a formula analogous to (3.4.2). When using (3.4.1) or (3.4.2) in the determination of $Q_1$ and $Q_3$, it must be understood that $L$ and $U$ now stand for the lower and upper boundaries of the classes into which the respective quartiles will fall, and that $f_M$ (we might now call it $f_Q$), represents the corresponding class frequencies.

*Deciles* are values that divide a distribution (or, better, the
total area of the rectangles of its histogram) into 10 equal parts.
We shall write $D_1$ for the *first decile* which exceeds 10 per cent and
is exceeded by 90 per cent of the data, $D_2$ for the *second decile* which
exceeds 20 per cent and is exceeded by 80 per cent of the data, and,
in general, $D_i$ for the *i*th *decile* which exceeds $i \cdot 10$ per cent and is
exceeded by $100 - i \cdot 10$ per cent of the data.

In order to reach any one of the $D_i$ (*i* can be either 1, 2, 3, . . . ,
or 9), we will have to count $n \cdot i/10$ cases starting at the bottom of
the distribution or *n minus* that many starting at the other end.
To illustrate the calculation of deciles, let us find $D_1$ and $D_8$ for the
speed-check distribution on page 17. In order to find $D_1$, we will
have to count $200 \cdot 1/10 = 20$ items starting at the bottom of the
distribution, and using a formula analogous to (3.4.1) we get

$$D_1 = 44.5 + 5 \cdot \frac{1}{40} = 44.6 \text{ mph}$$

rounded to the nearest tenth. Since 19 of the speeds fell below 44.5,
we needed 1 of the 40 falling into the next class to reach $D_1$. Similarly, $D_8$ may be obtained by counting $200 \cdot 8/10 = 160$ items starting
at the bottom of the distribution, and using a formula analogous to
(3.4.1) we get

$$D_8 = 54.5 + 5 \cdot \frac{36}{52} = 58.0 \text{ mph}$$

rounded to the nearest tenth. Had we wanted to find $D_8$ by counting
from the other end of the distribution, we would have obtained

$$D_8 = 59.5 - 5 \cdot \frac{16}{52} = 58.0 \text{ mph}$$

and the two answers are, of course, the same.

*Percentiles* are values that divide a distribution, or the total area
of the rectangles of its histogram, into 100 equal parts. For instance,
the *fifth percentile*, $P_5$, exceeds 5 per cent and is exceeded by 95 per
cent of the data, and the *eighty-fifth percentile*, $P_{85}$, exceeds 85 per
cent and is exceeded by 15 per cent of the data. Since the calculation
of percentiles is, for all practical purposes, identical with that of
quartiles and deciles, we shall give only one example; namely, find
$P_{85}$ for the speed-check data. Having the choice of counting
$200 \cdot 85/100 = 170$ cases starting at the bottom of the distribution

or $200 - 170 = 30$ cases starting at the top, let us choose the latter and write

$$P_{85} = 59.5 - 5 \cdot \frac{6}{52} = 58.9 \text{ mph}$$

rounded to the nearest tenth. Since 24 of the speeds exceeded 59.5, we had to count 6 of the 52 items falling into the next class.

## EXERCISES

1. Find $Q_1$ and $Q_3$ for the width-of-crab distribution on page 13.

2. Find $Q_1$ and $Q_3$ for the distribution of the numbers of defective shafts given in Exercise 8 on page 37.

3. Find $Q_1$ and $Q_3$ for the contest scores of Exercise 9 on page 38.

4. Find $Q_1$ and $Q_3$ for whichever data you grouped among those of Exercises 9, 11, 13, 14, 15, and 17 on pages 25 through 28.

5. It has been suggested that the *first quartile of ungrouped data* might be defined as the $(n + 3)/4$th largest. Check whether for $n = 9$, 13, and 17 observations (no two of which are alike) this will yield a value which is exceeded by three times as many values as it exceeds. Also, find a similar formula for the third quartile and verify it for the same values of $n$.

6. Find $D_1$ and $D_9$ for the distribution referred to in Exercise 2 above.

7. Find $D_2$ and $D_8$ for the distribution referred to in Exercise 3 above.

8. Find $D_3$ and $D_7$ for the distribution referred to in Exercise 4 above.

9. Find $P_{15}$ and $P_{85}$ for the distribution referred to in Exercise 2 above.

10. Find $P_5$ and $P_{95}$ for the distribution referred to in Exercise 3 above.

## 3.9 / Some Further Comparisons

The measures of location which we discussed in Sections 3.2 through 3.7 described the center, or middle, of a set of data in *specific ways*. Whereas the median represents the *middle* in as much as it is exceeded by as many items as it exceeds, the mode represents the value that is the *most common* and, in that sense, *most typical*, and the mean represents what might reasonably be called the "center of gravity" of the data. (Students of physics will note that a formula *mode = 3(median) − 2(mean)*   *mode = 3(median) − 2(me...*

analogous to (3.3.1) gives the center of gravity of a set of weights $f_i$ arranged along a horizontal line at distances $x_i$ from the origin.)

The question of what particular "average" should be used in a particular problem is not always easily answered. As we saw in Section 3.6, there are problems in which the nature of our data dictates the use of such special averages as the geometric and harmonic means. The nature of the data may also dictate the use of a weighted mean or, we did not mention this before, perhaps a *weighted* geometric mean. Finally, when dealing with qualitative data, we may have no choice but to use the mode or in some special instances the median.

A very interesting distinction between the mean, median, and mode will be brought out in Section 7.5, where we shall discuss their use in problems of *decision-making*. There we shall see that the choice between the three measures of central location may well depend on the risks, rewards, and penalties that are involved.

Generally speaking, the mean is by far the most widely used measure of central location, and we shall use it almost exclusively in Part Two of this book. In problems of estimation and tests of hypotheses the mean has such definite advantages that other measures, for instance, the median, are used only for reasons of computational ease. (This is why the median is used at times in *industrial quality control*, where it is important that inspectors can judge their data with a minimum of arithmetic.)

For fairly *symmetrical* distributions (see page 35), the problem of using the "right kind of average" is relatively unimportant since the mean, median, and mode will more or less coincide. Later on, in Section 5.2, we shall see how, in turn, differences between the mean, median, and mode can be used to measure the symmetry or skewness of a distribution. In connection with this it is interesting to note that for moderately skewed distributions the mean, median, and mode are roughly related as follows

$$mode = 3(\text{median}) - 2(\text{mean})$$

As the reader may wish to verify, this formula also indicates that the median will generally lie between the mean and the mode.

In problems in which it is appropriate to use any one of the measures of location, it is important that a choice be made *before the data are collected* or *before they are analyzed in any way*. The reason for this is that it is possible at times to arrive at opposite conclusions depending on the particular measure of location one happens to choose. This is illustrated in Exercise 14 on page 63, where we could arrive at one conclusion by using means and the opposite conclusion by using medians. It would hardly seem ethical in a situation like this to choose a statistical measure that happens to suit our objectives.

## BIBLIOGRAPHY

For more elaborate ways of defining the mode of a distribution see

Croxton, F. E., and Cowden, D. J., *Applied General Statistics*, 2nd ed. Englewood Cliffs, N. J.: Prentice-Hall, 1955, Chap. 9.

Waugh, A. E., *Elements of Statistical Method*, 3rd ed. New York: McGraw-Hill, 1952, p. 205. (This book also contains further material on desirable and undesirable properties of the various measures of location.)

Further information about the geometric and harmonic means may be found in the two books mentioned above and, among others, also in

Neiswanger, W. A., *Elementary Statistical Methods*, rev. ed. New York: Macmillan, 1956, Chap. 9.

With reference to the question of *ethics* in the selection of a measure of location, see the book by D. Huff mentioned on page 41.

# Chapter 4

# Measures of Variation

## 4.1 / Introduction

The mean, median, and most of the other "averages" discussed in the preceding chapter *each* provided a single number which is descriptive of a whole set of data. Although the information contained in a measure of location may be sufficient in some instances, there are many problems in which it is necessary to describe additional features of our data. The statistical measures which we shall study in this chapter are called *measures of variation, spread,* or *dispersion.* The following are a few examples to illustrate why knowledge of the mean (or some other measure of location) may have to be supplemented with information about the extent to which the data are dispersed, that is, the extent to which they are spread out or bunched.

Let us suppose, for instance, that the speed-check data on page 17 are to be used for deciding whether there is a need for erecting a speed limit sign in the vicinity of the checkpoint and that the person who has to make this decision is supplied only with the fact that the average (mean) of the speeds is 52.5 mph. If he decided on the basis of this figure, which is below the legal limit of 55 mph, that everything is under control and that there is no need to put up a sign, he might be making a serious mistake. *For all he knows, it is possible that half the cars passed the checkpoint going 32.5 mph while the other half speeded by at 72.5 mph.* Of course, this is an exaggeration and we would hardly expect it to happen, but it serves to illustrate that an intelligent decision cannot be reached in this matter on the basis of the mean alone. Something will have to be known about the interval over which the speeds are dispersed, how much they vary, how much they are spread out or bunched.

To consider another example, let us suppose that an executive has to choose one of two applicants for a secretarial position and that, to be objective, he asks them to copy five rather lengthy reports. If the results of this test show that each made on the average 6 mistakes per report, it would seem on the surface that the two applicants are equally good. However, before suggesting any such decision, let us take a brief look at the number of mistakes they made in copying the individual reports. Suppose then that the first applicant made 5, 8, 6, 7, and 4 mistakes, and the second applicant made 3, 12, 0, 0, and 15. This shows that *even though on the average their performances were the same* the first was fairly consistent, whereas the second was highly erratic. We shall not venture to guess whether the executive will prefer a secretary whose performance is consistently fair or one whose performance oscillates between perfection and utter carelessness, but the example serves to illustrate again why information about variability may be of importance.

The concept of variation or dispersion is of particular importance in inductive statistics, in problems where we have to make generalizations, because it is here that we have to cope with the question of *chance variation*. To illustrate the meaning of this term, let us suppose that a balanced coin is flipped 100 times. Although we may *expect* to get 50 heads and 50 tails, we would certainly not be surprised if we got, say, 53 heads and 47 tails, 48 heads and 52 tails, or 56 heads and 44 tails. We would probably ascribe the occurrence of a few extra heads or a few extra tails to chance. In order to study this effect of chance, let us suppose that we repeatedly flipped a balanced coin 100 times and that in 10 such "experiments" we got

48, 55, 49, 50, 52, 59, 43, 46, 51, and 48 heads

This gives us some idea about the magnitude of the fluctuations (variations) produced by chance in the number of times a coin comes up heads in 100 tries. Knowing this would be important, for example, if we wanted to decide whether there is something wrong with a coin which in 100 tosses came up with 30 heads and 70 tails. Judging by the above experiment, it would seem that most of the time we should get anywhere from 40 to 60 heads (in the experiment the number of heads ranged from 43 to 59) and, hence, we conclude that there is something wrong with the coin. In other words, we say that the difference between the 30 heads we got and the 50 we expected *is too big to be attributed to chance.* This argument has been presented on an intuitive basis to demonstrate the need for measuring chance variation; it will be treated formally in Part Two of this book.

To consider one more example in which the concept of variability plays a fundamental role, let us return to the example in which we tried to estimate $\mu$, the true average length of certain scorpions. Taking the results of Biologist A (see page 61), who obtained a mean of $\bar{x} = 1.9$ inches, we might be led to infer that $\mu = 1.9$ inches or, at least, that it is very close to 1.9. Clearly, this kind of reasoning involves a considerable generalization since we are using information about 3 scorpions to estimate the true average length of thousands. Whether such a generalization is reasonable, or justifiable, depends on many factors which we shall treat in detail in Chapter 10. For the moment, let us investigate one of them, namely, that of the *variability of the population* from which a sample is obtained. To explain what this means, let us consider the following possibilities:

1. The true average length of the given scorpions is $\mu = 2.0$ inches, *they are all very much alike*, and their lengths vary anywhere from 1.8 to 2.2 inches.

2. The true average length is $\mu = 2.0$ inches, *but there are enormous differences*, and the lengths vary anywhere from, say, 1.2 to 3.0 inches.

If the first alternative is true, we can be *sure* that our sample mean, $\bar{x}$, cannot possibly differ from the actual value of $\mu$ by more than 0.2 inches. After all, the worst that can happen is that all the scorpions in our sample have a length of 1.8 inches *or* that all of them have a length of 2.2 inches. In the second case the situation is quite different. Purely by chance we might pick only scorpions whose length is 3.0 inches, and $\bar{x}$ would then be "off" by as much as a whole inch. This illustrates the fact that *in order to evaluate the "closeness" of an estimate or the "goodness" of a generalization, we must know something about the variability of the population from which our sample is obtained.* If there is very little variation, as in the first case where the lengths of *all* scorpions were close to 2.0, the mean of a sample is apt to be very close to $\mu$. On the other hand, if there is a lot of variation, as in the second case where the lengths were spread over the interval from 1.2 to 3.0, the mean of a sample cannot reasonably be expected to be quite so close to the true mean.

We have given the four examples of this section to show that the concept of variability plays a fundamental role in the analysis of statistical data. In the remainder of this chapter we shall study several ways of describing (measuring) variation, dispersion, or spread.

### 4.2 / The Range

The *range* is a measure of variation that is easy to understand, easy to explain, and easy to obtain. For any set of numerical data it is defined simply as *the difference between the largest and the smallest*. For instance, in the speed-check example the lowest speed was 28 mph, the highest was 74 mph, and the *range* of the speeds is $74 - 28 = 46$. Similarly, the ranges of the numbers of mistakes made by the two secretaries on page 78 are, respectively, $8 - 4 = 4$ and $15 - 0 = 15$, and the range of the values obtained by Biologist B in the example on page 61 is $2.2 - 1.6 = 0.6$ inches.

Although the range is a measure of variation that is easy to understand and does not require lengthy calculations, it has many undesirable features. In fact, it is used mainly in situations where we are interested in getting a quick, though perhaps not very accurate, picture of the variability of a set of data.

The range is a poor measure of variability in the sense that it really accounts only for the two extreme values of a set of data. It does not say anything about the dispersion of the remaining data except, of course, that they lie on an interval whose length is specified by the range. If we take a look at the following three sets of numbers

$$
\begin{array}{cccccccc}
20, & 50, & 50, & 50, & 50, & 50, & 50, & 50 \\
20, & 20, & 20, & 20, & 50, & 50, & 50, & 50 \\
20, & 25, & 30, & 33, & 37, & 40, & 46, & 50
\end{array}
$$

it is apparent that the range is in each case equal to 30. Nevertheless, the *dispersion* of these numbers is by no means the same. In the first set all but one of the numbers are 50's, in the second half the numbers are 20's and half are 50's, and in the third the numbers are spread fairly evenly over the interval from 20 to 50. To bring out distinctions like these, we will have to describe variability with a statistical measure other than the range.

To give another illustration of the shortcomings of the range, let us suppose that we are told that the range of the salaries paid by a certain firm is \$55,000 and that the lowest salary is \$4,500. For all we know, all but one of the employees might be getting \$4,500, while one gets \$59,500. Of course, we could get a good picture of the dispersion of these salaries by looking at their distribution, for example, a distribution showing how many of them made less than \$5,000, less than \$6,000, ..., but let us remember that *our goal is to describe variability with a single number*. The range provides such a number but, unfortunately, it often does not tell us enough.

In view of these shortcomings of the range (and there are some that we have not even mentioned), we shall have to look for other ways of measuring what we have rather loosely referred to as variation or dispersion. To repeat, the main advantage (and about the only advantage) of the range is that it is very easy to find. It is sometimes used in problems of *industrial quality control*, where it is important that inspection work can be done quickly and, perhaps, even by mathematically untrained personnel.

## 4.3 / The Average Deviation

Since the dispersion of a set of numbers is *small* if they are bunched closely around the mean and it is *large* if they are spread over considerable distances away from the mean, it would seem reasonable to define variation in terms of the *distances (deviations) by which numbers depart from their mean*. Taking a set of numbers $x_1$, $x_2$, $x_3$, ..., $x_n$, whose mean is $\bar{x}$, we can write the amounts by which they differ from the mean as $x_1 - \bar{x}$, $x_2 - \bar{x}$, $x_3 - \bar{x}$, ..., and $x_n - \bar{x}$. These quantities are called the <u>deviations from the mean</u> and, offhand, it would seem reasonable to suggest that variability be measured in terms of their mean, namely, in terms of the quantity

$$\frac{\sum_{i=1}^{n} (x_i - \bar{x})}{n} \qquad (4.3.1)$$

Unfortunately, this does not measure the variation of the $x$'s; for that matter it does not measure anything, as it can be shown that it is always equal to zero. Using the rules of summation given in Appendix I, it can easily be seen that

$$\frac{\sum_{i=1}^{n}(x_i - \bar{x})}{n} = \frac{\sum_{i=1}^{n}x_i - \sum_{i=1}^{n}\bar{x}}{n} = \frac{\sum_{i=1}^{n}x_i}{n} - \bar{x}$$

and the last expression is *zero* since by definition the sum of the $x$'s divided by $n$ is $\bar{x}$. To give a numerical example, the mean of 5, 14, 10, 19, and 7 is $\bar{x} = 11$, the deviations from the mean are $-6$, 3, $-1$, 8, $-4$, and $(-6) + 3 + (-1) + 8 + (-4) = 0$.

Although formula (4.3.1) does not provide a measure of variation, the idea on which it was based, namely, the idea of expressing dispersion in terms of deviations from the mean, was not bad. As it happened, we made the unfortunate choice of using the *mean* of the deviations and this turned out to be zero regardless of the values of the $x$'s. In view of our goal of defining a measure of variation, it should be clear that we are really interested only in the *magnitude* of the deviations and not in their *signs*. Hence, we could "ignore" the minus signs and define a measure of variation in terms of the *absolute values* of the deviations from the mean. In mathematics, the absolute value of a *positive* number is the number itself, while the absolute value of a *negative* number is the number without its minus sign. For instance, the absolute value of 29 is 29, and the absolute value of $-13$ is 13. The notation that is used for the absolute value of $x$ is $|x|$, and we can thus write

$$|29| = 29 \quad \text{and} \quad |-13| = 13$$

Employing the absolute values of the deviations from the mean, let us now define the following measure of variation, called the *average* or *mean deviation*

$$\text{average deviation} = \frac{\sum_{i=1}^{n}|x_i - \bar{x}|}{n} \tag{4.3.2} \blacktriangle$$

It is similar to (4.3.1), the only difference being that the deviations from the mean are replaced by their absolute values.

To calculate a mean deviation, we must first find $\bar{x}$, then the deviations from the mean and their absolute values, and finally divide the sum of the absolute values by $n$. To illustrate, let us find the average deviation for the following data on the average relative humidity at 1:30 P.M. in Boise, Idaho, for each month of the year (based on 15 years' records of the Weather Bureau, Department of Commerce):

$$75, 71, 57, 47, 46, 44, 33, 33, 39, 48, 67, 76$$

First calculating the mean we get

$$\bar{x} = \frac{636}{12} = 53$$

and then

| $x_i$ | $x_i - \bar{x}$ | $\lvert x_i - \bar{x} \rvert$ |
|-------|------|------|
| 75 | 22 | 22 |
| 71 | 18 | 18 |
| 57 | 4 | 4 |
| 47 | $-6$ | 6 |
| 46 | $-7$ | 7 |
| 44 | $-9$ | 9 |
| 33 | $-20$ | 20 |
| 33 | $-20$ | 20 |
| 39 | $-14$ | 14 |
| 48 | $-5$ | 5 |
| 67 | 14 | 14 |
| 76 | 23 | 23 |
|  | 0 | 162 |

$$\text{average deviation} = \frac{162}{12} = 13.5$$

This value tells us that in Boise, Idaho, there are considerable fluctuations in relative humidity from month to month. Of course, we could have learned the same by merely looking at the data, but the average deviation tells us, specifically, that *on the average* the monthly figures deviate by 13.5 from the annual average of 53. Incidentally, in the calculation of the average deviation it is unnecessary to write down *both*, the deviations and their absolute values, but it is a good check to see whether the sum of the deviations is equal to zero.

The calculation of an average deviation can be quite cumbersome, particularly if $n$ is large and the mean has many digits or is given to many decimals. In that case it may be desirable to use a short-cut formula referred to in the Bibliography on page 98.

For grouped data, the average deviation can be found only if we make some assumption about the distribution of the measurements within each class. Assuming, as we did for the mean, that all measurements falling into a class are located at its class mark, we can write

$$\text{average deviation} = \frac{\sum_{i=1}^{k} |x_i - \bar{x}| \cdot f_i}{n} \qquad (4.3.3)\blacktriangle$$

where $x_i$ stands for the class mark of the $i$th class, $f_i$ for the corresponding class frequency, $k$ for the number of classes, and $n$ for the total frequency. Although formulas (4.3.2) and (4.3.3) define average deviations of *samples* (we used the symbol $\bar{x}$), analogous formulas for populations may be obtained by simply substituting $\mu$ for $\bar{x}$.

Although the average deviation may have intuitive appeal as a measure of variation, it is seldom used. Its main drawback is that, owing to the absolute values, it is difficult to subject it to any sort of mathematical, that is, theoretical, treatment. For example, it is very difficult to study mathematically how *in problems of sampling* average deviations are affected by chance. We have mentioned the average deviation mainly as a stepping-stone for the definition of the *standard deviation*, the much more important measure of variation which will be discussed in the following section.

### EXERCISES

1. Find the range of the ACE linguistic scores of Exercise 9 on page 26.

2. Find the range of the amounts spent on textbooks in Exercise 14 on page 26.

3. Find the range of the plating thicknesses of Exercise 16 on page 27.

4. Find the range of the time lapses between eruptions of Old Faithful for the data of Exercise 17 on page 28.

5. Find the average deviation of the grades of Exercise 2 on page 53.

6. Find the average deviation of the weights of Exercise 3 on page 53.

7. Find the average deviation of the thicknesses of grease coatings of Exercise 6 on page 53.

8. Use formula (4.3.3) to find the average deviation of the speed-check distribution on page 17.

9. Use formula (4.3.3) to find the average deviation of whichever data you grouped among those of Exercise 9, 11, 13, 14, 15, 16, and 17 on pages 25 through 28.

### 4.4 / The Standard Deviation

In the preceding section we used absolute values to eliminate the signs of the deviations from the mean. Being interested only in the size of the deviations and not in their signs, we could accomplish more or less the same by *squaring* the deviations and then averaging these squares. (Squares of real numbers are never negative.) To compensate for the fact that we averaged squared deviations, we could then take the square root of this average and use it as a measure of variation. Given a set of numbers $x_1, x_2, x_3, \ldots, x_n$, whose mean is $\bar{x}$, we would, thus, get

$$S = \sqrt{\frac{\sum_{i=1}^{n} (x_i - \bar{x})^2}{n}} \tag{4.4.1}$$

and this is how, traditionally, the *standard deviation* has been defined. It has also been known under the name of *root-mean-square deviation*, expressing the fact that it is literally the square *root* of the *mean* of the *squared* deviations.

In recent years there has been a growing tendency among statisticians and research workers in most fields to make a slight modification in this definition of the standard deviation. *It consists of dividing the sum of the squared deviations by n − 1 instead of n.* Following this practice, which we shall explain further in Section 4.6, let us define $s$, the *standard deviation of a sample,* as

$$s = \sqrt{\frac{\sum_{i=1}^{n} (x_i - \bar{x})^2}{n-1}} \tag{4.4.2}$$

(By using the symbol $\bar{x}$ we tacitly assumed that the $x$'s constitute a sample. However, substituting $\mu$ for $\bar{x}$ we could define an analogous measure for populations, and we shall have more to say about this on page 97.)

Since the practice of dividing by $n - 1$ instead of $n$ in the formula for the standard deviation is not yet universally accepted, let us point out that *there is no question of one formula being right and the other being wrong.* We are trying to describe the variability of a set of data, and the choice of any particular description, that is, of any particular formula, is really arbitrary. (To give an analogy, one person may wish to describe a dog as being a poodle and another person may wish to describe him as being black. If the dog is a black poodle, neither is wrong and the only question one might ask is whether one description is more useful than the other. *Indeed, the only reason why division by n — 1 is nowadays preferred is that it provides, in a certain sense, a more useful description.* We shall discuss this further in Section 4.6.)

While on the subject, let us add that the distinction between the two formulas is important only when *n* is very small. *If n is reasonably large, say, 100 or more, the difference between formulas (4.4.1) and (4.4.2) becomes negligible.* For instance, if for a given set of 100 numbers the first formula gives a standard deviation of 10, the second formula would give correspondingly 10.05. Clearly, a difference as small as this is for most practical purposes of no concern.

To illustrate the use of formula (4.4.2), let us find *s* for the "lifetimes" of the five electronic tubes given on page 47. The "lifetimes" of these tubes were

$$942, 820, 981, 929, 703 \text{ hours}$$

and the calculation of the standard deviation of these numbers may be arranged as follows:

| $x_i$ | $x_i - \bar{x}$ | $(x_i - \bar{x})^2$ |
|-------|-----------------|---------------------|
| 942   | 67              | 4,489               |
| 820   | −55             | 3,025               |
| 981   | 106             | 11,236              |
| 929   | 54              | 2,916               |
| 703   | −172            | 29,584              |
| 4,375 | 0               | 51,250              |

$$\bar{x} = \frac{4,375}{5} = 875$$

$$s = \sqrt{\frac{51,250}{4}}$$

$$= \sqrt{12,812.5}$$

Referring to Table VIII, whose use is explained in Appendix III, we find that the standard deviation of the lifetimes of the five tubes is approximately 113 hours. Knowledge of this value would be very important if we wanted to use $\bar{x} = 875$ as an estimate of $\mu$, the true average lifetime of all similar tubes made by the given firm. As we pointed out on page 79, it is essential to know something about the

6-7 Saturday

variability of these lifetimes if we want to judge whether the sample mean can be expected to be reasonably close to the true mean. This whole problem will be treated in detail in Chapter 10.

In the above example the calculation of $s$ was not very difficult, but it should be apparent that the work would have been much more involved if the mean had not been a whole number. In actual practice, formula (4.4.2) is seldom used, there being a short-cut formula which provides considerable simplifications *without being an approximation.* To derive this short-cut formula for $s$, let us begin with $s^2$, which, incidentally, is called the *sample variance,* and write

$$s^2 = \frac{\sum_{i=1}^{n}(x_i - \bar{x})^2}{n-1} = \frac{\sum_{i=1}^{n}(x_i^2 - 2x_i\bar{x} + \bar{x}^2)}{n-1}$$

Applying Rules A and B of Appendix I this becomes

$$s^2 = \frac{\sum_{i=1}^{n}x_i^2 - 2\bar{x}\sum_{i=1}^{n}x_i + \sum_{i=1}^{n}\bar{x}^2}{n-1}$$

and after multiplying numerator and denominator by $n$, using Rule C of Appendix I, and substituting $\sum_{i=1}^{n}x_i/n$ for $\bar{x}$, we get

$$s^2 = \frac{n \cdot \sum_{i=1}^{n}x_i^2 - (\sum_{i=1}^{n}x_i)^2}{n(n-1)}$$

The short-cut formula for the *standard deviation of a sample* can, thus, be written as

$$s = \sqrt{\frac{n \cdot \sum_{i=1}^{n}x_i^2 - (\sum_{i=1}^{n}x_i)^2}{n(n-1)}} \qquad (4.4.3)\blacktriangle$$

An important feature of this short-cut formula is that it enables us to find $s$ without having to go through the process of actually calculating the deviations from the mean. We have only to find the sum of the $x$'s, the sum of their squares, and then substitute into (4.4.3). Barring arithmetical mistakes or errors due to rounding, formulas (4.4.2) and (4.4.3) should always yield identical results; as we said before, the short-cut formula is not an approximation.

To demonstrate the advantages of formula (4.4.3), let us determine the standard deviation, $s$, of the numbers

$$12, 7, 9, 5, 4, 8, 17, 2, 11, 14, 13, 9$$

using first (4.4.2) and then (4.4.3). Working with (4.4.2) we get

| $x_i$ | $x_i - \bar{x}$ | $(x_i - \bar{x})^2$ |
|---|---|---|
| 12 | 2.75 | 7.5625 |
| 7 | −2.25 | 5.0625 |
| 9 | −0.25 | 0.0625 |
| 5 | −4.25 | 18.0625 |
| 4 | −5.25 | 27.5625 |
| 8 | −1.25 | 1.5625 |
| 17 | 7.75 | 60.0625 |
| 2 | −7.25 | 52.5625 |
| 11 | 1.75 | 3.0625 |
| 14 | 4.75 | 22.5625 |
| 13 | 3.75 | 14.0625 |
| 9 | −0.25 | 0.0625 |
| 111 | 0 | 212.2500 |

$$\bar{x} = \frac{111}{12} = 9.25$$

$$s = \sqrt{\frac{212.25}{11}}$$

$$= 4.4 \text{ (approx.)}$$

and working with short-cut formula (4.4.3) we get

| $x_i$ | $x_i^2$ |
|---|---|
| 12 | 144 |
| 7 | 49 |
| 9 | 81 |
| 5 | 25 |
| 4 | 16 |
| 8 | 64 |
| 17 | 289 |
| 2 | 4 |
| 11 | 121 |
| 14 | 196 |
| 13 | 169 |
| 9 | 81 |
| 111 | 1239 |

$$s = \sqrt{\frac{12(1239) - (111)^2}{12 \cdot 11}}$$

$$= \sqrt{\frac{2547}{132}}$$

$$= 4.4 \text{ (approx.)}$$

In this example the mean is 9.25, not a whole number, and the short-cut formula provided considerable simplifications. *Whereas formula (4.4.2) gives a clearer picture of what is meant by a standard deviation, formula (4.4.3) enables us to find s with greater ease.*

A further simplification in the calculation of s consists of adding or subtracting an arbitrary number to or from each measurement. It is not difficult to prove that if the same number is added to (or subtracted from) each measurement, the value of the standard deviation remains unchanged. Clearly, the variation or dispersion of a set of data should not be affected if the same constant is added to each number.

Had we used this trick in the last example, we might have subtracted 10 from each number, getting

$$2, -3, -1, -5, -6, -2, 7, -8, 1, 4, 3, -1$$

instead of the original measurements. The sum of these numbers is $-9$, the sum of their squares is 219, and substitution into (4.4.3) yields

$$s = \sqrt{\frac{12(219) - (-9)^2}{12 \cdot 11}}$$

$$= \sqrt{\frac{2547}{132}}$$

and this is exactly what we had before.

Since the purpose of this trick is to reduce the size of the numbers with which we have to work, it is usually desirable to subtract a number that is close to the mean. In our example the mean was 9.25, we subtracted 10, and the work might have been even simpler if we had subtracted 9.

The formulas given so far in this section apply essentially to samples. However, substituting $\mu$ for $\bar{x}$ in (4.4.1) and (4.4.2), we obtain analogous formulas for *standard deviations of populations* and both formulas are, in fact, widely used. It has become more or less general practice to denote population standard deviations calculated with (4.4.1), where we divide by $n$, as $\sigma$ (small Greek *sigma*), and those calculated with (4.4.2), where we divide by $n - 1$, as $S$ (capital letter S). So far as actual calculations are concerned, we can use short-cut formula (4.4.3), although for $\sigma$ (but not for $S$) the $n - 1$ in the denominator inside the square root must be replaced

$S = \div$ by $n-1$    sample

$\sigma = \div$ by $n$    population

with an $n$. Let us emphasize again that the difference between the two formulas is negligible unless $n$ is very small.

To calculate the standard deviation of a distribution, that is, of grouped data, we shall, as in the case of the mean, assume that all measurements falling into a class are located at its class mark. If we write $x_i$ for the class mark of the $i$th class, $f_i$ for its frequency, $k$ for the number of classes, and $n$ for the total frequency, formula (4.4.2) becomes

$$s = \sqrt{\frac{\sum_{i=1}^{k} (x_i - \bar{x})^2 \cdot f_i}{n - 1}} \qquad (4.4.4)$$

where each squared deviation is multiplied by $f_i$ to account for the $f_i$ values falling into the $i$th class.

Although (4.4.4) serves to *define* $s$ for grouped data, it is seldom used in actual practice. The calculation of the standard deviation of a distribution can be simplified considerably by employing the same change of scale which we introduced in Chapter 3 in connection with the short-cut formula for the mean. Choosing a $u$-scale in which the class marks become $\ldots, -3, -2, -1, 0, 1, 2, 3, \ldots$, the *short-cut formula for the standard deviation, $s$, of grouped data* can be written as

$$s = c \cdot \sqrt{\frac{n \cdot \sum_{i=1}^{k} u_i^2 f_i - (\sum_{i=1}^{k} u_i f_i)^2}{n(n - 1)}} \qquad (4.4.5) \blacktriangle$$

*applies also to population, replace $(n-1)$ c~N*

where $c$ is, as before, the class interval in the original scale. It is assumed here that all classes are of equal length. The steps needed to derive (4.4.5) from (4.4.4) are a combination of those used on pages 51 and 87.

Although the short-cut formula may look rather formidable, it makes the calculation of $s$ very easy. Instead of having to work with the actual class marks and the deviations from the mean, we have only to find the sum of the products obtained by multiplying each $u$ by the corresponding $f$, the sum of the products obtained by multiplying the square of each $u$ by the corresponding $f$, and substitute into (4.4.5).

To illustrate the use of the short-cut formula for $s$, let us calculate the standard deviation of the speed-check distribution on page 17. Introducing a suitable $u$-scale for the class marks of this distribution, we get

| Speed (miles per hour) | Class Marks $u_i$ | Number of Cars $f_i$ | $u_i f_i$ | $u_i^2 f_i$ |
|---|---|---|---|---|
| 25 – 29 | −5 | 1 | −5 | 25 |
| 30 – 34 | −4 | 1 | −4 | 16 |
| 35 – 39 | −3 | 4 | −12 | 36 |
| 40 – 44 | −2 | 13 | −26 | 52 |
| 45 – 49 | −1 | 40 | −40 | 40 |
| 50 – 54 | 0 | 65 | 0 | 0 |
| 55 – 59 | 1 | 52 | 52 | 52 |
| 60 – 64 | 2 | 18 | 36 | 72 |
| 65 – 69 | 3 | 5 | 15 | 45 |
| 70 – 74 | 4 | 1 | 4 | 16 |
| | | 200 | 20 | 354 |

and substituting the totals into (4.4.5) gives

$$s = 5 \cdot \sqrt{\frac{200(354) - (20)^2}{200 \cdot 199}}$$

$$= 6.65 \text{ mph}$$

The variation of the 200 speeds is, thus, measured by a standard deviation of, roughly, 6.6 mph.

We have computed this standard deviation under the assumption that all measurements falling into a class are located at its class mark. The error which is introduced by this assumption, and which is appropriately called a *grouping error*, can be fairly large, particularly when the class interval, $c$, is wide. A correction, called *Sheppard's correction*, which compensates for this error is mentioned in the Bibliography on page 98. Incidentally, the short-cut formula for grouped data applies also to *population standard deviations*, although it must be remembered that for $\sigma$ (but not for $S$) the $n - 1$ in the denominator inside the square root of (4.4.5) must be replaced with an $n$.

Having learned how to calculate standard deviations, let us now demonstrate how the knowledge of a standard deviation can play an important role in the analysis of experimental results. Referring again to the scorpions used as an example on page 61, let us suppose that the lengths of 50 such scorpions had a mean of $\bar{x} = 2.0$ inches and a standard deviation of $s = 0.15$ inches. If this is the only information available, we may want to infer (or we may have no choice but to infer) that $\mu$ and $\sigma$, *the true mean and standard deviation of the lengths of all scorpions of this kind*, are 2.0 and 0.15 inches, respectively.

Values of $\mu$ and $\sigma$ are important to know, that is, to estimate, because there are many populations in which roughly

*68 per cent of the values differ from the mean by less than one standard deviation,*

*95 per cent of the values differ from the mean by less than two standard deviations,*

*and more than 99 per cent of the values differ from the mean by less than three standard deviations.*

Assuming that these percentages apply to our example and that 2.0 and 0.15 are *very close* estimates of $\mu$ and $\sigma$, we can say that about 68 per cent of *all* scorpions of this kind have lengths from 2.0 − 0.15 = 1.85 to 2.0 + 0.15 = 2.15 inches, about 95 per cent have lengths from 1.70 to 2.30 inches, and that more than 99 per cent have lengths from 1.55 to 2.45 inches.

Another reason why it is sometimes important to have some knowledge about a population standard deviation, perhaps estimate it on the basis of a sample standard deviation, was already mentioned on page 79. In order to judge how close a sample mean, $\bar{x}$, might be to the true mean, $\mu$, we must have some information about the variability of the population from which our sample was obtained. For instance, to judge how close a sample mean of $\bar{x} = 2.0$ inches might be to the true average length of all these scorpions, we must know something about the *variability* of their lengths, and the necessary information is most commonly supplied by the sample standard deviation $s$.

Standard deviations are also useful for comparing numbers belonging to different sets of data. To illustrate, let us suppose that Mr. Jones received a grade of 72 in a final examination in sociology, in which the whole class averaged 54, and that he received a grade of 76 in a final examination in psychology, in which the whole class averaged 52. On the basis of these figures we can say that in each course Mr. Jones' grade was above average, but we could say *more* if we also knew the corresponding standard deviations. Let us suppose then that the sociology grades had a standard deviation of 20, and the psychology grades had a standard deviation of 12. Using this additional information, we can say that in sociology Mr. Jones was $\frac{72 - 54}{20} = 0.9$ standard deviations above average, whereas in psychology he was $\frac{76 - 52}{12} = 2$ standard deviation above the average of his class.  These figures indicate that, relatively speaking, his performance in psychology was *much better* than that in sociology, and this was not apparent by looking only at the means.

What we have done here consisted of converting the grades into so-called *standard units*.  If $x$ is a measurement belonging to a set of data having the mean $\bar{x}$ (or $\mu$) and the standard deviation $s$ (or $\sigma$), then its value in *standard units* is

$$\frac{x - \bar{x}}{s} \quad \text{or} \quad \frac{x - \mu}{\sigma}$$

*standard unit*

Standard units, *standard scores*, or *z-scores*, as they are also called, tell us how many standard deviations an item is above or below the mean of the set of data to which it belongs.  Their use is particularly important in the comparison of different kinds of measurements.  For example, the fact that a man's weight is 20 pounds above the average for his age, his blood pressure is 12 mm above average, and his pulse rate is 5 beats per minute below average, might be much more meaningful if all these quantities were expressed in terms of standard units.

## EXERCISES

1. Use formula (4.4.2) to find the standard deviation of the following sample of I.Q.'s: 97, 104, 98, 95, 105, and 101.

2. Find the standard deviation of the following sample of the ages of students attending a certain university using (a) formula (4.4.2) and (b) formula (4.4.3):

$$17, \quad 21, \quad 35, \quad 27, \quad 20, \quad 18, \quad 19, \quad 18$$

   *Time yourself on both methods and check how much time is saved by using the short-cut formula.*

3. Find $s$ for the number of heads obtained in the 10 series of 100 flips of a coin given on page 78.

4. Find $s$ for the daily high temperatures of Exercise 1 on page 53.  Use the simplification discussed on page 89.

5. Find $s$ for the 20 grades given in Exercise 2 on page 53.

6. Find $\sigma$ for the values of the 1954 *Wholesale Price Index* given in Exercise 4 on page 53.  Use the simplification suggested on page 89 and remember that for $\sigma$ the $n - 1$ in the denominator of (4.4.3) must be replaced with an $n$.

7. *Using a calculating machine*, find $s$ for the 200 ungrouped speeds given in the text on page 15.

8. *Using a calculating machine*, find $\sigma$ for the ungrouped ACE scores of Exercise 9 on page 25. Remember that for $\sigma$ the $n-1$ in the denominator of (4.4.3) must be replaced with an $n$.

9. Using the sums and sums of squares of the preceding exercise, calculate $S$ (see page 89) for these ACE scores and compare $\sigma$ with $S$.

10. Find $s$ for the width-of-crab distribution given in the text on page 13.

11. Find $s$ for whichever data you grouped among those of Exercises 11, 13, 14, 15, and 16 on pages 26 through 28.

12. Find $s$ for the time lapses between eruptions of Old Faithful on the basis of the distribution constructed in Exercise 17 on page 28.

13. Find $\sigma$ for the grouped contest scores of Exercise 9 on page 38. Remember that for $\sigma$ the $n-1$ in the denominator of (4.4.5) must be replaced with an $n$.

14. Mr. Jones' house costs \$13,500 and he lives in a tract in which house prices have a mean of \$11,500 and a standard deviation of \$2,000. Mr. Smith's house cost \$10,250 and he lives in a tract in which house prices have a mean of \$9,000 and a standard deviation of \$500. How do the costs of Jones' and Smith's houses compare to those of their respective tracts?

15. Mr. Brown belongs to an age group for which the average weight is 146 pounds with a standard deviation of 15 pounds, and Mr. Green belongs to an age group for which the average weight is 173 pounds with a standard deviation of 18 pounds. If Brown weighs 181 pounds and Green weighs 203 pounds, which of the two is more seriously overweight compared to his group?

## 4.5 / Other Measures of Variation

In some problems it is desirable to use a measure of variation that is easier to calculate than the standard deviation, yet more informative than the range. Such a measure is the *interquartile* range which gives the length of the interval containing the *middle* 50 per cent of the data. Its formula is

$$\text{interquartile range} = Q_3 - Q_1 \qquad (4.5.1)\blacktriangle$$

and it is easily calculated once we know $Q_1$ and $Q_3$. The interquartile range is more informative than the range in that it accounts for the spread of the middle, and in this sense most significant, part of our data. Unlike the range, it is not affected by one very small or very large value.

In Chapter 3 we found that the quartiles of the speed-check distribution were $Q_1 = 48.4$ mph and $Q_3 = 57.0$ mph. It follows immediately that the interquartile range of these data is 8.6, and this tells us that the middle 50 per cent of the speeds varied by this rather small amount.

Instead of the interquartile range, some research workers prefer to use the *semi-interquartile range*, also called the *quartile deviation*. As its name implies, it is half the interquartile range and, hence, its formula is $(Q_3 - Q_1)/2$. It measures the average amount by which the two quartiles deviate from the median.

In experiments, the standard deviation of a set of measurements is often used as an indication of their inherent precision. If we repeatedly measure something, say, the weight of a bird, the I.Q. of a student, or the circumference of the trunk of a tree, we would hardly expect always to get *identical* results. Consequently, the amount of variation that we find in repeated measurements of the same kind provide us with information about their inherent precision.

To give an example, let us suppose that 5 measurements of the length of a certain object have a standard deviation of 0.20 inch. Although this information may be important, it is not quite enough to enable us to decide whether we have a high precision; *we would have to know something about the size of the quantity we are trying to measure.* Clearly, if we had measured the height of a tall building, a standard deviation of 0.20 inch between 5 measurements would indicate that they are very precise. On the other hand, if we had measured the diameter of a tiny ball bearing, a standard deviation of 0.20 inch between 5 measurements would indicate considerable errors.

This serves to illustrate the need for measures of *relative variation,* that is, measures which express the magnitude of the variation relative to the size of whatever object we are trying to measure. The most widely used measure of relative variation is the *coefficient of variation,* $V$, which is defined as

$$V = \frac{s}{\bar{x}} \cdot 100 \qquad\qquad (4.5.2) \blacktriangle$$

with $s$ and $\bar{x}$ replaced by $\sigma$ and $\mu$ when dealing with populations. It is apparent from (4.5.2) that the coefficient of variation gives the standard deviation as a percentage of the mean.

If in the above example the standard deviation of 0.20 inch had referred to 5 measurements of the length of a room and if the mean of these measurements had been 240 inches, we would have had

$$V = \frac{0.2}{240} \cdot 100$$

or approximately *eight-hundredth of one per cent*. It would thus seem that the method of measurement is very precise.

By using the coefficient of variation it is possible to compare the dispersions of two or more sets of data that are given in *different units*. Instead of having to compare, say, the variability of weights in pounds, lengths in inches, ages in years, and prices in dollars, we can compare the respective coefficients of variation which are all percentages.

A second measure of relative variation that is sometimes used is called the *coefficient of quartile variation*. If, in the formula for $V$, we replace $s$ with the semi-interquartile range and $\bar{x}$ with the mean of $Q_1$ and $Q_3$, we get, after cancelling the 2's,

$$V_Q = \frac{Q_3 - Q_1}{Q_3 + Q_1} \cdot 100 \qquad (4.5.3) \blacktriangle$$

This is the *coefficient of quartile variation;* it provides a convenient substitute for the coefficient of variation in problems in which variability is expressed in terms of the quartiles rather than the standard deviation.

## EXERCISES

1. Use the results of Exercise 1 on page 74 to find the interquartile range and the coefficient of quartile deviation of the width-of-crab distribution.

2. Use the results of Exercise 3 on page 74 to find the interquartile range and the coefficient of quartile deviation of the contest scores.

3. Use the mean given in the text on page 52 and the result of Exercise 10 on page 94 to find the coefficient of variation of the width-of-crab distribution.

4. Using previously calculated values of $\bar{x}$ and $s$, find the coefficient of variation of whichever data you grouped among those of Exercises 11, 13, 14, 15, and 16 on pages 26 through 28.

5. Use the results of Exercise 4 on page 93 and Exercise 1 on page 53 to find the coefficient of variation of the daily high temperatures.

**6.** Use the results of Exercise 1 on page 74 to find the coefficient of quartile variation of the width-of-crab data.

**7.** Use the results of Exercise 3 on page 74 to find the coefficient of quartile variation for the contest scores.

## 4.6 / Some Further Remarks about the Standard Deviation

Unfortunately, there is no general agreement concerning the symbols and formulas used for standard deviations. In some books the same formula and the same symbol is used for standard deviations of samples as well as populations, in some books there are two different formulas for samples, and in some there are two different formulas for populations.

*In view of this lack of agreement, we would like to caution the reader to check the definition of each symbol whenever he uses other statistics books for reference or further study.* Some formulas arising in problems of estimation and in testing hypotheses can look different, depending on the symbols and formulas used for standard deviations. As we said earlier, *there is no question of one formula being right and the other being wrong,* but no formula can be used correctly unless its meaning is clearly understood.

Perhaps the main reason why division by $n - 1$ is advocated in the formula for the sample standard deviation, $s$, is that *it provides a better estimate of the population standard deviation, $\sigma$.* As we pointed out on page 79, it is necessary to know something about the variability of a population in order to judge whether an estimate based on a sample mean can be expected to be close to the true mean. Since, in most practical problems, estimates of the variability of a population will have to be based on samples, it is important that such estimates have as many desirable properties as possible. If we divide by $n - 1$, the sample variance $s^2$ is referred to as an *unbiased* estimate of $\sigma^2$. This means that if an experiment were repeated many times, the average of the values thus obtained for $s^2$ could be expected to equal $\sigma^2$. On the other hand, if we divide by $n$, the values obtained for $s^2$ would on the average be too small. The main reason for dividing by $n - 1$ instead of $n$ is, therefore, that we get a *better* estimate of $\sigma^2$. A more theoretical treatment of this argument is referred to in the Bibliography on page 98.

The quantity $n - 1$ by which we divide in the formula for $s$ is generally referred to as the number of *degrees of freedom*. The reason for this terminology may be explained as follows: on page 82 we showed that the sum of the deviations from the mean is always equal to 0. Hence, given any $n - 1$ of the deviations from the mean, the $n$th is automatically determined. For instance, if we have 5 measurements and 4 of the deviations from the mean are $-3$, 5, 8, and $-6$, then it is easily verified that the 5th deviation from the mean *must* equal $-4$. In view of the fact that the standard deviation measures variability in terms of the squared deviations from the mean, we can say that it is based on $n - 1$ *independent* quantities or, in other words, that we have $n - 1$ *degrees of freedom*. Incidentally, the fact that only $n - 1$ of the deviations from the mean are independent, namely, that $n - 1$ of them automatically determine the $n$th, is also sometimes advanced as a reason for dividing by $n - 1$ instead of $n$ in the formula for $s$.

## BIBLIOGRAPHY

Short-cut formulas for the average deviation of grouped and ungrouped data are given in

> Waugh, A. E. *Elements of Statistical Method*, 3rd ed. New York: McGraw-Hill, 1952, p. 132.

Sheppard's correction for the error introduced into the calculation of $s$ or $\sigma$ by the assumption that all measurements belonging to a class are located at its class mark is discussed in

> Mills, F. C., *Introduction to Statistics*. New York: Henry Holt, 1952, p. 121.

A slightly more formal discussion of the bias of the *sample variance* when dividing by $n$ instead of $n - 1$ is given in

> Freund, J. E., and Williams, F. J., *Modern Business Statistics*. Englewood Cliffs, N. J.: Prentice-Hall, 1958, p. 98.

A thorough theoretical treatment of this topic may be found in

> Hoel, P. G., *Introduction to Mathematical Statistics*, 2nd ed. New York: John Wiley, 1954, p. 198.

Chapter  5*

# Further Descriptions: Symmetry,

# Skewness, Peakedness

## 5.1 / Introduction

So far we have discussed only statistical descriptions coming under
the heading of "measures of location" and "measures of variation."
That there are others was already pointed out on page 42, where we
mentioned the existence of measures of the symmetry, skewness, and
peakedness of distributions. Indeed, there is no limit to the number
of ways in which statistical data can be described. Statisticians continually develop new methods of describing aspects of numerical data
that happen to be of relevance in particular problems. They have
defined a *coefficient of concordance* to measure, among other things,
the consistency of subjective rankings, a *coefficient of alienation* to
measure how little (or how much) one variable is affected by another,
and the author once suggested a *degree of stereotypy* to measure the
consistency of responses in multi-choice situations. In later chapters
we shall meet the widely used *coefficient of correlation*, the *contingency coefficient*, and others, but for the moment we shall limit our
discussion to measures providing further descriptions of the *shape* of
distributions. In Section 5.2 we shall go into the question of measur-

*This chapter may be omitted without loss of continuity.

ing symmetry and skewness, and in Section 5.3 we shall illustrate one method of describing the peakedness, or *kurtosis*, of a distribution. The use of these formulas is nowadays not as widespread as it was, say, a decade ago (see also discussion on page 188), and we are including them mainly for the sake of completeness. As is indicated in the footnote, this chapter may be omitted without loss of continuity.

## 5.2 / Symmetry and Skewness

The fact that two distributions can have *identical* means and standard deviations, yet differ considerably in their over-all appearance is illustrated in Figure 5.1. Here both distributions have means of 3.5, standard deviations of 1.2, but the first is perfectly symmetrical while the second is somewhat lopsided or skewed. This illustrates

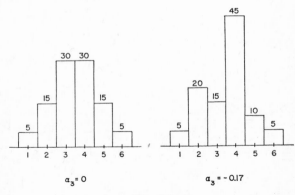

Fig. 5.1

why, at least in some problems, it may not suffice to measure only central location and variation. In problems of curve fitting, namely, in problems in which we are interested in approximating the histograms of distributions with smooth curves, it may well be necessary to measure additional features of their shapes.

The symmetry or lack of symmetry of a distribution (for that matter, also that of ungrouped data) can be expressed in terms of whatever differences there may exist between the mean, the median, and the mode. If a distribution is perfectly symmetrical (see Figure 2.11 on page 34) the mean will coincide with the median and the mode; if it is not, there will generally be discrepancies between these measures of central location. As can be seen from Figure 5.2,

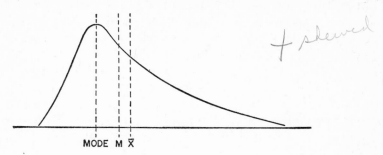

Fig. 5.2

*the mean of a distribution with a "tail" on the right will generally exceed the median, and the median will in turn exceed the mode. If the "tail" is on the left, this order will be reversed and the mode will exceed the median, which in turn will exceed the mean* (see Figure 5.3).

Whatever difference there may exist between the mean and the mode is used to measure symmetry and skewness by means of the formula

$$SK = \frac{\text{mean} - \text{mode}}{\text{standard deviation}} \qquad (5.2.1)\blacktriangle$$

called the *Pearsonian coefficient of skewness*. As in the case of the coefficient of variation where we divided by the mean, we are now

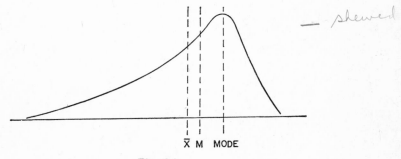

Fig. 5.3

dividing by the standard deviation to make the coefficient of skewness independent of the scale of measurement. This is important because it is supposed to describe the *shape* of a distribution and this should not be affected by a change in scale.

Formula (5.2.1) has the disadvantage that it involves the mode which, as we saw in Section 3.5, may not exist, may not be unique, and which is difficult to define for grouped data. Let us, therefore, use the approximate relationship between the mean, median, and mode mentioned on page 75, namely,

$$\text{mode} = 3(\text{median}) - 2(\text{mean})$$

and, substituting for the mode in (5.2.1), write the alternate form of the *Pearsonian coefficient of skewness* as

$$SK = \frac{3(\text{mean} - \text{median})}{\text{standard deviation}} \qquad (5.2.2)\blacktriangle$$

Applying this last formula to the two distributions of Figure 5.1, we find that for the first

$$SK = \frac{3(3.5 - 3.5)}{1.2} = 0$$

and that for the second, whose median is 3.72,

$$SK = \frac{3(3.5 - 3.72)}{1.2} = -0.55$$

The Pearsonian coefficient of skewness will be *positive* if the mean exceeds the median and the mode, and it will be *negative* if the mean is exceeded by the median and the mode. Hence, a distribution is said to be *positively skewed* if its tail is at the right, and *negatively skewed* if its tail is at the left (see Figures 5.2 and 5.3). Of course, for perfectly symmetrical distributions the mean, median, and mode coincide and the Pearsonian measures of skewness are both equal to zero.

The most widely used measure of skewness is called $\alpha_3$ (*alpha three*), and it is defined as *the average (mean) of the cubed deviations from the mean divided by the cube of the standard deviation.* Symbolically, it is written as

$$\alpha_3 = \frac{\dfrac{1}{n}\sum_{i=1}^{n}(x_i - \bar{x})^3}{s^3} \qquad (5.2.3)$$

for *ungrouped* data and as

$$\alpha_3 = \frac{\dfrac{1}{n}\sum_{i=1}^{n}(x_i - \bar{x})^3 \cdot f_i}{s^3} \qquad (5.2.4)$$

for *grouped* data. In these formulas the mean of the cubed deviations is divided by $s^3$ to make these "shape coefficients" independent of the scale of measurement. Incidentally, substituting $\mu$ and $\sigma$ for $\bar{x}$ and $s$, we can define analogous formulas for populations instead of samples.

Making the same change of scale as in the short-cut formulas for the mean and standard deviation, (5.2.4) can be written as

$$\alpha_3 = \frac{c^3}{s^3}\left[\frac{\sum_{i=1}^{k} u_i^3 f_i}{n} - 3\left(\frac{\sum_{i=1}^{k} u_i^2 f_i}{n}\right)\left(\frac{\sum_{i=1}^{k} u_i f_i}{n}\right) + 2\left(\frac{\sum_{i=1}^{k} u_i f_i}{n}\right)^3\right] \qquad (5.2.5)\blacktriangle$$

where $c$ is again the class interval of the distribution. Although this formula may look rather formidable, it is fairly easy to use. If we have already calculated the sum of the products $u_i f_i$ and the sum of the products $u_i^2 f_i$ in determining the standard deviation, we have only to calculate the sum of the products $u_i^3 f_i$ and then substitute into (5.2.5).

The work required to calculate $\alpha_3$ for the second distribution of Figure 5.1 is shown in the following table:

| Class mark | $f_i$ | $u_i$ | $u_i f_i$ | $u_i^2 f_i$ | $u_i^3 f_i$ |
|---|---|---|---|---|---|
| 1 | 5 | −2 | −10 | 20 | −40 |
| 2 | 20 | −1 | −20 | 20 | −20 |
| 3 | 15 | 0 | 0 | 0 | 0 |
| 4 | 45 | 1 | 45 | 45 | 45 |
| 5 | 10 | 2 | 20 | 40 | 80 |
| 6 | 5 | 3 | 15 | 45 | 135 |
|  | 100 |  | 50 | 170 | 200 |

$$s = \sqrt{\frac{100(170) - (50)^2}{100 \cdot 99}}$$

$$= 1.2 \text{ (approx.)}$$

and

$$\alpha_3 = \frac{1^3}{1.2^3}\left[\frac{200}{100} - 3\left(\frac{170}{100}\right)\left(\frac{50}{100}\right) + 2\left(\frac{50}{100}\right)^3\right] = -0.17$$

Had we used the same formula to calculate $\alpha_3$ for the first distribution of Figure 5.1, namely, the perfectly symmetrical distribution, we would have obtained $\alpha_3 = 0$.

## 5.3 / Peakedness

There are some problems, particularly problems of *curve fitting*, in which it is important to describe also the *peakedness* or *kurtosis* of a distribution (see Bibliography on page 105.) The measure that is most commonly used for this purpose is called $\alpha_4$ (*alpha four*), and it is defined as *the average (mean) of the fourth powers of the deviations from the mean divided by the fourth power of the standard deviation.* For grouped data it is written as

$$\alpha_4 = \frac{\dfrac{1}{n}\sum_{i=1}^{k}(x_i - \bar{x})^4 \cdot f_i}{s^4} \tag{5.3.1}$$

and analogous to (5.2.5) its *short-cut formula* is

$$\alpha_4 = \frac{c^4}{s^4}\left[\frac{\sum_{i=1}^{k}u_i^4 f_i}{n} - 4\left(\frac{\sum_{i=1}^{k}u_i^3 f_i}{n}\right)\left(\frac{\sum_{i=1}^{k}u_i f_i}{n}\right)\right.$$
$$\left. + 6\left(\frac{\sum_{i=1}^{k}u_i^2 f_i}{n}\right)\left(\frac{\sum_{i=1}^{k}u_i f_i}{n}\right)^2 - 3\left(\frac{\sum_{i=1}^{k}u_i f_i}{n}\right)^4\right] \tag{5.3.2} ▲$$

To determine $\alpha_4$ for the *first* distribution of Figure 5.1, we will have to calculate the sum of the products $u_i f_i$, that of the products $u_i^2 f_i$, that of the products $u_i^3 f_i$, and that of the products $u_i^4 f_i$. Using the same $u$-scale as on page 51, it can easily be checked that these sums are, respectively, 50, 170, 230, 770, and that $\alpha_4$ is equal to 2.63.

Distributions that are *very peaked* and have relatively *wide tails*

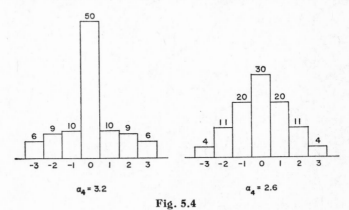

**Fig. 5.4**

are called *leptokurtic,* meaning "narrow humped," and distributions that are rather *flat in the middle* and have relatively *thin tails* are called *platykurtic,* meaning "broad humped." Thus, the first distribution of Figure 5.4 is leptokurtic while the second is platykurtic. In practice, one meets many distributions having the *bell shape* of the *normal distribution,* which will be discussed in Chapter 8, and for these distributions $\alpha_4$ is equal to 3. Hence, it has become the custom to refer to a distribution as leptokurtic if its value of $\alpha_4$ exceeds 3, and as platykurtic if its value of $\alpha_4$ is less than 3. The two distributions of Figure 5.4 have the same mean, the same standard deviation, they are both symmetrical, yet the first is leptokurtic with $\alpha_4 = 3.2$, while the second is platykurtic with $\alpha_4 = 2.6$.

## EXERCISES

1. Using the mean, median, and standard deviation of the speed-check distribution obtained in the text on pages 48, 58, and 91, measure its skewness with formula (5.2.2).

2. Use formula (5.2.2) to measure the skewness of whichever data you grouped among those of Exercises 11, 13, 14, 15, and 16 on pages 26 through 28. The mean and median were previously obtained in the problem sets on pages 54 and 62, and the standard deviation was found in Exercise 11 on page 94.

3. Use formula (5.2.2) to measure the skewness of the width-of-crab distribution on page 13. The mean is given on the text on page 52, while the median and standard deviation were obtained in Exercise 7 on page 62 and Exercise 10 on page 94.

4. Verify that $\alpha_3$ is zero for the first distribution of Figure 5.1 and calculate its value for the second distribution.

5. Verify that $\alpha_4$ is approximately 2.63 for the first distribution of Figure 5.1.

6. Calculate $\alpha_3$ and $\alpha_4$ for the speed-check distribution on page 17.

## BIBLIOGRAPHY

A somewhat more detailed treatment of the material covered in this chapter may be found in

> Croxton, F. E., and Cowden, D. J., *Applied General Statistics*, 2nd ed. Englewood Cliffs, N. J.: Prentice-Hall, 1955, Chap. 10.

> Waugh, A. E., *Elements of Statistical Method*, 3rd ed. New York: McGraw-Hill, 1952, Chap. 8.

The use of $\alpha_3$ and $\alpha_4$ in problems of curve fitting is discussed in the two books mentioned above (in Chapter 23 of the book by Croxton and Cowden and in Chapter 9 of the book by Waugh). A more theoretical treatment may be found in

> Kendall, M. G., *The Advanced Theory of Statistics, Vol. I*, 5th ed. London: Charles Griffin, 1952, Chap. 6.

# Chapter 6

# Further Descriptions: Index Numbers

## 6.1 / Introduction

High on the list of statistical measures that are the most useful to social scientists, particularly economists, are those telling them how much certain things have changed or how they compare with one another. They may want to know, for example, that in 1950 the size of the population of the United States was 114.5 per cent of what it was in 1940, that the 1957 average retail price of milk was 119 per cent of what it was in 1950, and that the 1955 production of barley in the United States was 77.7 per cent of what it was in 1950. These percentages, each of which compares two things, are the most primitive of a large set of statistical measures called *index numbers*. They are the most primitive, because there are also index numbers expressing changes in such complex phenomena as the cost of living, total industrial production, and business cycles. This, of course, involves combining many prices and (or) quantities in such a way that a single number can serve to indicate over-all changes.

Although index numbers are commonly associated with business and economics, they are also used in other fields. Psychologists measure intelligence quotients, which are essentially index numbers

*This chapter may be omitted without loss of continuity.

comparing a person's intelligence with that of an average for his or her age; health authorities prepare indexes to display changes in the adequacy of hospital facilities; educational research organizations devise indexes to measure the effectiveness of school systems; and sociologists may be interested in indexes measuring population changes. In practice, index numbers are used mainly to make comparisons between two different periods of time, but they can serve equally well to indicate comparisons between different locations, different industries, different nationalities, and so on.

During the past few years the use of index numbers has extended to many new fields of human activity. They are now of vital interest to millions of workers whose wages automatically go up or down with the value of the *Consumer Price Index* of the Bureau of Labor Statistics, they are of great concern to farmers whose subsidies depend on the *Parity Index* of the federal government, and they are no less important to business firms and individuals for whom they provide actual insurance against changing prices. Index numbers have even found their way into alimony agreements and trust fund payments, which can thus be made to vary with the value of the dollar.

Some knowledge of index numbers nowadays almost belongs under the heading of "general education," and it is for this reason that we have included this rather brief chapter on the subject. In Section 6.2 we shall discuss some of the basic problems met in index number construction, in Sections 6.3 and 6.4 we shall treat some of the formulas that are the most widely used, and in Section 6.5 we shall go into some mathematical properties of index number formulas.

## 6.2 / Basic Problems in Index Number Construction

The following are the most basic problems met in index number construction: (1) *The availability and comparability of data*, (2) *The selection of items to be included in the comparison*, (3) *The choice of time periods (localities, etc.) that are to be compared*, (4) *The selection of appropriate weights*, and (5) *The choice of a suitable formula*.

Before going into any of these problems in detail, let us point out that generally none of them can be solved unless the purpose of the index we want to construct has been formulated in a precise way. For instance, if we are asked to construct an index to measure the change in ingot production of the Republic Steel Corporation from

1949 to 1955, we have only to look at this company's Annual Report, copy the appropriate production figures which are, respectively, 6804 and 9680 thousand tons, and write

$$\text{index} = \frac{9680}{6804} = 1.42 \text{ or } 142 \text{ per cent}$$

In contrast to this example, where the statement of the purpose of the index solved all problems, there are many situations in which the formulation of the problem raises complex issues like those to be discussed below.

1. *The availability and comparability of data.* It would hardly seem necessary to point out that comparisons cannot be made, indexes cannot be constructed, unless the required statistical data can be obtained. Many research workers have been frustrated by the fact that essential information needed by townships was tabulated by counties, sales data needed by brand were available only by type of merchandise, insurance losses were given per risk and not per claim, and so on. Unfortunately, there often is a considerable lack of uniformity in the methods used in reporting statistical data and this can lead to difficulties in index number construction.

The question of availability also enters the picture if we want to make a comparison, say, of the cost of living in 1958 with that of the year 1914. Nowadays television sets, frozen foods, and appliances of all sorts are found in wide use, but none of them were sold commercially in 1914. We may thus be forced to invent fictitious prices for what such items might have cost had they been available in 1914.

The question of comparability can also be quite troublesome. In recent congressional hearings some labor organizations complained that, to some extent, the *Consumer Price Index* reflects deterioration in quality rather than an actual change in prices. It does not matter here whether this criticism was valid, but it serves to indicate that it can be a very difficult problem to make sure that prices are actually comparable, that is, that they refer to goods and services which are identical in quality.

The comparability of statistical data may also be questioned if parts of the data are obtained from different sources. It is very confusing, for example, to note that the Bureau of Census reports that the 1939 production of nonferrous minerals in the United States had a total value of $350 million, while the Bureau of Mines reports a corresponding figure of $434 million. (This discrepancy arises from the fact that the Bureau of Census figures are those given by producers while the Bureau of Mines figures are those given by purchasers and transportation companies.) Similar difficulties can arise also in connection with import-export data supplied by different governments, employment and production figures quoted by different sources, sickness and accident data supplied by different agencies, and so on.

2. *The selection of items to be included in the comparison.* If an index is designed for the special purpose of comparing the prices of a commodity at two different times, there is no question as to what figures should be included. The situation is entirely different, however, in the construction of so-called *general purpose indexes* such as those designed to measure general changes in wholesale or consumer prices. It must be clear that it is physically impossible, or at least highly impractical, to include in such a comparison all commodities from aspirin to zithers and to include, furthermore, *all* prices at which these commodities are traded in every single transaction throughout the entire country. The only reasonable alternative is to take samples in such a way that the items and transactions included adequately reflect the over-all situation. For example, the *Consumer Price Index* is based on about 300 items (goods and services) playing a significant role in the average budget of persons belonging to a certain population group. The prices included in this index are samples with respect to the goods and services that are included and also with respect to the stores and cities that are canvassed in the necessary surveys.

The sampling methods used in selecting commodities for an index often come under the heading of what we shall later refer to as "judgment sampling." This means that the selection is *not* left to chance, but that the person who is responsible for the construction of an index selects those items which, in his professional judgment, best reflect the general situation the index is supposed to describe.

3. *The choice of time periods that are to be compared.* If an index number is designed for the specific purpose of comparing 1958 figures with those of some other year, say, 1949, it is customary to refer to 1958 as the *given year*, to 1949 as the *base year*, and the latter is usually indicated by writing 1949 = 100. In general, the year or period which we want to compare is called the *given year* or *given period*, while the year or period relative to which the comparison is made is called the *base year* or *base period*.

The choice of the base year or base period does not present any problems if an index is constructed for a specific comparison. So far as general purpose indexes describing complex phenomena are concerned, it is generally desirable to base the comparison on a period of *relative economic stability* as well as a period that is *not too distant in the past*. The reason for the first stipulation is that during periods of abnormal economic conditions (for example, during a war) there may be no free trading of some commodities, there may be black markets, and the buying habits of the public may be irregular due to shortages of products that would otherwise figure in the average person's budget.

One reason for choosing base periods that are not too far in the distant past is that rapid changes in the availability of commercial products make it difficult, sometimes impossible, to obtain required information. Base periods that are too far in the past also raise problems not unlike those faced by an art critic who, instead of judging two paintings by holding them next to one another, is forced to compare them individually with a third, and then compare the individual comparisons.

Most current government indexes have as their base the three-year period 1947–1949. Although this period can hardly be described as one of economic stability in the classical sense, it has the advantage that it is relatively recent and that it is at least as stable as any period within the last two decades. Some government indexes are still tied by law to the pre-World War I period from 1910 to 1914.

4. *The selection of appropriate weights.* As we pointed out in Section 3.7, there are many situations in which figures cannot be averaged without paying due attention to their relative importance, and this applies particularly to index numbers. Let us suppose, for example, that we want to construct an index comparing the 1949 and 1958 prices of wood products used in the home, and that we arbitrarily decide to include the two items *toothpicks and furniture*. Let us suppose, furthermore, that for *furniture alone* the index is 160 per cent, while for *toothpicks alone* it is 110. We could go ahead and claim on the basis of these figures that the price of wood products used in the home in 1958 is $\dfrac{160 + 110}{2} = 135$ per cent of what it was in 1949, but it must be clear that this average is not very useful. To get a more meaningful result we would have to *weight* the items in some way to account for their significance in the over-all situation

we are trying to describe.  This is precisely the problem which we discussed in Section 3.7.

The problem of choosing suitable weights in the construction of an index is not an easy one.  It depends on whether we want to average prices, quantities, or, as in the illustration given, indexes of individual commodities.  Since it is difficult to treat this problem without referring to specific index number formulas, let us defer further discussion of this matter until Section 6.4, where we shall study weighted index number formulas.

5.  *The choice of a suitable formula.*  In the same way in which the *average* of a set of data can be described by using the mean, median, mode, and other measures of central location, relative changes can be described by employing any one of a great number of formulas, all of which by definition provide index numbers.  In the next two sections we shall treat some of these formulas and some of the factors that must be taken into account in choosing an appropriate one for a given problem.  After having read these sections it should be clear to the reader that any such choice will ultimately have to depend on practical considerations as well as on mathematical niceties of the formulas.

The symbolism which we shall use in the remainder of this chapter consists of referring to index numbers as $I$, base-year prices as $p_0$, given-year prices as $p_n$, base-year quantities as $q_0$, and given-year quantities as $q_n$.

## 6.3 / Unweighted Index Numbers

To illustrate some of the simplest methods used in index number construction, let us compare the March 1957 and (average) 1950 retail prices of certain kinds of meat.  The following prices, copied from the *Monthly Labor Review*, are all in cents per pound

|               | March 1957 | 1950 |
|---------------|:----------:|:----:|
| Round steak   | 87.1       | 93.6 |
| Chuck roast   | 48.7       | 61.6 |
| Pork chops    | 81.4       | 75.4 |
| Bacon, sliced | 67.7       | 63.7 |
| Ham, whole    | 61.7       | 62.0 |
| Lamb, leg     | 67.2       | 74.4 |

Adding the March 1957 prices and dividing their sum by that of the corresponding 1950 prices, we get

$$\frac{87.1 + 48.7 + 81.4 + 67.7 + 61.7 + 67.2}{93.6 + 61.6 + 75.4 + 63.7 + 62.0 + 74.4} = \frac{413.8}{430.7} = 0.96$$

and this tells us that the combined March 1957 prices are 96 per cent of those of 1950. In other words, *the index stands at 96 per cent.* The method which we employed here is called the *simple aggregative method* and the resulting index is accordingly called a *simple aggregative index.* In general, the formula for a *simple aggregative index* is

$$I = \frac{\sum p_n}{\sum p_0} \cdot 100 \qquad (6.3.1)\blacktriangle$$

where $\sum p_n$ is the sum of the given-year prices, $\sum p_0$ the sum of the base-year prices, and the ratio of the two is multiplied by 100 to express the index as a percentage.

The greatest weakness of a simple aggregative index is that it fails the so-called *units test.* It can produce vastly divergent results depending on the units for which the prices of the various commodities are quoted. We might have gotten an entirely different answer in our example if we had combined the prices of, say, a ton of round steak, a pound of chuck roast, three pork chops, half a pound of bacon, a whole ham, and a whole leg of lamb. It is mainly for this reason that simple aggregative indexes are nowadays rarely used. Among the few published indexes that are still of this type, perhaps the most widely known, is the *Dun and Bradstreet Wholesale Food Price Index* which has appeared monthly in *Dun's Statistical Review* since 1916.

An alternate way of comparing the two sets of prices given on page 111 would be to calculate first a separate index for each of the six kinds of meat, and then to average the individual *price relatives,* with any one of the many measures of central location. Writing the price relatives as percentages, we obtain

*Price Relatives*

| | |
|---|---|
| Round steak | $\dfrac{87.1}{93.6} \cdot 100 = \quad 93$ per cent |
| Chuck roast | $\dfrac{48.7}{61.6} \cdot 100 = \quad 79$ per cent |
| Pork chops | $\dfrac{81.4}{75.4} \cdot 100 = 108$ per cent |
| Bacon, sliced | $\dfrac{67.7}{63.7} \cdot 100 = 106$ per cent |
| Ham, whole | $\dfrac{61.7}{62.0} \cdot 100 = 100$ per cent |
| Lamb, leg | $\dfrac{67.2}{74.4} \cdot 100 = \quad 90$ per cent |

To construct an over-all index comparing the prices of these six kinds of meat, we can now take the mean, median, mode or some other "average" of the six price relatives. Choosing the mean, we get

$$\frac{93 + 79 + 108 + 106 + 100 + 90}{6} = 96$$

and this index is appropriately called an *arithmetic mean of price relatives*. Symbolically, the formula for this kind of index is

$$I = \frac{\sum \frac{p_n}{p_0} \cdot 100}{k} \qquad (6.3.2) \blacktriangle$$

where $k$ is the number of items (commodities) whose price relatives are being combined.

Had we used the median of the price relatives we would have obtained 96.5 per cent, and had we computed the geometric mean with formula (3.6.2) we would have obtained 95 per cent. Although any measure of central location can be used, price relatives are usually averaged with either the arithmetic mean or the geometric mean. Incidentally, formulas (6.3.1) and (6.3.2) define *price indexes*, but they can easily be changed to *quantity indexes* by replacing the $p$'s with $q$'s.

It is a matter of historical interest that the earliest index number on record is an arithmetic mean of price relatives. In the middle of the eighteenth century G. R. Carli, an Italian, calculated the effect of the import of silver from America on the value of money, using a formula like (6.3.2) to compare the 1750 prices of oil, grain, and wine with those of the year 1500.

Today the need for employing weights has been almost universally accepted and very few indexes are actually computed with formulas as simple as (6.3.1) and (6.3.2). Among the important government indexes only the daily *Index of Spot Market Prices* is still calculated as a simple geometric mean of price relatives, and prior to 1914 the *Wholesale Price Index* of the Bureau of Labor Statistics was an arithmetic mean of the price relatives of about 250 commodities. It was changed to a weighted index as the result of the well-known study by W. C. Mitchell (see Bibliography on page 120), which since its publication in 1915 has had a pronounced effect on index number construction.

## EXERCISES

**1.** The following are the average hourly earnings (in dollars) of production workers in printing, publishing, and allied industries:

|  | *1950* | *1954* | *1955* |
|---|---|---|---|
| Newspapers | 2.17 | 2.59 | 2.67 |
| Periodicals | 1.88 | 2.24 | 2.33 |
| Books | 1.64 | 1.94 | 2.01 |
| Commercial printing | 1.81 | 2.17 | 2.25 |
| Lithographing | 1.83 | 2.18 | 2.28 |

(a) Find simple aggregative indexes comparing the 1954 and 1955 average hourly earnings of these workers with those of 1950.

(b) Find the mean and the median of the price relatives comparing the 1955 average hourly earnings of these workers with those of 1954.

**2.** The following are figures on silver production in thousands of fine ounces:

|  | *1939* | *1954* |
|---|---|---|
| Canada | 1930 | 2557 |
| Mexico | 6322 | 3325 |
| United States | 4817 | 3172 |

Substituting $q$'s for $p$'s, use formula (6.3.1) to compute a simple aggregative index comparing the 1954 silver production in these countries with that of 1939.

**3.** Use the data of Exercise 2 to find the arithmetic mean of the quantity relatives comparing the 1954 production of silver with that of 1939.

**4.** The following are average retail prices of butter and cheese in cents per pound, milk in cents per quart, and eggs in cents per dozen:

|  | *1948* | *1955* | *March 1957* |
|---|---|---|---|
| Butter | 86.7 | 70.9 | 74.1 |
| Cheese | 65.6 | 57.7 | 52.5 |
| Milk | 21.8 | 23.1 | 24.6 |
| Eggs | 72.3 | 60.6 | 50.5 |

(a) Find a simple aggregative index comparing the March 1957 prices of these dairy products with those of 1948.

(b) Find the mean of the price relatives comparing the March 1957 prices of these dairy products with those of 1948.

(c) Find the median of the price relatives comparing the March 1957 prices of these dairy products with those of 1955.

(d) Find a simple aggregative index comparing the March 1957 prices of these dairy products with those of 1955.

## 6.4 / Weighted Index Numbers

To show how an index number can be made to account for differences in importance, let us consider the following data on the prices of five major crops in cents per bushel and their production in millions of bushels

|  | Prices 1936 – 1940 | 1955 | Quantities 1936 – 1940 |
|---|---|---|---|
| Wheat | 77 | 198 | 796 |
| Corn | 61 | 135 | 2347 |
| Oats | 31 | 60 | 1053 |
| Rye | 51 | 105 | 41 |
| Barley | 47 | 92 | 113 |

As we pointed out on page 69, it is customary and appropriate to average prices by using as weights the corresponding quantities sold, consumed, or produced. Hence, using the average production figures for the five-year period 1936–1940 as weights, let us calculate a *weighted mean* of the 1955 prices, another of the 1936–1940 prices, and define an index in terms of the ratio of the two. Ignoring the denominators of the two weighted means which cancel, we thus get

$$\frac{198(796) + 135(2347) + 60(1053) + 105(41) + 92(113)}{77(796) + 61(2347) + 31(1053) + 51(41) + 47(113)} \cdot 100 = 226 \text{ per cent}$$

The index which we have constructed here is called a *weighted aggregative index with base-year weights*. It is also known as a Laspeyres Index, named after the statistician who first suggested its use. In general, its formula is

$$I = \frac{\sum p_n q_0}{\sum p_0 q_0} \cdot 100 \qquad (6.4.1) \blacktriangle$$

where the numerator contains the sum of the products of the respective given-year prices and base-year quantities, whereas the denominator contains the sum of the products of the respective base-year prices and base-year quantities.

In case the reader is curious why we did not weight the base-year prices with base-year quantities and the given-year prices with given-year quantities, let us point out that this would have given us a *value index* rather than a price index. It would have compared the *total values* of the five crops and not comparable averages of their prices.

Instead of using base-year quantities as weights, we could also have used given-year quantities or, for that matter, quantities referring to any other year. Employing given-year quantity weights, we obtain a second *weighted aggregative index*, sometimes called a Paasche Index, whose formula is

$$I = \frac{\sum p_n q_n}{\sum p_0 q_n} \cdot 100 \qquad (6.4.2)\blacktriangle$$

Given that the 1955 production totals for the five crops mentioned on page 115 are, respectively, 935, 3223, 1503, 29, and 368 million bushels, the reader can easily verify that formula (6.4.2) gives an index of 224 per cent (see Exercise 1 on page 117).

Most of the important index numbers constructed by the federal government are published *in series*, that is, regularly every day, week, month, or year. For these it would be highly impractical to use (6.4.2), since this formula would continually require new quantity weights. An index that is currently in great favor is the *fixed-weight aggregative index*, whose formula is

$$I = \frac{\sum p_n q_a}{\sum p_0 q_a} \cdot 100 \qquad (6.4.3)\blacktriangle$$

Here the weights are quantities referring to some period other than the base year $o$ or the given year $n$. One of the most important fixed-weight aggregative indexes is the *Wholesale Price Index* of the Bureau of Labor Statistics. Its current base period is the three-year period 1947–1949 and the $q_a$ are quantities marketed in 1947. We shall not illustrate the use of (6.4.3) since the calculations required are identical with those needed for (6.4.1) or (6.4.2).

In Section 6.3 we discussed two kinds of index numbers, those of the aggregative type and those that are averages of individual price relatives. Having treated weighted aggregative indexes, let us now in a parallel fashion present *weighted averages of price relatives*. For example, we can write the formula for a *weighted arithmetic mean of price relatives* as

$$I = \frac{\sum \dfrac{p_n}{p_0} \cdot w}{\sum w} \cdot 100 \qquad (6.4.4)\blacktriangle$$

where the $w$'s are suitable weights assigned to the individual price relatives, now written as proportions.

Since the importance of a relative change in the price of a commodity is most adequately reflected by the *total amount of money* that is spent on it, it is customary to use *value weights* for the $w$'s of formula (6.4.4). This raises the question whether one should use the values (prices times quantities) of the base year, those of the given year, or perhaps some other fixed-value weights. It will be left to the reader to show in Exercise 6 on page 118 that base-year value weights $p_0 q_0$ would not yield a new index. With these weights (6.4.4) reduces to the formula of the Laspeyres Index given in (6.4.1). To give one example in which we use *given-year value weights* let us refer to the prices given on page 115 and the 1955 production figures given on page 116. Calculating the necessary price relatives and value weights we get

| | Price relatives $p_n/p_0$ | Values* $p_n \cdot q_n$ |
|---|---|---|
| Wheat | 2.57 | 185,130 |
| Corn | 2.21 | 435,105 |
| Oats | 1.94 | 90,180 |
| Rye | 2.06 | 3,045 |
| Barley | 1.96 | 33,856 |

and formula (6.4.4) with *given-year value weights* gives

$$\frac{2.57(185,130) + 2.21(435,105) + 1.94(90,180) + 2.06(3,045) + 1.96(33,856)}{185,130 + 435,105 + 90,180 + 3,045 + 33,856} \cdot 100$$
$$= 225 \text{ per cent}$$

Having compared the prices of the five crops in three different ways, we obtained indexes of 226, 224, and 225. The differences are evidently not very large, but if millions of dollars ride on an increase or decrease of one point (as in some labor-management agreements containing escalator clauses), the question of choosing an appropriate index is a serious matter. Some further considerations for choosing between index number formulas will be given in Section 6.5.

### EXERCISES

1. Using the prices given on page 115 and the 1955 production figures given on page 116, verify that formula (6.4.2) gives an index of 224 for the prices of the five crops.

2. The following are the prices in cents per pound and production totals in thousands of short tons of selected minerals:

*Since the prices were given in cents per bushel and the quantities in millions of bushels, the units of these values are $10,000.

| | Prices | | | Quantities | |
|---|---|---|---|---|---|
| | 1949 | 1952 | 1955 | 1949 | 1952 |
| Copper | 19.2 | 24.2 | 37.5 | 88 | 99 |
| Lead | 15.4 | 16.5 | 15.1 | 45 | 44 |
| Zinc | 12.1 | 16.2 | 12.2 | 72 | 80 |

(a) Using 1949 quantities as weights and 1949 = 100, find weighted aggregative indexes for the 1952 and 1955 prices of the minerals.

(b) Using 1952 quantities as weights and 1949 = 100, find a weighted aggregative index for the 1952 prices of these minerals.

(c) Using 1952 quantities as weights and 1949 = 100, find a fixed-weight aggregative index for the 1955 prices of these minerals.

3. Given that the 1950 production of wheat, corn, oats, rye, and barley was, respectively, 1019, 3075, 1369, 21, and 358 million bushels, calculate a fixed-weight aggregative index comparing the 1955 prices of these crops with average prices for the period 1936-1940 using 1950 quantity weights. The prices are given in the text on page 115.

4. Calculate a weighted arithmetic mean of price relatives comparing the 1955 prices of the minerals of Exercise 2 with those of 1949 using 1952 value weights.

5. Given that the total copper, lead, and zinc production in the United States in 1953 had values of 532, 90, and 125 million dollars, find a weighted arithmetic mean of price relatives comparing the 1955 prices of these minerals with those of 1949 using 1953 value weights. The prices are given above in Exercise 2.

6. Prove that if we substitute base-year values for the $w$'s of formula (6.4.4), this index reduces to a Laspeyres Index.

## 6.5 / Properties of Index Numbers

Statisticians have devised several mathematical criteria for choosing between index number formulas, among them the *units test* mentioned on page 112. This test requires that an index be independent of the units in which, or for which, prices and quantities are quoted. Of all the index numbers met in this chapter, only the simple (unweighted) aggregative index failed to meet this test.

Two other interesting criteria for choosing between index number formulas are the *time reversal test* and the *factor reversal test*. The *time reversal test* expresses the intuitive notion that if an index comparing 1958 prices with those of 1939 is 200 per cent, then the same index comparing 1939 prices with those of 1958 should be 50 per cent. In other words, if one thing is twice as big as another, the second must be half as big as the first. Symbolically, if $I_{o,n}$ stands for an index comparing prices in the year $n$ with those in the year $o$, the time reversal test demands that $I_{o,n}$ (expressed as a proportion) be the reciprocal of $I_{n,o}$. To check whether an index number formula satisfies this test, we have only to interchange the subscripts $o$ and $n$ wherever they appear in the formula, and then see whether the resulting index is the reciprocal of the first. In spite of the evident desirability of this property, the time reversal test is *not* satisfied by many index number formulas. It will be left to the reader to show in Exercise 1 on page 120 that among the formulas we have discussed only (6.3.1) and (6.4.3) satisfy this test.

We mentioned earlier that the various index number formulas in this chapter can be converted to *quantity indexes* by simply replacing the $p$'s with $q$'s and $q$'s with $p$'s. Using this relationship between the formula for a price index and that for the corresponding quantity index, the *factor reversal test* demands that the product of the two equal the *value index*

$$V = \frac{\sum p_n q_n}{\sum p_0 q_0}$$

This criterion is satisfied if we compare the prices, quantities, and values of a *single* commodity at times $o$ and $n$, but it is not satisfied by any of the index number formulas given in this chapter. One index which does satisfy the factor reversal test is the so-called *Ideal Index*. It was formulated originally by Irving Fisher and it is the *geometric mean* of the two indexes defined by (6.4.1) and (6.4.2). Thus, the formula for the *Ideal Index* is

$$I = \sqrt{\frac{\sum p_n q_0}{\sum p_0 q_0} \cdot \frac{\sum p_n q_n}{\sum p_0 q_n}} \qquad (6.5.1)\blacktriangle$$

It will be left to the reader to verify that the Ideal Index does satisfy the factor reversal test.

It would be erroneous to assume that the units test, the time reversal test, and the factor reversal test provide absolute yardsticks by which to measure the relative merits of index numbers. When practical advantages clash with theoretical considerations, practical needs are usually given the most attention.

## EXERCISES

**1.** Check each formula in Sections 6.3 and 6.4 to show that only (6.3.1) and (6.4.3) satisfy the time reversal test. Does the Ideal Index satisfy the time reversal test?

**2.** Show that the Ideal Index given by (6.5.1) satisfies the factor reversal test.

**3.** Calculate an Ideal Index comparing the 1952 prices of copper, lead, and zinc with those of 1949. The necessary figures are given in Exercise 2 on page 118.

**4.** Using the results obtained in the text on pages 115 and 116, find the Ideal Index for the 1955 and 1936–1940 prices of the five crops.

## BIBLIOGRAPHY

More detailed discussions of index numbers, their theory, construction, and application, may be found in most textbooks on business statistics. The following are a few books and pamphlets devoted exclusively to problems of index number construction:

Fisher, I., *The Making of Index Numbers*. Boston: Houghton Mifflin, 1923.

Mitchell, W. C., *The Making and Using of Index Numbers*. Bulletin 656, Bureau of Labor Statistics, Washington, D. C., 1938.

Mudgett, B. D., *Index Numbers*. New York: John Wiley, 1951.
A thorough treatment of the major index numbers published by the federal government is given in

Hauser, P. M., and Leonard, W. R., *Government Statistics for Business Use*, 2nd ed. New York: John Wiley, 1956.

# PART TWO

# Probability, Estimation, and Tests of Hypotheses

Chapter 7

# Probability, Expectation,

# and Decision-Making

## 7.1 / Introduction

Directly or indirectly, the concept of probability plays an important role in all problems of science, business, and everyday life that involve *an element of uncertainty*. Having stated in Chapter 1 that statistics may be identified with the art, or science, of making decisions in the face of uncertainty, it follows that questions concerning probabilities, their meaning, their estimation, and their manipulation are basic in any treatment of the subject of statistics. In view of its importance, it is unfortunate in a way that the term "probability," itself, is difficult to define. At least, there is no general agreement, and there are still many people who associate it with nebulous and mystic ideas.

So long as we concern ourselves only with conversational language, it does not really matter whether we use such terms as "probably," "possibly," and "likely" without giving them a strict definition. However, we find ourselves in difficulties if we try to use them in statistics, or in science in general, without stating precisely what they are supposed to mean. Before going much further, we shall, therefore, have to explain what we mean when we say, for example, "the probability that it will rain tomorrow is 0.30," "the probability that the candidate will be elected is 0.72," or "the probability that the price of a stock will go up is 0.60."

Philosophical arguments about the various theories of probability that have been proposed make interesting reading (see Bibliography on page 148, but in view of our interests and objectives in this book, we shall limit our discussion to the so-called *objectivistic view*. After all, objectivity is the keynote of science, and, more generally, it forms the basis of all rational thought.

In statistics, probabilities are defined as *relative frequencies,* or to be more exact as *limits of relative frequencies*. When we say "the probability that it will rain tomorrow in Chicago is 0.30," we mean that in the long run it will rain there on that date 30 per cent of the time; when we say "the probability that a student who enters a given college will graduate is 0.45," we mean that in the long run 45 per cent of the students who enter this college will graduate; and when we say "the probability that a man aged 50 will live to be 65 is 0.71," we mean that if present conditions prevail 71 per cent of all men aged 50 will live to be 65. *The proportion of the time that an event takes place is called its relative frequency, and the relative frequency with which it takes place in the long run is called its probability.*

When we say "the probability of getting *heads* with a balanced coin is $\frac{1}{2}$," this means that in the long run we will get 50 per cent heads and 50 per cent tails. It does not mean that we must necessarily get 5 heads and 5 tails in 10 flips of a coin or 50 heads and 50 tails in 100. No, it would be unreasonable always to expect an equal number of heads and tails, but if a balanced coin is flipped a large number of times we can usually expect to get very close to 50 per cent heads and 50 per cent tails.

Since "in the long run" is not a very precise term, the probability of an event is actually defined as the *limit of the relative frequency* with which it occurs. If an event occurs $x$ times out of $n$, its relative frequency is $x/n$, and the value approached by $x/n$ when $n$ becomes infinite is called the limit of the relative frequency. Since limits, which belong to the subject of calculus, are difficult to explain without assuming more knowledge of mathematics than we did for this book, we shall be contented using the more intuitive and easier to understand expression "in the long run."

The role played by probability in statistics is that of a substitute for certainty. There being very few occasions in which we actually have *complete* information, that is, *all* relevant facts, we really have no choice but to generalize from samples, and we cannot be absolutely certain of whatever conclusions we may reach. To illustrate, let us suppose that Mr. Jones is planning to open a furniture store and that he consults an expert about the chances of its becoming a success. If the expert could tell him for sure that the store will be a financial success, Mr. Jones would know precisely where he stands. Similarly, a definite negative reply, if followed, would prevent him from having a financial loss. In reality, the kind of answer he can reasonably expect from the expert, who is not clairvoyant, is that his chances of succeeding in this venture are very good, average, or fairly poor. To interpret such a reply in the light of what we have said about probabilities, let us suppose that the expert asserts more specifically that the probability of the store's success is 0.75. *Where does Mr. Jones stand now? Should he go ahead and open the store even though there is the chance that it may fail? Would he have the right to blame the expert if he opened the store and it failed? Should he put the expert on a pedestal if he opened the store and it became a success? Would he have the right to blame the expert if he did not open the store, but a competitor who did turned it into a success?*

Ultimately, the answer to the question whether he should open the store is entirely Mr. Jones', and if he is an intelligent business-man he will base it on many factors including the opinion expressed by the expert. The answer to the other questions is that the "good-ness" of the expert cannot (and should not) be evaluated in terms of what happens to this particular store. When he says that the probability for success is 0.75, he means that *among a large number of similar stores built in similar locations and under similar circum-stances 75 per cent will succeed and 25 per cent will fail.*

The foregoing example illustrates the fact that in order to quote a probability for the occurrence of an event we must refer to what will happen in the long run in a large number of similar events. There are some who object to this, being unwilling to settle for anything short of absolute certainty and absolute truth, but unless we discover an accurate crystal ball, we will have to resign ourselves to the fact that statistical predictions must necessarily be similar in kind to that of the expert mentioned above.

The fact that probability statements cannot be proven right or wrong on the basis of the occurrence (or non-occurrence) of single events does not imply that we should go ahead and make wild predic-tions in terms of probabilities. *It is as important in science as it is in business and everyday life to make correct predictions and correct decisions as often as possible and, hence, it is essential to know at least approximately what the correct values of relevant probabilities are.* For instance, if the probability of catching a cold at a football game is 0.08 if we do not wear a heavy coat and 0.01 if we do, it will be smart to play the odds by wearing a heavy coat. Of course, this will not protect us completely from catching colds, but in the long run we will catch fewer.

Let us discuss briefly how probabilities are used in statistics to judge the merits of generalizations, the closeness of estimates, and the goodness of decisions. Suppose, for instance, that we are asked to predict an election on the basis of a sample taken from the electorate. If on the basis of this sample and appropriate statistical techniques we arrive at the conclusion that Candidate A will receive anywhere from 57 to 59 per cent of the vote, we cannot be absolutely certain that this is correct. *We assumed a certain risk by generalizing on the basis of a sample.* Since we cannot be sure that the candidate will receive from 57 to 59 per cent of the vote, we are open to the question as to "how sure" we really are. Suppose then that we say that we are "95 per cent sure," or in other words that we assign our estimate a probability of 0.95. To explain what this means, let us point out first that we are talking about a *specific* election; the probability of 0.95 is not meant to imply that Candidate A would receive the estimated per cent of the vote 95 per cent of the time if he ran for office a great number of times. No, if we assign an estimate a probability of 0.95 this means that *we employed a method of estimation which in the long run will be successful 95 per cent of the time. In other words, the probability which we assign to an estimate is really a measure of the "goodness" of the method of estimation we happen to employ.*

In the same way we shall express the "goodness" of decisions based on samples by giving the *success ratio* of the statistical criteria which we employ. For example, if we decide on the basis of samples of grades obtained in a French vocabulary test that students in one school are superior to those of another *and* if we say that we are 99 per cent sure that this decision is not in error, *we are really saying that our decision is based on a statistical technique which exposes us to the risk of making such an error about 1 per cent of the time.* In statistics, all probabilities that are used to express the merits of estimates, predictions, and decisions are really indications of the "goodness" of the methods which we employ.

In the study of probability there are essentially three kinds of questions: the question of what we mean when we say a probability is 0.75, 0.32, ..., the question of how to obtain numerical values of probabilities, and the question of how to use known probabilities to calculate others. Having resolved the first question by defining probabilities in terms of relative frequencies, the problem of obtaining numerical values for probabilities becomes a problem of *estimation*. For instance, if we want to estimate the probability that a moving van will arrive in time at its destination, we refer to past experience and check what proportion of the time such shipments have arrived on time. Assuming that what happened in the past is an indication of what will happen in the future, we thus get an estimate of the desired probability. In actual practice, probabilities are usually estimated by observing the relative frequency with which similar events have occurred in the past.

Since the problem of estimation will be treated separately in Chapter 10, we shall limit the discussion of this chapter mainly to the third kind of question, namely, the question of how to calculate the probabilities of relatively complex events in terms of known (or assumed values of the probabilities of simpler kinds of events. Thus, in Sections 7.2 and 7.3 we shall study what is often called the *calculus of probabilities*. In Section 7.4 we shall introduce the concept of *mathematical expectation*, and in Section 7.5 we shall use it to study the general problem of decision-making in the face of uncertainty.

## 7.2 / Rules of Probability

In this section we shall study some of the basic rules of probability, and we shall illustrate them with reference to the occurrence (or nonoccurrence) of physical events. Since most of these rules are easier to explain and easier to understand with reference to games of chance, where we can apply a special rule of probability for *equiprobable events* (see page 135), further illustrations will be given in Section 7.3.

The symbol which we shall use for the probability of the occurrence of an event $A$ is $P(A)$. Generally speaking, there is no uniformity in this respect; instead of $P(A)$ some authors use $Pr(A)$, $p(A)$, $pr(A)$, or simply $p$ without any qualification as to the event to which the probability is supposed to refer. Later we shall use $P(A \text{ or } B)$ for the probability that $A$ *or* $B$ (*or both*) occur and $P(A \text{ and } B)$ for the probability that $A$ *and* $B$ both occur.

The first rule of probability which we shall discuss states that $P(A)$ *cannot be negative or exceed 1*, namely, that it must be a number on the interval from 0 to 1. This agrees with our definition on page 124. A relative frequency, that is, a proportion, cannot be negative or exceed 1. Although the distinction is rather fine, $P(A) = 0$ does not necessarily mean that the occurrence of event $A$ is beyond the realm of possibility, and $P(A) = 1$ does not necessarily imply that the occurrence of event $A$ is absolutely certain. It is customary to assign *zero* probabilities to events which in colloquial terms "would not happen in a million years," and probabilities of *one* to events whose occurrence is "practically certain." If a monkey were set loose on a typewriter it is not impossible that he might (purely by chance) type the complete works of Shakespeare without a mistake, but it is so unlikely that we put the probability of this happening equal to 0. Similarly, we are practically certain that it will not snow in Phoenix, Arizona, in the month of July, although logically speaking it could, and we put this probability (the probability that it will *not* snow) equal to 1. An interesting discussion about probabilities that may be considered as negligible or practically certain from the human, terrestrial, cosmic, and super-cosmic perspective is given in the book by Borel referred to in the Bibliography on page 148.

A second rule of probability states that if the probability of the occurrence of event $A$ is $P(A)$, *the probability that it will not occur is* $1 - P(A)$. This also agrees with the frequency theory of probability. If the probability that it will rain on a certain day is 0.12, the probability that it will not rain is $1 - 0.12 = 0.88$. In other words, 12 per cent of the time it will rain and 88 per cent of the time it will not. Similarly, if the probability that a student will pass a test is 0.75, the probability that he will not pass is 0.25, and if the probability that a patient will recover from a disease is 0.84, the probability that he will not recover is 0.16.

If the probability that something will happen is $\frac{3}{4}$ and the probability that it will not happen is $\frac{1}{4}$, it is customary to say that *the odds are 3 to 1* in favor of the occurrence of the event. Also, if $P(A) = \frac{5}{9}$, the odds for the occurrence of $A$ are 5 to 4, and if $P(B) = \frac{3}{8}$, the odds for the occurrence of $B$ are 3 to 5. *By "odds" we mean the ratio of the probability that a certain event will happen to the probability that it will not take place.*

The next rule of probability refers to special kinds of events, events that are *mutually exclusive*. *Two or more events are said to be mutually exclusive if the occurrence of one precludes the occurrence of the others.* If we toss a coin, heads and tails are mutually exclusive since we can get one or the other but never both.  Similarly, a person's being born in New York City, San Francisco, or St. Louis are mutually exclusive events, and so are the Cleveland Indians', Detroit Tigers', or Baltimore Orioles' winning the championship of the American League.  On the other hand, having ice cream or apple pie for dessert are *not* mutually exclusive events since a person can have apple pie à la mode, and neither are the Los Angeles Dodgers' and the New York Yankees' winning the championships of their respective leagues.

If two events $A$ and $B$ are mutually exclusive, the probability that *A or B* will occur is given by the following rule

SPECIAL RULE OF ADDITION:

*If A and B are mutually exclusive,*

*then $P(A \text{ or } B) = P(A) + P(B)$.*                    (7.2.1)▲

In other words, if $A$ and $B$ are mutually exclusive, the probability that either will occur equals the sum of their individual probabilities.

If the probability that a student receives an A in a given course is 0.35 and the probability that he receives a B is 0.55, then the probability that he receives an A or a B is $0.35 + 0.55 = 0.90$.  Also, if the probability that a person shopping at the El Rancho supermarket has an income under \$6,000 is 0.54 and the probability that he has an income over \$10,000 is 0.18, then the probability that his income is under \$6,000 or over \$10,000 is $0.54 + 0.18 = 0.72$. (Further illustrations of the special rule of addition will be given on page 136.)

The special rule of addition can easily be generalized to apply to more than two mutually exclusive events.  Given $k$ mutually exclusive events $A_1, A_2, \ldots,$ and $A_k$, the probability that one of them will occur is

$$P(A_1 \text{ or } A_2 \text{ or } \ldots \text{ or } A_k) =$$

$$P(A_1) + P(A_2) + \ldots + P(A_k) \qquad (7.2.2)▲$$

If the probabilities that a person interviewed in a house-to-house canvass is a member of a Baptist, Catholic, Methodist, or Presbyterian church are, respectively, 0.09, 0.20, 0.06, and 0.02, then the probability that he is a member of one of these churches is $0.09 + 0.20 + 0.06 + 0.02 = 0.37$.  If the probabilities that a person who immigrated to the United States in 1955 came from England, Germany, or

Italy are, respectively, 0.06, 0.12, and 0.13, then the probability that he came from one of these countries is $0.06 + 0.12 + 0.13 = 0.31$. An application of rule (7.2.2) to a game of chance will be given on page 136.

If the probability that a man who enters a department store will buy a shirt is 0.04 and the probability that he will buy a tie is 0.05, formula (7.2.1) cannot be used to calculate the probability that he will buy either a shirt or a tie. The two events are not mutually exclusive, since he could very well buy a shirt *and* a tie.

Before we formulate a general rule of addition that applies also to events that are not mutually exclusive, let us first explain what is meant by *independent* and *dependent* events. *Two or more events are said to be independent if the occurrence or non-occurrence of one does in no way affect the occurrence of any of the others.* If $A$ and $B$ stand for getting heads in two successive flips of a coin, then $A$ and $B$ are independent. The outcome of the second flip is in no way affected by what happened in the first. Similarly, if $A$ stands for Mr. Smith's having an egg for breakfast, and $B$ stands for his having a flat tire while driving to work, it is difficult to see how these two events can possibly be dependent. Incidentally, *if two events are mutually exclusive, they are also dependent;* by definition, the occurrence of one precludes the occurrence of the other.

If two events are independent, the probability that they will both occur is given by the following rule*

SPECIAL RULE OF MULTIPLICATION:

> *If $A$ and $B$ are independent,*
>
> *then $P(A \text{ and } B) = P(A) \cdot P(B)$*  (7.2.3) ▲

This formula tells us that the probability of the occurrence of two independent events equals the product of their individual probabilities.

Applying (7.2.3) to the game of "heads or tails," we find that the probability of getting heads in each of two flips of a balanced coin is the probability of getting heads in the first *times* the probability of getting heads in the second, or $\frac{1}{2} \cdot \frac{1}{2} = \frac{1}{4}$. This is discussed further on page 136. Also, if the probability that a person 25 years or older (who

---

*This rule may actually be used to give a more rigorous mathematical definition of what is meant by independent events. Accordingly, two events are said to be independent if and only if $P(A \text{ and } B)$ equals the product of $P(A)$ and $P(B)$.

is interviewed in a survey) has completed four years of college is 0.07 and the probability that he has blond hair is 0.20, then the probability that he has blond hair *and* has completed four years of college is $(0.07) \cdot (0.20) = 0.014$.

The special rule of multiplication can easily be extended to more than two independent events. Given $k$ *independent* events $A_1$, $A_2$, ..., and $A_k$, the probability that *all* will occur is

$$P(A_1 \text{ and } A_2 \text{ and } \ldots \text{ and } A_k) =$$

$$P(A_1) \cdot P(A_2) \cdot \ldots \cdot P(A_k) \qquad (7.2.4) \blacktriangle$$

For instance, the probability of getting 3 heads in a row with a balanced coin is $\frac{1}{2} \cdot \frac{1}{2} \cdot \frac{1}{2} = \frac{1}{8}$. Another illustration of this rule will be given on page 137.

Actually, it is easier to give examples of events that are dependent than of events that are independent. For instance, if $A$ and $B$ stand, respectively, for a husband and his wife having completed four years of college, these events are *not* independent; and the probability that a person contacted in a survey is a banker *and* that he has an income of over \$15,000 a year is *not* the product of the two individual probabilities.

A very important concept of probability is that of a *conditional probability*. The probability that event $B$ will take place provided that event $A$ has taken place (is taking place or will for sure take place) is called the *conditional probability of B relative to A*. Symbolically, it is written as $P(B|A)$. If $A$ stands for a man's being a banker and $B$ stands for his having an income of over \$15,000 a year, then $P(B|A)$ is the probability that a *banker has an income of over \$15,000* and $P(A|B)$ is the probability that *a man with an income of over \$15,000 is a banker*. Similarly, if $C$ stands for a student's being a scholar and $D$ stands for his being an athlete, then $P(D|C)$ is the probability that a scholar is an athlete and $P(C|D)$ is the probability that an athlete is a scholar.

On page 130 we said that if two events are mutually exclusive, they are necessarily dependent. We can now add in terms of conditional probabilities that if $A$ and $B$ are *mutually exclusive*, then $P(B|A)$ and $P(A|B)$ are both equal to zero.

Using conditional probabilities, we can now formulate a more general rule for the probability that two events $A$ and $B$ will both occur.

GENERAL RULE OF MULTIPLICATION:

$$P(A \text{ and } B) = P(A) \cdot P(B|A)$$

$$\text{or} \quad P(A \text{ and } B) = P(B) \cdot P(A|B) \qquad (7.2.5)\blacktriangle$$

These two formulas are really the same since we are merely interchanging $A$ and $B$ on the right-hand side and "$A$ and $B$" is the same as "$B$ and $A$." Incidentally, the general rule of multiplication is no longer restricted to independent events, but if they *are* independent, then $P(B|A) = P(B)$, $P(A|B) = P(A)$, and (7.2.5) reduces to (7.2.3).

To illustrate the use of (7.2.5), let us suppose that $A$ stands for a student's passing an examination in mathematics while $B$ stands for his passing an examination in physics. Then $P(B)$ is the probability of his passing in physics while $P(B|A)$ is the probability of his passing in physics provided that he passes in mathematics. Since a student who is good in one of these subjects is apt to be good also in the other, the two events are dependent and $P(B|A)$ is, in fact, greater than $P(B)$. If $P(A) = 0.80$, $P(B) = 0.75$, and $P(B|A) = 0.90$, substitution into the first equation of (7.2.5) gives

$$P(A \text{ and } B) = (0.80)(0.90) = \mathbf{0.72}$$

This is the probability that a student will pass both exams. The reader may wish to verify that on the basis of the given figures it can also be shown that $P(A|B) = 0.96$.

Returning now to the problem of finding a rule of addition for events that are not necessarily mutually exclusive, let us suppose that $P(A)$ is the probability that it will rain (in a certain place on a certain day) and that $P(B)$ is the probability that it will snow. If $P(A) = 0.70$ and $P(B) = 0.35$, substitution into (7.2.1) yields the *impossible* result that $P(A \text{ or } B) = 0.70 + 0.35 = 1.05$. By using the formula that applies only to mutually exclusive events we made the mistake of *counting twice all days on which there is (or was) both rain and snow*. To compensate for this we will have to subtract the days (proportion of the days) that were counted twice or, which is the same, use the following rule

GENERAL RULE OF ADDITION:

$$P(A \text{ or } B) = P(A) + P(B) - P(A \text{ and } B) \qquad (7.2.6)\blacktriangle$$

If in the last example it had been known that there is *both* rain and snow (at the given time and place) about 15 per cent of the time, formula (7.2.6) would have given

$$P(A \text{ or } B) = 0.70 + 0.35 - 0.15 = 0.90$$

for the probability that it will rain or snow. Similarly, in the example of the student taking tests in mathematics and physics the figures on page 132 yield

$$P(A \text{ or } B) = 0.80 + 0.75 - 0.72 = 0.83$$

for the probability that he will pass at least one of the two exams.

These examples emphasize the fact that the "or" in $P(A \text{ or } B)$ is what is called the "inclusive or." $P(A \text{ or } B)$ stands for the probability that $A$, $B$, *or both* occur; in other words, that *at least one of the two events occurs*. It should also be noted that if $A$ and $B$ are mutually exclusive, then $P(A \text{ and } B) = 0$ since the two events cannot both happen, and (7.2.6) reduces to (7.2.1).

### EXERCISES

1. If $A$ stands for a male college student's belonging to a fraternity and $B$ stands for his being on the football team, write each of the following probabilities in symbolic form:
   (a) The probability that a fraternity man is on the football team.
   (b) The probability that a member of the football team belongs to a fraternity.
   (c) The probability that a male college student is not on the football team.

2. If $A$ stands for a person's being a college graduate and $B$ stands for his being wealthy, what probabilities are expressed by each of the following:

   (a) $P(A \mid B)$      (c) $P(B \mid A)$      (e) $1 - P(A)$

   (b) $P(A \text{ or } B)$      (d) $P(A \text{ and } B)$      (f) $1 - P(B)$

3. If $A$ and $B$ are mutually exclusive events, $P(A) = 0.30$, and $P(B) = 0.40$, find each of the following probabilities:

   (a) $P(A \mid B)$    (b) $P(B \mid A)$    (c) $P(A \text{ or } B)$    (d) $P(A \text{ and } B)$

   (e) $P(\text{neither } A \text{ nor } B)$

4. If $A$ and $B$ are independent events, $P(A) = 0.20$, and $P(B) = 0.50$, find each of the following probabilities:

   (a) $P(A \mid B)$    (b) $P(B \mid A)$    (c) $P(A \text{ or } B)$    (d) $P(A \text{ and } B)$

   (e) $P(\text{neither } A \text{ nor } B)$

5. Which of the following pairs of events are mutually exclusive?
   (a) Rolling a 7 or a 9 with a pair of dice.
   (b) Being the son of a lawyer and being born in Chicago.
   (c) Being under 25 years of age and being President of the United States.
   (d) Drawing a king or a black card out of a standard deck of 52 playing cards.
   (e) Owning a Chevrolet and owning a Ford.

6. Which of the following pairs of events are independent?
   (a) Getting sixes in two successive rolls of a die.
   (b) Being intoxicated and having an accident.
   (c) Being a journalist and having blue eyes.
   (d) Wearing a white shirt and wearing a red shirt.
   (e) Being on time for work and the weather being good.

7. Sometimes Mr. Brown has lunch at a cafeteria, sometimes he goes to a restaurant in the building in which he works, and sometimes he brings his own lunch. If the probability that he will go to the cafeteria is 0.25 and the probability that he will go to the restaurant is 0.45, what is the probability that on any given day he will go to either one or the other? Assuming that there are no other alternatives, what is the probability that on a given day he will bring his own lunch?

8. If the probability of drawing a king from deck of cards is $\frac{1}{13}$ and the probability of drawing a queen is $\frac{1}{13}$, what is the probability of drawing either a king or a queen?

9. The probability that a customer in a certain restaurant will order steak is 0.40, and the probability that he will order ice cream for dessert is 0.25. Assuming independence, what is the probability that a customer will order both steak and ice cream?

10. Suppose that the probability of getting a busy signal when calling a friend is 0.04. Would it be reasonable to say that the probability of getting busy signals when calling two friends, one right after the other, is 0.0016?

11. If the probability of rolling a seven with a pair of dice is $\frac{1}{6}$, what is the probability of *not* rolling two sevens in a row with a pair of dice?

12. If the probability that a married man will vote in a given election is 0.50 and the probability that a woman will vote provided that her husband votes is 0.90, what is the probability that a husband and wife will both vote in this election?

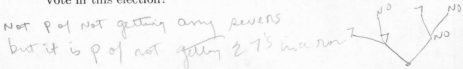

13. If in addition to the information given in Exercise 12 it is known that the probability that a married woman will vote in the election is 0.60, find (a) the probability that a man will vote given that his wife votes in the election, and (b) the probability that at least one of a married couple will vote.

14. If the probability that it rains in a certain town on an April day is 0.20, and the probability that it rains there on an April day is 0.60 if it is known to have rained the day before, what is the probability that it will rain in this town on two successive April days?

15. What assumption would have to be made in the preceding example to say that the probability that it will rain in the given town on *three* successive April days may be obtained by multiplying the answer to Exercise 14 by 0.60?

16. What are the *odds* for the occurrence of $A$ if:

    (a)   $P(A) = \frac{3}{7}$          (b)   $P(A) = \frac{8}{11}$       (c)   $P(A) = 0.85$


## 7.3 / Probabilities in Games of Chance

Although we are not directly concerned with games of chance, the rules of probability are easier to explain, illustrate, and understand, with reference to such games. If cards are thoroughly shuffled, dice are properly shaken, coins are properly flipped, and numbered slips are thoroughly mixed, it is generally assumed that each card has the same probability of being drawn and that, similarly, equal probabilities are associated with the six faces of a die, heads and tails, and each numbered slip. Making this assumption, many probabilities can be calculated with the following rule

SPECIAL RULE FOR EQUIPROBABLE EVENTS:

> *If n mutually exclusive events have equal probabilities and s of them are labeled "success," then the probability of a success is s/n.*

This special rule can be derived fairly easily from the rules of Section 7.2.

To illustrate the special rule for equiprobable events, let us first find the probability of drawing an ace out of a well-shuffled deck of cards. Since there are 4 aces, 4 "successess," among the usual 52 cards, the probability of getting an ace is $s/n = \frac{4}{52}$ or $\frac{1}{13}$. Similarly, there are 13 spades, 2 red queens, 1 ace of clubs, and the probabilities of getting a spade, a red queen, or the ace of clubs are, respectively, $\frac{13}{52}$, $\frac{2}{52}$, and $\frac{1}{52}$.

To give an example illustrating formula (7.2.1), the special rule of addition, let us find the probability of drawing *either a spade or a red queen* out of an ordinary deck of 52 playing cards. Since there are 13 spades and 2 red queens, there are altogether $13 + 2 = 15$ successes among the 52 cards, and the desired probability is $\frac{15}{52}$. We could also have argued that the probability of getting a spade is $\frac{13}{52}$, the probability of getting a red queen is $\frac{2}{52}$, and since the two are mutually exclusive, the probability of getting either is the sum of the probabilities or $\frac{15}{52}$.

To consider a slightly more complicated example, let us look for the probability of rolling a 7 or an 11 with a pair of balanced dice. Here $n = 36$ since there are 36 possible outcomes of the form *1 and 6, 2 and 3, 3 and 5, 4 and 1, . . .*, and $s = 8$ since "7 or 11" may be obtained by rolling *1 and 6, 2 and 5, 3 and 4, 4 and 3, 5 and 2, 6 and 1, 5 and 6*, or *6 and 5*. Hence the desired probability is $s/n = \frac{8}{36}$. We could also have argued that there are 6 ways of getting a *seven*, 2 ways of getting an *eleven*, that their respective probabilities are $\frac{6}{36}$ and $\frac{2}{36}$, and that according to (7.2.1) the probability of getting 7 or 11 is $\frac{6}{36} + \frac{2}{36} = \frac{8}{36}$.

To illustrate (7.2.2) let us find the probability of drawing either a spade, a red queen, or the ace of clubs out of an ordinary deck of 52 playing cards. Having already shown above that the respective probabilities of these mutually exclusive events are $\frac{13}{52}$, $\frac{2}{52}$, and $\frac{1}{52}$, we find with the use of (7.2.2) that the desired probability is $\frac{13}{52} + \frac{2}{52} + \frac{1}{52} = \frac{16}{52}$. We could have argued also that there are altogether 13 spades, 2 red queens, 1 ace of clubs and, hence, 16 successes among $n = 52$ equally likely possibilities. The special rule for equiprobable events would then have given us directly a probability of $s/n = \frac{16}{52}$.

To illustrate the use of (7.2.3), the special rule of multiplication, let us look again for the probability of getting heads in two successive flips of a balanced coin. On page 130 we said that since the two events are independent the probability is $\frac{1}{2} \cdot \frac{1}{2} = \frac{1}{4}$; using the special rule of this section we could argue that there are 4 equiprobable outcomes *heads and heads, heads and tails, tails and heads, tails and tails*, and that therefore the probability of getting two heads is $s/n = \frac{1}{4}$. If we tried to use this argument to find the probability of getting 2 sixes in a row with a die we would run into difficulties. There are again 4 possible outcomes, namely, *six and six, six and non-six, non-six and six, non-six and non-six,* but they are not equiprobable. (This problem will be discussed further in Section 8.2.) Of course, using (7.2.3) we find that the probability of getting 2 sixes in a row is $\frac{1}{6} \cdot \frac{1}{6} = \frac{1}{36}$.

Formula (7.2.4) enables us to find probabilities such as those of getting heads in each of 3 flips of a coin, four sixes in a row with a balanced die, .... For 3 heads the probability is $\frac{1}{2} \cdot \frac{1}{2} \cdot \frac{1}{2} = \frac{1}{8}$, and for 4 sixes in a row it is $\frac{1}{6} \cdot \frac{1}{6} \cdot \frac{1}{6} \cdot \frac{1}{6} = \frac{1}{1296}$. As we shall see in Section 8.2, the first of these probabilities can also be found by enumerating all possible equiprobable outcomes and using the formula $s/n$.

So far we have discussed only independent events. To illustrate the use of (7.2.5) in calculating $P(A \text{ and } B)$ for _dependent_ events, let us find the probability of drawing two aces in a row out of an ordinary deck of playing cards, assuming that the first card is not replaced before the second is drawn. Since there are 4 aces among the 52 cards, the probability of getting an ace in the first draw is $\frac{4}{52}$. After that there are only 3 aces left among 51 cards and the probability of getting an ace in the second draw (given that the first draw yielded an ace) is $\frac{3}{51}$. According to (7.2.5) we can then say that the probability of getting 2 aces in a row is $\frac{4}{52} \cdot \frac{3}{51} = \frac{1}{221}$. In this example the two drawings are *not* independent because the probability of getting an ace in the second draw is $\frac{3}{51}$ if the first is an ace and $\frac{4}{51}$ if it is not. (We could have solved this problem by enumerating all equiprobable outcomes such as *2 of clubs and queen of hearts, 7 of spades and ace of diamonds,* ..., or use theory about permutations and combinations to show that $s = 12$, $n = 2652$, and $s/n = \frac{12}{2652} = \frac{1}{221}$.)

Finally, to illustrate (7.2.6) the general rule of addition, let us look for the probability of getting either a red card or a king in one draw from an ordinary deck of 52 playing cards. Since there are 26 red cards, 4 kings, and 2 red kings, the probabilities of getting a red card, a king, or a red king are, respectively, $\frac{26}{52}$, $\frac{4}{52}$, and $\frac{2}{52}$. Hence, substitution into (7.2.6) gives $\frac{26}{52} + \frac{4}{52} - \frac{2}{52} = \frac{28}{52}$ for the probability of getting a red card or a king. To obtain this result, we could also have argued that there are 26 red cards, 2 black kings, and hence a total of $26 + 2 = 28$ "successes" among the 52 cards. Substituting $s = 28$ and $n = 52$ into the special formula for equiprobable events, we find immediately that the desired probability is $\frac{28}{52}$. In this example the two events (getting a red card and getting a king) were *not* mutually exclusive since there are two red kings.

## EXERCISES

**1.** What is the probability of drawing an 8 or a 10 out of a standard deck of 52 playing cards?

**2.** What is the probability of rolling a *six* with a pair of dice?

**3.** Find the probability of rolling less than 5 with one die.

**4.** Find the probability of drawing a black ace out of a standard deck of 52 playing cards.

**5.** If the numbers from 1 through 50 are written on slips of paper that are thoroughly mixed in a goldfish bowl, what is the probability of drawing a number divisible by 7?

**6.** If an urn contains 6 red marbles and 4 blue marbles, what is the probability of getting two red marbles in a row (a) if the first marble is replaced before the second is drawn, (b) if the first marble is not replaced?

**7.** What is the probability of getting four heads in a row with a balanced coin?

**8.** What is the probability of getting an ace and a queen, not necessarily in that order, in two draws from a standard deck of 52 playing cards? The first card is not replaced before the second is drawn.

**9.** What would be the answer to Exercise 8 if the first card were replaced before the second is drawn?

**10.** Find the probability of rolling first a 5, then a 3, and then a 1 or a 6 with a balanced die.

**11.** What is the probability of getting three aces in three successive drawings from a standard deck of 52 playing cards (a) if each card is replaced before the next one is drawn, (b) if the cards are not replaced?

**12.** In rolling a balanced die, what is the probability that the first 3 will come on the fourth try?

**13.** In drawing one card at a time without replacement from a standard deck of 52 playing cards, what is the probability that the first spade is the third card drawn?

**14.** Among the 500 freshman attending a certain college 80 own cars, 140 are from out-of-state, and 50 of the out-of-state students own cars. If one of these students is selected (with equal probabilities), find (a) the probability of getting an out-of-state student without a car, (b) the probability of getting a resident of the state with a car, and (c) the probability of getting an out-of-state student with a car.

## 7.4 / Mathematical Expectation

If the probability that an insurance company has to pay off on an air-travel policy with a face value of $10,000 is 0.00001, its losses will *average* 10 cents per policy. If it charges a premium of 25 cents for each policy, it can *expect* to gain 15 cents per policy not counting overhead and other expenses. If in the game of "heads or tails" we receive $1.00 for each head and nothing for each tail, we will get a dollar about half the time, nothing the other half of the time, and we can *expect* to get *on the average* 50 cents per toss. These two examples illustrate what is meant by a *mathematical expectation*. The insurance company does not "expect" to gain 15 cents per policy in the sense of wishful thinking or on the basis of strong convictions, and we do not "expect" to win 50 cents per toss in the above-mentioned game because this is what we may want to occur. *A mathematical expectation* is an average or, to be more exact, an average "in the long run." Defining it in terms of probabilities, *if the probability of getting an amount $A$ is $P(A)$, the mathematical expectation is $A \cdot P(A)$, namely, the product of the amount we stand to receive and the probability of getting it.* In the insurance example the probability of a policy holder's estate collecting the $10,000 is 0.00001, and the mathematical expectation for each policy is $10{,}000(0.00001) = 0.10$ or 10 cents; in the coin-tossing example the amount $A$ is $1.00, $P(A) = \frac{1}{2}$, and the mathematical expectation is $(1.00)(\frac{1}{2}) = 0.50$ or 50 cents per toss.

The above game of heads and tails was not very realistic, as it was arranged so that we could not possibly lose. To make it equitable, let us suppose that we receive $1.00 for each head but lose $1.00 for each tail. In the long run we will then win $1.00 about half the time, lose $1.00 about half the time, and on the average we can *expect* to break even. To make the concept of a mathematical expectation applicable also to this kind of situation, let us extend it by means of the following definition:

*If the probabilities of obtaining amounts $A_1$, $A_2 \ldots$, and $A_k$ are $P(A_1)$, $P(A_2)$, $\ldots$, and $P(A_k)$, respectively, and if the possibilities of getting these amounts are mutually exclusive, the mathematical expectation is*

$$A_1 \cdot P(A_1) + A_2 \cdot P(A_2) + \ldots + A_k \cdot P(A_k) \qquad (7.4.1) \blacktriangle$$

It should be noted that the amounts referred to in this definition need not be positive. If we stand to *win* $1.00, the corresponding $A$ is $+1$; and if we stand to *lose* $1.00, the corresponding $A$ is $-1$. In the last example we can, thus, say that the mathematical expectation is $(+1)(\frac{1}{2}) + (-1)(\frac{1}{2}) = 0$, assuming that the probability for heads and tails is $\frac{1}{2}$. *A mathematical expectation of zero defines what is meant by a fair or equitable game.*

To give another example illustrating (7.4.1), let us suppose that someone suggests the following game: we are to pay him $1.00 for each roll of a die and he will pay us back $3.00 if we roll a 6, $1.50 if we roll a 5, $0.75 if we roll a 4, and nothing if we roll a 1, 2, or 3. We will, thus *win* $2.00 if we roll a 6, $0.50 if we roll a 5, but *lose* $0.25 if we roll a 4, and $1.00 if we roll a 1, 2, or 3. Letting these amounts be $A_1$, $A_2$, $A_3$, and $A_4$ we have

$$A_1 = 2.00 \qquad A_2 = 0.50 \qquad A_3 = -0.25 \qquad A_4 = -1.00$$

$$P(A_1) = \tfrac{1}{6} \qquad P(A_2) = \tfrac{1}{6} \qquad P(A_3) = \tfrac{1}{6} \qquad P(A_4) = \tfrac{1}{2}$$

and the mathematical expectation is

$$(200)(\tfrac{1}{6}) + (0.50)(\tfrac{1}{6}) - (0.25)(\tfrac{1}{6}) - (1.00)(\tfrac{1}{2}) = -0.125$$

This means that on the *average* we stand to lose 12.5 cents each time we play this game. Evidently, it is not an equitable game.

Let us also point out that mathematical expectations need not be in terms of money and the $A$'s do not have to be cash penalities or rewards. We might say, for example, that the average married couple in the United States can *expect* to have 1.13 children or that a person residing in the United States can *expect* to be fed 417 eggs a year. In the first case the figure 1.13 is the sum of the products obtained by multiplying 0, 1, 2, ..., respectively, by the probabilities that a couple will have that many children. The $A$'s of (7.4.1) thus stand here for the number of children a couple has and they can, similarly, stand for the number of eggs a person eats per year, the number of heads one obtains when flipping 10 coins, or the number of times a person visits his doctor per month.

### EXERCISES

1. The organizers of a raffle plan to give a grand prize of $5,000 and to sell 10,000 tickets. What is the mathematical expectation for each ticket?

2. Suppose that someone will give us $4.00 each time that we roll a 1 with a balanced die. How much should we pay him when we roll a 2, 3, 4, 5, or 6 to make this game equitable?

3. If the probability that a baseball player will reach first base is 0.42, and the probabilities that he will get a two-base hit, a three-base hit, or a home run are, respectively, 0.02, 0.01, and 0.03, how many bases can this ball player *expect* for each time at bat? (Ignore the possibility that he might advance beyond first base on an error.)

4. If the two teams are evenly matched, the probabilities that the World Series will end in 4, 5, 6, or 7 games are, respectively, $\frac{1}{8}$, $\frac{1}{4}$, $\frac{5}{16}$, and $\frac{5}{16}$. Assuming that the two teams are evenly matched, how many games can we *expect* a World Series to last?

5. If the probability that the value of a certain stock will remain the same is 0.46, the probabilities that its value will increase by $0.50 or $1.00 per share are, respectively, 0.17 and 0.23, and the probability that its value will decrease by $0.25 per share is 0.14, what is the *expected* gain per share?

6. If the probabilities that there will be 2, 3, 4, 5, 6, or 7 persons in a tourist party visiting the Grand Canyon by private car are, respectively, 0.46, 0.27, 0.15, 0.08, 0.03, and 0.01, how many tourists can be *expected* per car?

## 7.5 / Decision-Making

It has been suggested that a person's behavior is *rational* if in situations involving uncertainties and risks he always chooses the alternative having the highest mathematical expectation. Although this may seem reasonable, it involves a number of difficulties to be discussed below. For the moment let us consider an example. Let us suppose that Mr. Black is in charge of a dinner party whose purpose is to raise money for a worthy cause, and that he has to decide whether to plan an outdoor picnic or a buffet supper to be held indoors. Let us suppose also that on the basis of past experience he has the following information: *if it does not rain* the outdoor picnic will yield a profit of $500 whereas the indoor buffet supper will yield a profit of $170; on the other hand, if it *rains* the outdoor picnic will yield a profit of $80 whereas the indoor buffet supper will yield a profit of $440. Schematically, this information may be arranged in the following table

|  | No Rain | Rain |
|---|---|---|
| Outdoor picnic | $500 | $80 |
| Indoor buffet supper | $170 | $440 |

It is apparent that Mr. Black will be better off holding the party *indoors* if it rains, and that he will be better off holding it *outdoors* if it does not. To plan intelligently, he will thus have to weigh the chances that it might rain and, for the sake of argument, let us suppose that the probability for rain on that day is $\frac{1}{3}$. Mr. Black might then argue as follows: if he holds the affair outdoors the *expected profit is*

$$500(\tfrac{2}{3}) + 80(\tfrac{1}{3}) = \$360 \quad EP$$

and if he holds it indoors the *expected profit* is

$$170(\tfrac{2}{3}) + 440(\tfrac{1}{3}) = \$260 \quad EP$$

Being "rational" in the sense of choosing the alternative having the highest expectation, he will decide to have the outdoor picnic and, perhaps, keep his fingers crossed that it will not rain. In calculating the expected profits we used (7.4.1); we added the products obtained by multiplying each possible profit by the probability of its being attained.

If mathematical expectations are to serve as aids in making rational decisions, it is essential that the correct values of all relevant probabilities are known. Had the probability for rain been $\frac{1}{2}$ in the above example, the *expected profit* for an outdoor picnic would have been

$$500(\tfrac{1}{2}) + 80(\tfrac{1}{2}) = \$290$$

the *expected profit* for an indoor buffet supper would have been

$$170(\tfrac{1}{2}) + 440(\tfrac{1}{2}) = \$305$$

and it would have been smarter to decide on a buffet supper to be held indoors.

Having shown how mathematical expectations can serve as bases for rational decisions when the values of relevant probabilities are known, let us now investigate briefly what Mr. Black might have done if he had not had the vaguest idea about the probability that it might rain. To consider one line of attack, let us suppose that Mr. Black is a *confirmed optimist*, always expecting (in the sense of wishful thinking) that the best possible thing will occur. Looking at the situation through rose-colored glasses, he sees that if the party is held outdoors he can make as much as $500 whereas an indoor buffet supper will yield at most $440, *and he decides to hold the party outdoors.* If, on the other hand, Mr. Black is a *confirmed pessimist*, who always expects (in the sense of resignation or fear) the worst, he notes that the indoor party will make at least $170, the outdoor party might make only $80, *and he decides to hold the party indoors.*

Since decisions based mainly on optimism or pessimism can hardly be called rational, let us see whether there are, perhaps, other ways in which Mr. Black's dilemma might be resolved. Let us suppose, for instance, that in desperation he decides to leave the final decision to *chance,* writing "outdoors" on a number of slips of paper, "indoors" on a number of others, mixing them up, and planning his party according to whichever he draws. In numbering the slips he, furthermore, wants to *fix the odds* in such a way that *his expected profit is the same regardless of whether or not it rains.* To show how this can be done, let us write $p$ for the probability that he will draw a slip marked "outdoors" and, accordingly, $1 - p$ for the probability that he will draw a slip marked "indoors." Then *if it does not rain* the expected profit is

$$500p + 170(1 - p)$$

*if it rains* the expected profit is

$$80p + 440(1 - p)$$

and putting the two equal to one another we get

$$500p + 170(1 - p) = 80p + 440(1 - p)$$

and

$$p = \tfrac{9}{23}$$

By labeling 9 slips "outdoors," 14 slips "indoors," and acting according to what is written on the slip he draws, Mr. Black can thus make sure that the *expected* profit is the same regardless of whether or not it rains. As a matter of fact, substituting $p = \tfrac{9}{23}$ into either of the two expected profits, we find that the expected profit is $299\tfrac{3}{23}$ regardless of whether or not it rains.

This last decision procedure, in which the ultimate decision is left to chance, is usually referred to as *randomized* or *mixed.* Although it may seem strange that a "rational" decision should be left to chance, there are situations in which randomized decision procedures actually provide the most desirable results. For example, if Nature, which has control over whether it does or does not rain on the day of the party, were *malevolently* inclined towards Mr. Black, it could take advantage of knowing that his decisions are generally guided by optimism or pessimism. (We are assuming that Nature knows something about Mr. Black's habits but that it is not informed of his actual plans.) On the other hand, if Mr. Black uses the randomized decision procedure outlined above, his expected profit is $299\frac{3}{23}$ regardless of what Nature does.

The preceding paragraph may have given the impression that Nature and Mr. Black are playing a *game* in which each is trying to outwit the other. Indeed, what we have discussed belongs to a branch of mathematics called the *Theory of Games*. Applied to statistical problems it forms part of *Decision Theory*, under which heading is included the entire problem of making decisions in the face of uncertainty.

The main difficulties in applying the methods which we discussed with reference to the picnic and the buffet supper to more realistic problems in statistics are that *we seldom know the exact values of all risks that are involved*, namely, the exact values of the "pay off" corresponding to the various eventualities, and that *we seldom have much information about relevant probabilities*. For instance, if we have to decide on the basis of a sample whether or not a new drug is really effective, *how can we put a cash value on the lives that might be lost if we decide not to release the drug when actually it sometimes provides a cure?* Similarly, if we have to decide on the basis of a test which of two students is superior or which is to receive a scholarship, *how can we foresee all consequences that might be involved?*

The fact that we seldom have adequate information about relevant probabilities also provides obstacles to finding suitable decision criteria. Without them, is it "reasonable" to base decisions on optimism, pessimism, or the assumption that we are playing against a malevolent opponent? Although these questions are difficult to answer, their analysis, including the material presented in this section, is important inasmuch as it constitutes the logic behind most statistical reasoning. The methods of statistical inference are easier to grasp if, at least tacitly, we formulate them as if they deal with "games" in which we have to select one of a number of courses of action, in which all sorts of things can happen (our opponent has various moves), and in which there are consequences on which we may or may not be able to put cash values. In later chapters dealing with problems of estimation and tests of hypotheses we shall have the occasion to remind the reader of this analogy.

While on the subject of decision-making, let us illustrate an interesting distinction between properties of the *mean, median, and mode* — three of the measures of central location we discussed in Chapter 3. Let us suppose that the numbers 11, 15, 19, 20, and 20 are written on five slips of paper which are thoroughly mixed in a bowl, that one slip is to be drawn, and that *we are to predict the number that is on this slip.* We are thus faced with making a decision, and, in view of what we have said in this section, it must be clear that any such decision will have to depend not only on the probabilities that are involved, but also on the consequences (penalties or rewards) to which we might be exposed. So far as the probabilities are concerned we shall assume that each slip has an equal chance of being drawn. Hence, the probabilities of getting 11, 15, 19, and 20 are $\frac{1}{5}$, $\frac{1}{5}$, $\frac{1}{5}$, and $\frac{2}{5}$, respectively.

Before going any further, we shall also have to know something about the consequences to which our decision, that is, prediction, might lead. After all, if there are no penalties for being wrong, no rewards for being right or close, *there is nothing at stake* and we might just as well predict that the number drawn is 37 or 55.1 even though we know that there are no such numbers on the slips. To make the problem interesting, let us investigate what decisions we might reach in each of the following situations:

(1) *We are given a reward of $10 if the exact number we predict is drawn, and we are fined $3 if a different number is drawn.*    Mode

(2) *We are paid a fee of $5 for making the prediction, but fined an amount of money equal in dollars to the size of our error. (If we predict 19 and the number drawn is 15, the fine is $4; if we predict 11 and the number drawn is 20, the fine is $9.)*    Median

(3) *We are paid a fee of $15 for making the prediction, but fined an amount of money equal in dollars to the square of our error. (If we predict 19 and the number drawn is 15, the fine is $16; if we predict 11 and the number drawn is 20, the fine is $81.)*    Mean

To select in each case a "best possible" prediction, we shall again use the criterion of *maximizing expected profits* or *minimizing expected fines*, which is the same.

Investigating first alternative (1), we find that if we predict the number 20, the *mode* of the 5 numbers, we stand to make $10 with a probability of $\frac{2}{5}$; we stand to lose $3 with a probability of $\frac{3}{5}$, and our *expected* profit is

$$10(\tfrac{2}{5}) - 3(\tfrac{3}{5}) = \$2.20$$

The reader can easily verify that this is the *best* prediction since the expected profit for predictions of 11, 15, and 19 is $-0.40$ or a *loss* of \$0.40, while any other prediction, say, 8 or 13, entails a *sure loss* of \$3.00. This illustrates the fact that in a situation where we have to pick the right value on the nose, where there is no reward for being close, the best prediction is the mode.

In alternative (2) it is the *median* which yields the most profitable predictions. Predicting that the number drawn will be 19, the *median* of the 5 numbers, the fine will be \$8, \$4, \$0, or \$1, depending on whether the number drawn is 11, 15, 19, or 20. Hence, the *expected fine* is

$$8(\tfrac{1}{5}) + 4(\tfrac{1}{5}) + 0(\tfrac{1}{5}) + 1(\tfrac{2}{5}) = \$2.80$$

and it can be shown that it would have been greater for any other prediction. (A proof of this is referred to in the Bibliography on page 148.) For instance, had we predicted the mean of the 5 numbers, namely, 17, the fine would have been \$6, \$2, \$2, or \$3, depending on whether the number drawn had been 11, 15, 19, or 20, and the *expected fine* would have been

$$6(\tfrac{1}{5}) + 2(\tfrac{1}{5}) + 2(\tfrac{1}{5}) + 3(\tfrac{2}{5}) = \$3.20$$

With reference to the financial arrangements of alternative (2), the median thus provides a better prediction than the mean or, for that matter, any other prediction.

The *mean* comes into its own rights in alternative (3), where the fine goes up very rapidly with the size of the error. Predicting that the number drawn will be 17, the *mean* of the 5 numbers, the fine will be \$36, \$4, \$4, or \$9, depending on whether the number drawn is 11, 15, 19, or 20, and the *expected fine* is

$$36(\tfrac{1}{5}) + 4(\tfrac{1}{5}) + 4(\tfrac{1}{5}) + 9(\tfrac{2}{5}) = \$12.40$$

It can easily be shown that the expected fine would have been greater for any other prediction, and it will be left to the reader to show that it would have been \$16.40 if we had used the median, that is, predicted 19. (A general proof is referred to in the Bibliography on page 148.)

Alternative (3), in which we are concerned with the *squares* of the errors, plays a very important role in statistical theory; it ties in closely with the *method of least squares* which we shall study in Chapter 14. The idea of trying to minimize squared errors is justifiable on the grounds that in actual practice the seriousness of an error often increases very rapidly with the size of the error, *more* rapidly than the magnitude of the error itself.

To consider one more variation of our problem, let us suppose that the bowl contains *several* slips of paper marked 11, *several* marked 15, *several* marked 19, *several* marked 20, and that we do not know how many of each. The "pay off" is as in Alternative (2). Having no probabilities to go by, we can no longer calculate expected profits or expected fines, and we find ourselves in a position similar to that on page 142, where we had to decide between an outdoor picnic and an indoor buffet supper without knowledge of the probability that it might rain. One criterion that suggests itself is to *minimize the greatest possible error.* If we predict the number 20, the greatest possible error is 9, the fine is $9, and it occurs when the number drawn is 11; if we predict 15, the greatest possible error is 5, the fine is $5, and it occurs when the number drawn is 20. It should not be very difficult to see that the greatest possible error is the *least,* if our prediction is halfway between the two extremes, namely $\frac{11 + 20}{2} = 15.5$. Although we are predicting a number which cannot possibly occur, the greatest possible error is 4.5 and *this is less than the greatest possible error for any other prediction.* The statistic we are using here is called the *mid-range,* it is the mean of the smallest and largest values of a set of numbers.

## EXERCISES

1. A company operating a chain of drugstores plans to open a new store in one of two locations. The management of the company figures that in the first location the new store will show an annual profit of $20,000 if it is successful and an annual loss of $2,000 if it is not. So far as the second location is concerned, the store will show an annual profit of $25,000 if it is successful and an annual loss of $5,000 if it is not. If the probability of success is $\frac{1}{2}$ for each location, where should the company open the store so as to maximize its expected profit? (Note that a loss of $2,000 is the same as a "profit" of $-$2,000.)

2. How would the management's decision have been affected in Exercise 1 if the probability of success had been $\frac{1}{4}$ instead of $\frac{1}{2}$ for each store? What if the probability of success had been $\frac{3}{8}$ for each store?

3. Where would the company referred to in Exercise 1 build the new store if there were no information about the probability of success and its

management consisted of confirmed pessimists? What if its management consisted of confirmed optimists?

4. The ages of six finalists in a beauty contest are 17, 17, 17, 19, 20, and 21. What prediction of the winner's age would maximize one's *expected profit* if (a) there is a reward for being exactly right, none for being close, (b) there is a penalty proportional to the size of the error, and (c) there is a penalty proportional to the square of the error?

5. With reference to Exercise 4, what prediction would minimize the greatest possible error?

## BIBLIOGRAPHY

An interesting discussion of various philosophical views on objective, subjective, and logical probabilities may be found in

> Nagel, E., *Principles of the Theory of Probability*. Chicago: University of Chicago Press, 1939.

The question as to what probabilities are negligible or practically equal to 1 is treated in

> Borel, E., *Elements de la Theorie des Probabilites*. Paris: Editions Albin Michel, 1950.

Further problems dealing with probabilities in games of chance may be found in most textbooks of college algebra. Interesting examples are given in

> Levinson, H. C., *The Science of Chance*. New York: Rinehart, 1950.

Informal introductions to game theory and decision theory are given in

> Bross, I. D. J., *Design for Decision*. New York: Macmillan, 1953.

> Williams, J. D., *The Compleat Strategyst*. New York: McGraw-Hill, 1954.

A proof of the fact that the sum of the magnitudes of the deviations (errors) is least for the *median* is given in

> Mode, E. B., *The Elements of Statistics, 1st ed.* Englewood Cliffs, New Jersey. Prentice-Hall, 1941, p. 105.

A proof showing that the sum of the *squares* of the deviations (errors) is least for the *mean* is given in

> Waugh, A. E., *Elements of Statistical Method, 3rd ed.* New York: McGraw-Hill, 1952, p. 110.

Chapter **8**

# Theoretical Distributions

*distributions that can be*
*expected on the basis of*
*past experience,*

## 8.1 / Introduction

In Chapter 2 we studied distributions obtained by grouping observed data. Now we shall study distributions that can be *expected* on the basis of past experience or theoretical considerations. To illustrate the importance of expected distributions we have only to consider the proprietor of a dress shop, who must know something about the distribution of his potential customers' sizes; the executive of a publishing firm, who must know something about the distribution of the public's literary tastes; or the manager of a restaurant who must know something about the distribution of people's likes and dislikes for various foods. Unless he knows what to *expect*, the proprietor of the dress shop may overstock with size 16 dresses he cannot sell, the executive of the publishing firm may put out a book nobody wants to read, and the manager of the restaurant may find himself with a refrigerator full of chops and not enough steaks.

In contrast to the above examples, in which the expected distributions of dress sizes, literary tastes, and preferences for foods can only be based on past experience, there are many situations in which expected distributions can be based on *theoretical considerations*. To give an example, let us consider the game of "heads or tails," and let us suppose that 200 flips yielded 86 heads and 114 tails. If we must decide on the basis of these flips whether the coin we are using is balanced, it stands to reason that we will have to know what to expect from a balanced coin. Since "balanced," as it is used here, means that the probabilities for heads and tails both equal $\frac{1}{2}$, it would seem reasonable to say that we *expect* as many heads as tails or, in other words, the following distribution

|  | Expected Frequency |
|---|---|
| Heads | 100 |
| Tails | 100 |

It must be understood, of course, that we are now using the word "expect" in the sense of a mathematical expectation, namely, *in the sense of an average*. Among 200 flips we will sometimes get 94 heads and 106 tails, sometimes 109 heads and 91 tails, sometimes 88 heads and 112 tails, but in the long run, if the series of flips is repeated a great many times, we will *on the average* get close to 100 heads and 100 tails.

In order to convert the *categorical distribution* shown above into a *numerical distribution*, let us simply count the number of heads observed in each flip of the coin, referring, thus, to *tails* as "0 heads" and *heads* as "1 heads." The observed frequencies and the corresponding expectations may then be presented together in the following fashion

| Number of Heads | Observed Frequency | Expected Frequency |
|---|---|---|
| 0 | 114 | 100 |
| 1 | 86 | 100 |

Later, in Chapter 12, we shall learn how to decide on the basis of such distributions whether discrepancies existing between observed and expected frequencies may reasonably be attributed to chance.

To give a slightly more complicated example of a theoretical distribution, let us find the frequencies with which 0, 1, and 2 heads can be expected in, say, 160 flips of *two* balanced coins. As we have pointed out earlier, there are four equally likely cases, that is

$$TT \quad TH \quad HT \quad HH$$

where $H$ stands for heads and $T$ for tails. Hence, the probability for 0 heads is $\frac{1}{4}$, the probability for 1 head is $\frac{1}{4} + \frac{1}{4} = \frac{1}{2}$, and that for 2 heads is $\frac{1}{4}$. Expecting thus 0 heads $\frac{1}{4}$ of the time, 1 head $\frac{1}{2}$ the time, and 2 heads $\frac{1}{4}$ of the time, the expected distribution for 160 flips of two balanced coins is

| Number of Heads | Expected Frequency |
|:---:|:---:|
| 0 | 40 |
| 1 | 80 |
| 2 | 40 |

If *three* coins are flipped simultaneously, there are eight possible outcomes which (if the coins are balanced) may be considered as equiprobable. They are

$$TTT \quad TTH \quad THT \quad HTT$$

$$HHT \quad HTH \quad THH \quad HHH$$

Since we can thus expect 0 heads $\frac{1}{8}$ of the time, 1 head $\frac{3}{8}$ of the time, 2 heads $\frac{3}{8}$ of the time, and 3 heads $\frac{1}{8}$ of the time, the expected distribution for, say, 120 tosses of three balanced coins is

| Number of Heads | Expected Frequency |
|:---:|:---:|
| 0 | 15 |
| 1 | 45 |
| 2 | 45 |
| 3 | 15 |

Again, the expected frequencies were obtained by multiplying the respective probabilities by the total number of flips, in this case by 120.

In the preceding examples, in which we considered 200 flips of *one* coin, 160 flips of *two* coins, and 120 of *three* coins, the expected frequencies depended in each case on the probabilities of getting the respective number of heads and the total number of flips. In order to make theoretical distributions like the ones we obtained applicable to more general situations (we might, for example, want to vary the total number of flips), it is often desirable to list the probabilities corresponding to the various number of heads instead of the expected frequencies. For *one* flip of a balanced coin we can thus write

| Number of Heads | Probability |
|:---:|:---:|
| 0 | $\frac{1}{2}$ |
| 1 | $\frac{1}{2}$ |

and this distribution is appropriately called a *probability distribution*. It shows how the total probability of 1 is distributed among the various eventualities. Similarly, the probability distribution for the number of heads obtained with *two* balanced coins is

$$\sigma = \left(-\frac{9}{8}\right)^2 1 + \left(\frac{9}{8}\right)^2 2 + \left(-\frac{11}{8}\right)^2 3$$

$$\frac{81 + 81(2) + (121)3}{64}$$

$$\frac{81 + 162 + 363}{64} =$$

| Number of Heads | Probability |
|:---:|:---:|
| 0 | $\frac{1}{4}$ |
| 1 | $\frac{1}{2}$ |
| 2 | $\frac{1}{4}$ |

and that for the number of heads obtained with *three* balanced coins is

$$\frac{3}{8} + \frac{6}{8} + \frac{3}{8} = \frac{12}{8}$$

$$\mu = 1.5$$

$$\sigma = \sqrt{\frac{3 \cdot 5}{3 \cdot 2}} \qquad \sigma = 3$$

| Number of Heads | Probability |
|:---:|:---:|
| 0 | $\frac{1}{8}$ |
| 1 | $\frac{3}{8}$ |
| 2 | $\frac{3}{8}$ |
| 3 | $\frac{1}{8}$ |

It should be noted that if probability distributions like these are known, we can always find the expected frequencies for *any* number of flips by multiplying the probabilities by the total number of flips.

All three of the probability distributions we have discussed are shown graphically in the form of histograms in Figure 8.1. It should be noted that by drawing the rectangles so that there are no gaps, we are again "spreading" the classes over a continuous scale. Although the number of heads must be 0, 1, 2, 3, ..., and cannot be $\frac{1}{3}$ or $\frac{3}{4}$, the

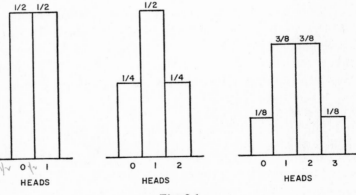

**Fig. 8.1**

bases of the rectangles go from $-\frac{1}{2}$ to $\frac{1}{2}$, from $\frac{1}{2}$ to $1\frac{1}{2}$, from $1\frac{1}{2}$ to $2\frac{1}{2}$, and so on. Thus the *areas* of the rectangles measure the probabilities for the corresponding number of heads.

## EXERCISES

**1.** Toss *four* coins 160 times and construct a distribution showing the frequencies with which 0, 1, 2, 3, and 4 heads occurred. Also find the corresponding expected frequencies by enumerating the 16 equiprobable cases *TTTT, THHT, HTTT,* ...

**2.** Draw histograms like those of Figure 8.1 for the observed and expected distributions of Exercise 1.

**3.** Toss *five* coins 160 times and construct a distributions showing the frequencies with which 0, 1, 2, 3, 4, and 5 heads occurred. Also find the corresponding probabilities and expected frequencies for 160 tosses by enumerating the 32 equiprobable cases *TTHHH, THTHT,* ...

**4.** Draw a histogram of the probability distribution obtained in Exercise 3.

**5.** Draw 40 cards from an ordinary deck of 52 playing cards, replacing each card before the next one is drawn, and construct a distribution showing the frequencies with which the four suits occurred. What are the corresponding expected frequencies?

**6.** Roll *one* die 120 times and construct a table showing the proportions of the time that each face appeared. Compare this with the corresponding probability distribution by drawing superimposed histograms of the two.

**7.** Suppose that a balanced coin is flipped 4 times and that after each flip we check whether we are ahead, even, or behind as in the example on page 36. Enumerate the 16 equiprobable cases to find the probabilities of being ahead 0, 1, 2, 3, and 4 times out of 4. Also draw a histogram of this U-shaped distribution.

## 8.2 / The Binomial Distribution

The probability distributions of the preceding section were easily obtained by enumerating all possible outcomes and assigning them equal probabilities. To consider a somewhat more complicated example, let us determine the probability distribution for getting 0, 1, and 2 *sixes* in two rolls of a balanced die. Letting $S$ and $N$ stand for "six" and "not a six," the four possible outcomes are $SS$, $SN$, $NS$, and $NN$, analogous to the $HH, HT, TH,$ and $TT$ for the tosses of two coins. However, whereas $HH, HT, TH,$ and $TT$ were *equiprobable*, $SS$, $SN$, $NS$, and $NN$ are *not*. Since the probability of *rolling a six* with a balanced die is $\frac{1}{6}$, the probability of *not rolling a six* is $\frac{5}{6}$, and since two successive rolls of a die are presumably independent, we can use formula (7.2.3) on page 130 and write

the probability of getting $SS$ is $\frac{1}{6} \cdot \frac{1}{6} = \frac{1}{36}$

the probability of getting $SN$ is $\frac{1}{6} \cdot \frac{5}{6} = \frac{5}{36}$

the probability of getting $NS$ is $\frac{5}{6} \cdot \frac{1}{6} = \frac{5}{36}$

the probability of getting $NN$ is $\frac{5}{6} \cdot \frac{5}{6} = \frac{25}{36}$

Hence the probability for 0 *sixes* is $\frac{25}{36}$, the probability for 1 *six* is $\frac{5}{36} + \frac{5}{36} = \frac{10}{36}$, and the probability for 2 *sixes* is $\frac{1}{36}$. The probability distribution of the number of sixes obtained in two rolls of a balanced die is thus

| Number of Sixes | Probability |
|:---:|:---:|
| 0 | $\frac{25}{36}$ |
| 1 | $\frac{10}{36}$ |
| 2 | $\frac{1}{36}$ |

and its histogram is shown in Figure 8.2.

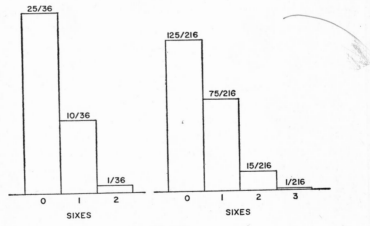

Fig. 8.2

To go one step further, let us determine the probability distribution of the number of *sixes* obtained in three rolls of a balanced die (or one roll of three balanced dice). Using the same notation as before, the 8 possible outcomes are $SSS$, $SSN$, $SNS$, $NSS$, $NNS$, $NSN$, $SNN$, $NNN$, and these arrangements of the letters $S$ and $N$

are again *not* equiprobable. Using probabilities of $\frac{1}{6}$ and $\frac{5}{6}$ for $S$ and $N$, and formula (7.2.4) on page 131, we get

the probability of getting $SSS$ is $\frac{1}{6} \cdot \frac{1}{6} \cdot \frac{1}{6} = \frac{1}{216}$

the probability of getting $SSN$ is $\frac{1}{6} \cdot \frac{1}{6} \cdot \frac{5}{6} = \frac{5}{216}$

the probability of getting $NSN$ is $\frac{5}{6} \cdot \frac{1}{6} \cdot \frac{5}{6} = \frac{25}{216}$

$\cdots$

$\cdots$

After adding the probabilities of the various arrangements yielding 0, 1, 2, and 3 *sixes*, we find that the desired probability distribution for the number of sixes obtained in three rolls of a balanced die is

| Number of Sixes | Probability |
|:---:|:---:|
| 0 | 125/216 |
| 1 | 75/216 |
| 2 | 15/216 |
| 3 | 1/216 |

A histogram of this probability distribution is shown in Figure 8.2.

Before studying the general case, let us consider one more example and look for the probability of getting exactly 3 *sixes* in 5 rolls of a balanced die. Enumerating the 32 possible outcomes, we find that 10 of them, namely

$$SSSNN \quad SSNSN \quad SSNNS \quad SNSSN \quad SNSNS$$

$$SNNSS \quad NSSSN \quad NSSNS \quad NSNSS \quad NNSSS$$

contain 3 letters $S$ and 2 letters $N$. Using formula (7.2.4) on page 131, we find that each of the 10 arrangements has the probability $(\frac{1}{6})^3 \cdot (\frac{5}{6})^2$; there are always three factors $\frac{1}{6}$ corresponding to the three $S$'s and two factors $\frac{5}{6}$ corresponding to the two $N$'s. Since the 10 arrangements are, furthermore, mutually exclusive, we can add their probabilities and arrive at the result that the probability of getting 3 *sixes* in 5 rolls of a balanced die is 10 *times* $(\frac{1}{6})^3$ *times* $(\frac{5}{6})^2$ or 250/7776.

The process of enumerating all possible outcomes and calculating the probability associated with each would become rather tedious if we were interested, for example, in finding the probability distribution for the number of heads obtained in 10 flips of a coin *or* the number of sixes obtained in 20 rolls of a die. For 10 flips of a coin the number of arrangements is 1024, and for 20 rolls of a die it is over a million.

Although probabilities connected with games of chance are not our immediate concern, there are many practical problems in which we must determine probabilities of a similar type. For instance, an inspection engineer may have to know the probability of getting 3 defective tubes in a sample of 20, assuming that the sample is taken from a large shipment in which 1 per cent of the tubes is defective; *or* an election forecaster may have to know the probability of getting a sample in which 32 out of 50 persons are for Candidate Jones, assuming that the probability of any voter being for Mr. Jones is 0.60. To investigate problems like these in a general fashion, let us look for the probability that *an event will take place exactly x times in n "trials", in other words, x times out of n, if the probability that it will take place in any one trial is some number p and the trials are independent.* Referring to the occurrence of the event as a "success" and its non-occurrence as a "failure," we are thus interested in the probability of *"x successes in n trials."**

Proceeding as in Section 8.1, let us refer to a success as $S$, a failure as $F$, and enumerate all possible arrangements in which there are $x$ letters $S$ and $n - x$ letters $F$. We could then find the probability associated with each, and the sum of the probabilities would give us the desired probability. To demonstrate that all this is not necessary, let us observe that if the probability of a "success" is $p$ and that of a "failure" is $1 - p$, the probability of getting $x$ successes and $n - x$ *failures* ($x$ letters $S$ and $n - x$ letters $F$) *in some specific order* is $p^x(1 - p)^{n-x}$. In this expression there are $x$ factors $p$ for the $x$ letters $S$ and $n - x$ factors $1 - p$ for the $n - x$ letters $F$. Since this probability is the same for each arrangement containing $x$ letters $S$ and $n - x$ letters $F$, the probability of getting *"x successes in n trials"* can be obtained by multiplying $p^x(1 - p)^{n-x}$ by the number of distinct ways in which $x$ letters $S$ and $n - x$ letters $F$ can be ar-

---

*Although we are using the term "success," this does not mean that the event to which we are referring must necessarily be advantageous or desirable. If a doctor wants to know the probability that 5 of 30 pneumonia patients will die, he is concerned with the probability of "5 successes in 30 trials;" if an insurance company wants to know the probability that 20 of its 400 policy holders will have accidents, it is interested in the probability of "20 successes in 400 trials;" and if an economist wants to know the probability that 15 of 250 stores will go bankrupt, he is interested in the probability of "15 successes in 250 trials." This usage of "success" and "failure" is a holdover from the days when probabilities were studies almost exclusively with reference to games of chance.

ranged. Denoting the number of such arrangements, that is, *combinations*, with the symbol $\binom{n}{x}$, we can finally write the probability of "*x* successes in *n* trials" as

$$P(x;n,p) = \binom{n}{x}p^x(1 - p)^{n-x} \qquad (8.2.1)\blacktriangle$$

Although this formula may look involved, let us point out that it was derived by exactly duplicating the steps used on page 155 to find the probability of getting 3 sixes in 5 rolls of a balanced die. The symbol $P(x;n,p)$, being fairly explicit, stands for the probability of getting $x$ successes in $n$ trials when the probability of success in any one trial is equal to $p$. It is important to note that (8.2.1) applies only when the trials are *independent;* if they were not, we could not have used formula (7.2.4), that is, we could not have multiplied the probabilities of the individual $S$'s and $F$'s.

Formula (8.2.1) presents a *probability distribution* in as much as it gives the probabilities of 0, 1, 2, 3, ..., and $n$ successes upon substitution of $x = 0, 1, 2, 3, \ldots$, and $n$. In view of its importance it has a special name, it is called the *binomial distribution*. This term derives from the fact that the expressions yielded by (8.2.1) for $x = 0, 1, 2, \ldots$, and $n$ are the corresponding terms of the binomial expansion of $[(1 - p) + p]^n$, as can be checked in most college algebra texts.

The quantities $\binom{n}{x}$ are called *binomial coefficients*. For $n = 2$ they are the coefficients 1, 2, 1 arising in the binomial expansion

$$(a + b)^2 = a^2 + 2ab + b^2$$

for $n = 3$ they are the coefficients 1, 3, 3, 1 arising in the binomial expansion

$$(a + b)^3 = a^3 + 3a^2b + 3ab^2 + b^3$$

and so forth. These coefficients may be obtained by enumerating all possible cases, as we did earlier in this section, they may be obtained from special tables, or they may be calculated with the formula

$$\binom{n}{x} = \frac{n(n - 1)(n - 2) \cdot \ldots \cdot (n - x + 1)}{x(x - 1)(x - 2) \cdot \ldots \cdot 2 \cdot 1} \qquad (8.2.2)\blacktriangle$$

for $x = 1, 2, \ldots$, and $n$. For $x = 0$ there is obviously only 1 arrangement of 0 letters $S$ and $n$ letters $F$, and $\binom{n}{0} = 1$. In the examples that follow we shall use Table VI on page 390; it gives the binomial coefficients for $n = 2$ to $n = 20$.

To illustrate the use of (8.2.1), let us find the probability of getting 3 heads and 6 tails in 9 flips of a balanced coin. Substituting $x = 3$, $n = 9$, and $p = \frac{1}{2}$, we obtain

$$P(3;9,\tfrac{1}{2}) = \binom{9}{3}(\tfrac{1}{2})^3(1 - \tfrac{1}{2})^{9-3}$$

and since Table IV shows that $\binom{9}{3} = 84$, the desired probability for 3 heads and 6 tails is

$$P(3;9,\tfrac{1}{2}) = 84 \cdot \tfrac{1}{8} \cdot \tfrac{1}{64} = 21/128$$

or approximately 0.16. Similarly, the probability of getting exactly 1 six in 5 rolls of a balanced die is

$$P(1;5,\tfrac{1}{6}) = \binom{5}{1}\left(\frac{1}{6}\right)^1\left(1 - \frac{1}{6}\right)^{5-1}$$

$$= 5 \cdot \frac{1}{6} \cdot \frac{625}{1296}$$

$$= \frac{3125}{7776}$$

or approximately 0.40. In this example we substituted $x = 1$, $n = 5$, and $\binom{5}{1} = 5$ into (8.2.1).

To consider an example in which we actually compute the entire probability distribution, namely, the probabilities for all values of $x$, let us suppose that the probability of a person's responding to a mail order solicitation is 0.20, and that we want to find the probabilities of getting 0, 1, 2, 3, 4, 5, or 6 responses to solicitations mailed to 6 individuals. Here $n = 6$, $p = 0.20$, and according to Table IV the binomial coefficients are 1, 6, 15, 20, 15, 6, 1. Substituting these values together with $x = 0, 1, 2, 3, 4, 5$, and 6 into (8.2.1), and rounding to four decimals, we get

$$P(0;6,0.20) = 1(0.20)^0(0.80)^6 = 0.2621$$

$$P(1;6,0.20) = 6(0.20)^1(0.80)^5 = 0.3932$$

$$P(2;6,0.20) = 15(0.20)^2(0.80)^4 = 0.2458$$

$$P(3;6,0.20) = 20(0.20)^3(0.80)^3 = 0.0819$$

$$P(4;6,0.20) = 15(0.20)^4(0.80)^2 = 0.0154$$

$$P(5;6,0.20) = 6(0.20)^5(0.80)^1 = 0.0015$$

$$P(6;6,0.20) = 1(0.20)^6(0.80)^0 = 0.0001$$

This binomial distribution, which is also shown in Figure 8.3, indicates that about 26 per cent of the time there will be no responses at all, about 39 per cent of the time there will be 1 response, about 25 per cent of the time there will be 2, and so on.

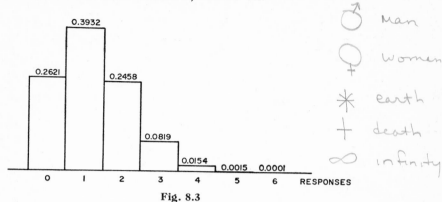

Fig. 8.3

The binomial distribution has many important applications which we shall study later in Chapters 10 and 11. Although formula (8.2.1) provides all probabilities related to the binomial distribution, it is actually seldom used. Its application would be much too tedious, for example, for finding the probability that among 500 school children there will be 5 with I.Q.'s over 130 given the probability that any one child has such an I.Q. Similarly, it would require an enormous amount of arithmetic to use (8.2.1) to find the probability of getting anywhere from 46 to 54 heads in 100 tosses of a balanced coin. [We would have to calculate $P(x;100,0.50)$ for $x = 46, 47, \ldots,$ 54, and then add the results.] Instead of using formula (8.2.1) *directly*, it is often preferable to refer to special tables of binomial probabilities such as those referred to in the Bibliography on page 190, or to employ approximations, for example, the one which will be discussed in Section 8.7.

Before we proceed to further problems dealing with the binomial distribution, let us add a word of caution about its use. *Formula (8.2.1) applies only if p, the probability of a "success," remains constant from trial to trial and if, furthermore, the trials are independent.* The formula cannot be used, therefore, to find the probability that it will rain, say, 30 out of 120 consecutive days. Not only does the daily probability for rain vary over such a lengthy period of time, but the "trials" are not even independent. Clearly, the probability that it will rain on a given day will depend to some extent on whether it did or did not rain on the preceding day.

## EXERCISES

1. Use formula (8.2.1) to find the probability of getting 6 heads and 6 tails in 12 flips of a balanced coin.

2. Use formula (8.2.1) to find the probability of getting exactly 2 fives in 5 rolls of a balanced die.

3. An urn contains 10 red marbles and 30 white ones. What is the probability of getting 2 red marbles and 5 white ones in 7 draws if each marble is replaced before the next one is drawn? Could formula (8.2.1) be used if the marbles were not replaced?

4. Find the probability of getting *at least* 6 heads in 8 flips of a balanced coin. Use formula (8.2.1) with $x = 6$, 7, and 8, and add the results in accordance with formula (7.2.2).

5. In a multiple-choice test there are 8 questions and 4 answers to each question. If each question is answered by drawing one card from an ordinary deck of 52 playing cards and checking answer 1, 2, 3, or 4 depending on whether the card drawn is a spade, heart, diamond, or club, what is the probability of getting 3 correct and 5 incorrect answers?

6. If a rifleman averages 8 hits out of 10 shots at a target, what is the probability that he will hit the target in 3 out of 4 shots?

7. If 50 per cent of all children born in a certain hospital are boys, what is the probability that among 9 children born on a certain day there are 4 boys and 5 girls?

8. If the probability that a combat plane returns from a mission undamaged is 0.85, find the probability that 2 of 4 planes sent out on different missions will return undamaged.

9. Given that the probability of a patient's recovery from a certain disease is 0.75, find the probabilities that among 3 patients having this disease 0, 1, 2, or 3 will recover. Also draw a histogram of this binomial distribution.

10. Calculate the probabilities of the binomial distributions having (a) $n = 5$ and $p = \frac{1}{3}$, and (b) $n = 4$ and $p = \frac{1}{10}$.

## 8.3 / The Mean and Standard Deviation of the Binomial Distribution

In Chapter 3 we defined the mean of a distribution (looked upon as a population) by means of the formula

$$\mu = \frac{\sum_{i=1}^{k} x_i f_i}{n}$$

assuming that all values falling into the $i$th class equal the class mark $x_i$ or, in other words, that the $x_i$ occur with frequencies $f_i$. If we now divide $n$, the total frequency appearing in the denominator, into the $f_i$, we get

$$\mu = \sum_{i=1}^{k} x_i (f_i/n) \qquad (8.3.1)$$

It is important to note that here each $x_i$ is multiplied by the proportion $f_i/n$, namely the proportion of the time that it occurs.

If we now substitute in (8.3.1) the probability of getting $x_i$, namely, $P(x_i)$, for the proportion $f_i/n$, we have

*Mean of a probability distribution*

*# of success*

$P(x_i) = (f_i/n)$

$$\mu = \sum_{i=1}^{k} x_i \cdot P(x_i) \qquad (8.3.2)▲$$

and this *defines* the *mean of a probability distribution*. To justify this definition, let us remind the reader that we originally defined probability as the limit of a relative frequency, namely, as the proportion of the time that an event will occur in the long run.

Another way of looking at (8.3.2) is to consider it as a *mathematical expectation*. In accordance with (7.4.1) each $x_i$ is multiplied by its probability, and the sum of the products $x_i \cdot P(x_i)$ thus tells us what value we can on the average expect to obtain. To illustrate, on page 152 we showed that the probabilities of getting 0, 1, and 2 heads in 2 flips of a balanced coin are $\frac{1}{4}$, $\frac{1}{2}$, and $\frac{1}{4}$, and we can now say that we expect *on the average* $0(\frac{1}{4}) + 1(\frac{1}{2}) + 2(\frac{1}{4}) = 1$ head in 2 flips of a balanced coin.

When dealing with *binomial distributions*, $x_i$ in (8.3.2) stands for the number of successes, that is, 0, 1, $\ldots$, and $n$, while $P(x_i)$ stands for the probability of getting "$x_i$ successes in $n$ trials" as given by formula (8.2.1). If we actually substituted $P(x;n,p)$ into (8.3.2), a certain amount of algebraic manipulation would yield the result that the formula for the *mean of the binomial distribution* reduces to

*mean of binomial distribution*

$$\mu = np \qquad (8.3.3)▲$$

Although the derivation of this formula is not very difficult, we shall not give it here. A suitable reference may be found in the Bibliography on page 190.

The result expressed by (8.3.3) might well have been expected. If a balanced coin is flipped 100 times, we would expect on the average 50 heads and formula (8.3.3) yields, indeed, $\mu = np = 100(\frac{1}{2}) = 50$. Similarly, we would expect to get on the average 10 sixes in 60 rolls of a die and for $n = 60$ and $p = \frac{1}{6}$ formula (8.3.3) yields $\mu = np = 60(\frac{1}{6}) = 10$. To provide further verification, the reader will be asked (Exercise 2 on page 164) to demonstrate that (8.3.2) and (8.3.3) both give $\mu = \frac{1}{2}$ for the expected (or average) number of sixes obtained in 3 rolls of a balanced die. This illustrates the fact that although we cannot possibly get $\frac{1}{2}$ six in 3 rolls of a die, we will sometimes get 0, sometimes 1, sometimes 2, sometimes 3, but *on the average* 0.5.

In Chapter 4 we defined the standard deviation, essentially, in terms of the *average of the squares deviations from the mean*. Proceeding in a similar fashion, let us now define the *standard deviation of a probability distribution* as

$$\sigma = \sqrt{\sum_{i=1}^{k} (x_i - \mu)^2 P(x_i)} \qquad (8.3.4)\blacktriangle$$

where the quantity inside the radical is the value we can *expect on the average* for the squared deviation from the mean. It is a mathematical expectation as defined by (7.4.1) in so far as it is the sum of the products obtained by multiplying each squared deviation $(x_i - \mu)^2$ by the probability of getting this particular deviation from the mean. For example, if the $x_i$ are 0, 1, and 2, the number of heads obtained in 2 flips of a balanced coin, then $\mu = 1$, the squared deviations from the mean are $(0 - 1)^2$, $(1 - 1)^2$, $(2 - 1)^2$, the corresponding probabilities are $\frac{1}{4}$, $\frac{1}{2}$, $\frac{1}{4}$, and the standard deviation is

$$\sigma = \sqrt{(0 - 1)^2(\tfrac{1}{4}) + (1 - 1)^2(\tfrac{1}{2}) + (2 - 1)^2(\tfrac{1}{4})}$$
$$= \sqrt{\tfrac{1}{2}}$$

Using formula (8.3.4) to find the standard deviation of a probability distribution can entail a good deal of work, particularly when there are many $x_i$ and the calculations of the probabilities get involved. In actual practice, formula (8.3.4) is never used directly to find the *standard deviation of a binomial distribution*. Instead we use the formula

$$\sigma = \sqrt{np(1 - p)} \qquad (8.3.5)\blacktriangle$$

which can be derived by substituting the binomial probabilities of (8.2.1) for the $P(x_i)$ of (8.3.4) and performing suitable algebraic simplifications. A reference to the derivation of (8.3.5) is given in the Bibliography on page 190.

To verify the special formula for the standard deviation of a binomial distribution, let us consider again the distribution of the number of heads obtained in 2 flips of a balanced coin. Using (8.3.4) directly we showed above that $\sigma = \sqrt{\tfrac{1}{2}}$; substituting $n = 2$ and $p = \tfrac{1}{2}$ into (8.3.5) we find that the result is again $\sigma = \sqrt{np(1 - p)} = \sqrt{2(\tfrac{1}{2})(\tfrac{1}{2})} = \sqrt{\tfrac{1}{2}}$.

In Chapter 4 we introduced the standard deviation as a measure of *variability* and $\sigma = \sqrt{np(1 - p)}$, indeed, tells us *how much variation there is due to chance in the number of successes obtained in n trials when the probability of success in an individual trail is p.* To give the reader some idea of a possible application, let us refer to what we said on page 92, namely, that for certain distributions about 95 per cent of all values fall within 2 standard deviations on either side of the mean. Assuming for the moment that this holds for the binomial distribution of, say, the number of heads obtained in 300 flips of a balanced coin, we find that

$$\mu = 300(\tfrac{1}{2}) = 150$$

$$\sigma = \sqrt{300(\tfrac{1}{2})(\tfrac{1}{2})} = 8.66$$

and we can say that *95 per cent of the time* we will get anywhere from $150 - 2(8.66)$ to $150 + 2(8.66)$ or, roughly, from 133 to 167 heads in 300 flips of a balanced coin. This kind of problem will be discussed further in Section 8.7.

The reader may have noted that we used the Greek letters $\mu$ and $\sigma$, originally reserved for populations, to denote the mean and standard deviation of the binomial distribution (and probability distributions in general). Indeed, statisticians often refer to binomial distributions as "binomial populations." If a balanced coin is flipped, say, 50 times, the number of heads obtained constitutes a *sample* of the results we would get if we repeated the 50 flips over and over again. The hypothetical population from which we are, thus, sampling is described by the corresponding binomial distribution with $n = 50$ and $p = \tfrac{1}{2}$.

## EXERCISES

1. Use the probabilities on page 152 and formulas (8.3.2 and 8.3.4) to find $\mu$ and $\sigma$ for the distribution of the number of heads obtained in 3 flips

of a balanced coin.  Check your results against formulas (8.3.3) and (8.3.5).

2. Use the probabilities on page 155 and formulas (8.3.2) and (8.3.4) to find $\mu$ and $\sigma$ for the distribution of the number of sixes obtained in 3 rolls of a balanced die.  Check your results against formulas (8.3.3) and (8.3.5).

3. Use formulas (8.3.3) and (8.3.5) to find the means and standard deviations of the binomial distributions of Exercise 10 on page 160.

4. Use formulas (8.3.3) and (8.3.5) to find the means and standard deviations of binomial distributions having

$$\text{(a)} \quad n = 900 \text{ and } p = \tfrac{1}{2}$$

$$\text{(b)} \quad n = 128 \text{ and } p = \tfrac{8}{9}$$

$$\text{(c)} \quad n = 100 \text{ and } p = \tfrac{4}{5}$$

## 8.4 / Continuous Distributions

If $x$ stands for the number of heads obtained in 20 flips of a coin, the number of sixes obtained in 3 rolls of a die, or the number of rainy days in Chicago in September, it is called a *chance* or *random variable*. In each case the variable $x$ can assume a variety of values with certain associated probabilities.  For the binomial distribution the random variable is the number of successes, and the probabilities that it will assume the values 0, 1, 2, ..., and $n$ are given by the formula on page 157.

Variables are usually classified according to the kinds of values they can assume.  They are said to be *discrete* if they can assume only a finite number of values or as many values as there are whole numbers.  The number of heads obtained in 20 flips of a coin is a *discrete random variable* as it cannot assume values other than 0, 1, 2, ..., and 20.  There is a finite number of values — 21 to be exact.  If we rolled a die until the first six appears, the number of the particular roll on which this occurs is also a *discrete random variable*.  It could occur on the first roll, the second, the third, the fourth, ..., and the random variable can assume as many values as there are whole numbers.

In contrast to discrete variables, we shall say that a variable is *continuous* if it can assume all values of a continuous scale.  Such quantities as time, length, and temperature are measured on continuous scales and their measurements may be referred to as *continuous variables*. A definition of what is meant by a continuous random variable will be deferred until later (it will be given on page 167).

When we first discussed histograms in Chapter 2, we pointed out that the frequencies, percentages, (and we might now add probabilities) which are associated with the various classes are represented by the *areas* of the rectangles. For example, the areas of the rectangles of Figure 8.4 represent the probabilities of getting 0, 1, 2, ..., and 10 heads in 10 flips of a balanced coin or, better, they are equal or

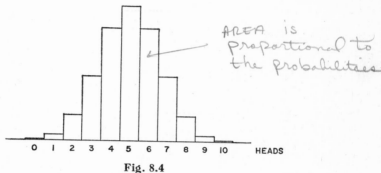

AREA is
proportional to
the probabilities

O 1 2 3 4 5 6 7 8 9 10    HEADS

Fig. 8.4

proportional to these probabilities. If we look at Figure 8.5, which is an enlargement of a portion of Figure 8.4, it is apparent that the area of rectangle *ABCD* is nearly equal to the shaded area under the continuous curve which we have drawn to approximate the histogram. Since the area of rectangle *ABCD* is equal to (or proportional to) the probability of getting 3 heads in 10 flips of a balanced coin, we can say that this probability, itself, is given by the shaded area under the continuous curve. More generally, *if a histogram is approximated by means of a smooth curve, the frequency, percentage, or probability of any given class is represented by the corresponding area under the curve*.

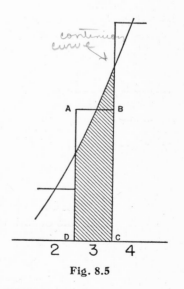

continuous curve

A    B

D    C

2    3    4

Fig. 8.5

If we approximate the distribution of 1953 family incomes in the

United States with a smooth curve, as we did in Figure 8.6, we can determine the proportion of incomes falling into any given interval by looking at the corresponding area under the curve. By comparing

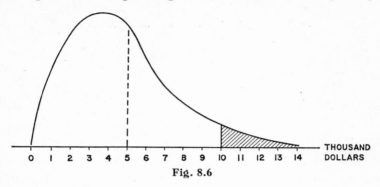

Fig. 8.6

the shaded area of Figure 8.6 with the total area under the curve (representing 100 per cent), we can judge that roughly 7 or 8 per cent of all families had incomes of $10,000 or more. It can, similarly, be seen from Figure 8.6 that about 58 per cent of the families had incomes of $5,000 or less. We obtained these percentages by (mentally) dividing the corresponding areas by the total area under the curve.

Had we drawn Figure 8.6 so that the total area under the curve is equal to 1, the proportion of the families belonging to any income class would have been given directly by the corresponding area under the curve. Indeed, we shall refer to a curve as a *distribution curve* or a *continuous distribution* if the area under the curve between two values *a* and *b* (see Figure 8.7) is *equal* to the proportion of the cases falling between *a* and *b*.

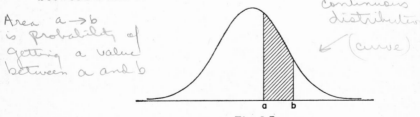

Fig. 8.7

Going again from proportions to probabilities, *we shall refer to a curve as a continuous distribution curve* if the area under the curve between a and b equals the probability of getting a value between a and b.

*It is also customary to use the terms *density function* or *probability density function*.

For example, if the curve of Figure 8.8 is a distribution curve that approximates the probability distribution of the number of heads obtained in 100 flips of a balanced coin, the probability of getting anywhere from 45 to 55 heads, inclusive, is given by the shaded area

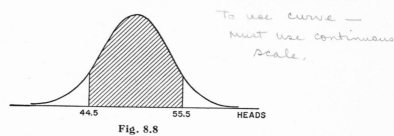

*To use curve —
Must use continuous
scale.*

44.5　　　　　55.5　　　　**HEADS**

**Fig. 8.8**

under the curve and, as can be verified later, it is approximately equal to 0.73. It should be noted that we have shaded the area between 44.5 and 55.5 and *not* the area between 45 and 55. The number of heads obtained in $n$ flips of a coin is a *discrete* variable and its probability distribution cannot be approximated with a smooth curve unless we let the intervals from $-\frac{1}{2}$ to $\frac{1}{2}$, from $\frac{1}{2}$ to $1\frac{1}{2}$, from $1\frac{1}{2}$ to $2\frac{1}{2}$, ..., represent 0 heads, 1 head, 2 heads, .... If we thus spread the discrete variable over a continuous scale, "45 to 55 heads" is represented by the interval from 44.5 to 55.5.

With the definition given above we can now explain, at least informally, what is meant by a *continuous random variable*. A variable is said to be a *continuous random variable* if it can assume all values of a continuous scale *and* if the probability that it assumes a value in any interval equals the corresponding area under a given distribution curve.

*Def
Continuous
Variable*

Continuous random variables and their distribution curves play a very important role in statistical theory. Continuous distributions provide close approximations to the probability distributions of discrete variables and, what is even more important, they provide the basis for most of the theory used in problems of estimation, prediction, and in testing hypotheses.

Since continuous distribution curves can always be looked upon as close approximations to histograms, we can define, informally, the *mean and standard deviation of a continuous distribution* in the following manner: If a continuous distribution is approximated with a sequence of histograms having narrower and narrower classes, the means of the distributions represented by the histograms will approach the mean of the continuous distribution. Similarly, the standard deviations will approach the standard deviation of the continuous distribution. Intuitively speaking, *the mean and standard deviation of a continuous distribution measure the identical features as the mean and standard deviation of an ordinary frequency distribution, namely, its center and its spread.* More rigorous definitions of the mean and standard deviation of continuous distributions are referred to in the Bibliography on page 190. They cannot be given without the use of integral calculus.

## 8.5 / The Normal Curve

One continuous distribution, the *normal curve*, is in many respects the cornerstone of modern statistical theory. Its mathematical study dates back to the eighteenth century when scientists observed an astonishing degree of regularity in errors of measurements, that is, in repeated measurements of one and the same quantity. They found that the patterns (distributions) which they observed were closely approximated by a continuous distribution curve which they

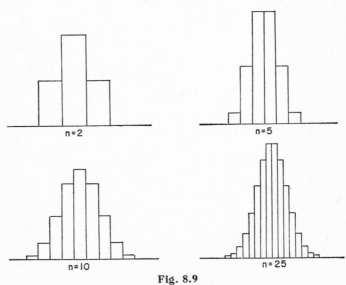

Fig. 8.9

referred to as the "normal curve of errors" and attributed to the laws of chance. The mathematical properties of this continuous distribution and its theoretical basis were first investigated by Pierre

Laplace (1749–1827), Abraham de Moivre (1667–1745), and Carl Gauss (1777–1855). In honor of the last, normal curves are sometimes also referred to as *Gaussian distributions*.

There are several ways in which the normal curve can be introduced. Although, historically speaking, the normal curve was originally related to "laws of error," it is, perhaps, easier to look upon it as a continuous distribution curve which provides a very close approximation to binomial distributions when $n$, the number of trials, is large and $p$, the probability of a success, is close to $\frac{1}{2}$. Figure 8.9 contains the histograms of binomial distributions having $p = \frac{1}{2}$ and $n = 2, 5, 10,$ and 25, and it can be seen that with increasing $n$ these distributions approach the *symmetrical bell-shaped* pattern on the normal curve shown in Figure 8.10.

The normal curve is a bell-shaped curve that extends indefinitely in both directions. Although this may not be apparent from Figure 8.10, the curve comes closer and closer to the horizontal axis without

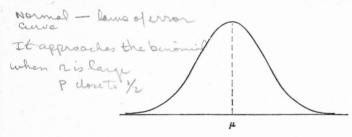

*Normal — laws of error*
*curve*
*It approaches the binomial*
*when n is large*
*P close to ½*

$\mu$

**Fig. 8.10**

ever reaching it, no matter how far we might go in either direction. Fortunately, it is seldom necessary to extend the "tails" of the normal curve very far, because the area under the curve becomes negligible if we go more than 4 or 5 standard deviations away from the mean.

An important property of a normal curve is that it is completely determined if we are given its mean and standard deviation. In other words, the mathematical equation of the normal curve is such that if we are given $\mu$ and $\sigma$ we can calculate the *height* of the curve corresponding to any point and we can determine the *area* under the curve between any two points on the horizontal scale. Although both, heights and areas, have been tabulated, we shall be interested mainly in areas under the normal curve, that is, those given in Table I on page 384. *Let us remind the reader that it is the areas under*

*areas*

*the curve that provide the probabilities of values' falling into given intervals.*

Before we will be able to use Table I, we shall have to explain what is meant by a normal curve in its *standard form*. As we pointed out earlier, the equation of the normal curve depends on $\mu$ and $\sigma$ and we will, thus, get different curves and different areas under these curves if we refer to different values of $\mu$ and $\sigma$. For instance, Figure 8.11 shows the superimposed graphs of two normal curves, one having $\mu = 10$ and $\sigma = 5$, the other having $\mu = 20$ and $\sigma = 10$. This means that unless there exists another way of handling this, we have to construct *separate tables* of normal curve areas for each pair of values of $\mu$ and $\sigma$. Fortunately, there is such a way and we shall

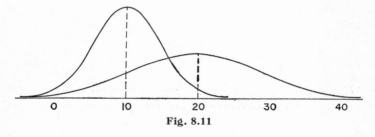

Fig. 8.11

presently see how any normal curve area may be found, referring only to a table of areas under a normal curve having $\mu = 0$ and $\sigma = 1$. *Incidentally, such a normal curve with zero mean and unit standard deviation is called a standard normal curve.*

Given a normal curve with the mean $\mu$ and the standard deviation $\sigma$, it is always possible to convert it into a standard normal curve by

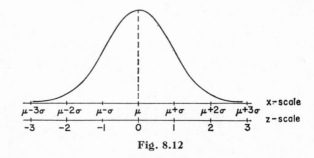

Fig. 8.12

performing the *change of scale* indicated in Figure 8.12. Whereas in the original scale (the $x$-scale) the mean and standard deviation are $\mu$ and $\sigma$, in the new scale (the $z$-scale) they are 0 and 1. The fact that in the $z$-scale the mean is 0 and the standard deviation is 1 can be seen directly from Figure 8.12. Using the method indicated in this diagram, we can change any normal curve into the standard form by leaving the curve, so to speak, as is *but changing the scale.*

It can easily be verified that the formula which enables us to change from the $x$-scale to the $z$-scale of Figure 8.12 and vice versa is

*Change to the standard units z*

$$z = \frac{x - \mu}{\sigma}$$

(8.5.1)▲

and this is precisely the formula we used in Chapter 4 (see page 93) to convert measurements into what we then called *standard units* or *standard scores.* Hence, when we change a normal curve into the standard form we are, in fact, changing the scale of measurement into standard units.

To find areas under normal curves whose mean and standard deviation are *not* 0 and 1, we have only to convert the $x$'s (to the left of which, to the right of which, or between which we want to determine areas under the curve) into $z$'s and then use Table I on page 384 This table contains normal curve areas, like that shaded in Figure 8.13, for values of $z$ from 0.00 to 3.09. In other words, *the entries in*

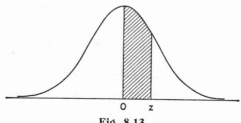

0   z

**Fig. 8.13**

*Table I are the areas under the normal curve between the mean ($z = 0$) and the values of z given in the left-hand column.* For example, the entry corresponding to $z = 1.15$ is 0.3749 and this measures the

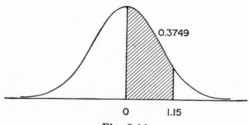

0.3749

0    1.15

**Fig. 8.14**

shaded area of Figure 8.14, namely, the area under the normal curve between $z = 0$ and $z = 1.15$.

Table I has no entries for *negative* values of $z$, but since the normal curve is symmetrical we can find the area between, say, $z = -1.28$ and $z = 0$ by looking up the area corresponding to $z = 1.28$. We, thus, find that the desired area, the shaded area of Figure 8.15, is 0.3997.

In order to determine a normal curve area *to the right of a positive value of z*, we have only to subtract the tabular value from 0.5000. Since the normal curve is symmetrical and the total area under the curve is equal to 1, the area to the right of the mean is 0.5000 and the

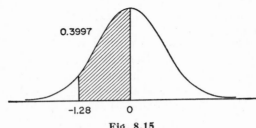

0.3997

-1.28     O

**Fig. 8.15**

area to the right of a positive value of $z$ is 0.5000 *minus* the tabular value given for this $z$. For instance, to find the area to the right of $z = 0.72$, we subtract 0.2642 (the entry given in Table I for $z = 0.72$)

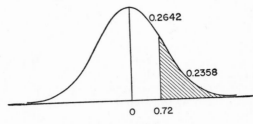

0.2642

0.2358

O     0.72

**Fig. 8.16**

from 0.5000, getting $0.5000 - 0.2642 = 0.2358$ (see Figure 8.16).

In order to find an area *to the left of a positive value of z*, we merely *add* 0.5000 to the tabular value given for this $z$. For instance, the area to the left of $z = 1.84$, the shaded area of Figure 8.17, is $0.4671 + 0.5000 = 0.9671$.

When dealing with normal curve areas it is always best to begin by making a drawing which clearly shows whatever area is to be determined. It will then be apparent whether we can take the value given in Table I, whether we have to subtract it from 0.5000,

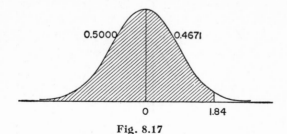

Fig. 8.17

whether we have to add 0.5000, or perhaps perform some other calculation. For example, to find the area to the right of $z = -1.39$ we immediately note from Figure 8.18 that 0.5000 must be added to the

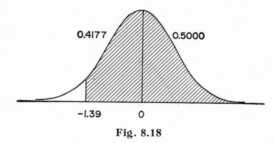

Fig. 8.18

tabular value corresponding to $z = 1.39$, and we get $0.4177 + 0.5000 = 0.9177$.

　　There are problems in which it will be necessary to find normal curve areas lying *between* two given values of $z$. If both $z$'s are on the *same* side of the mean (if they are both positive or both negative), the area between them is given by the *difference* of the tabular values of the two $z$'s. For instance, the normal curve area between $z = 0.61$ and $z = 1.55$ is $0.4394 - 0.2291 = 0.2103$ (see Figure 8.19). If the

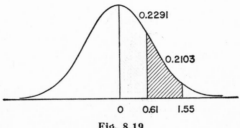

Fig. 8.19

two $z$'s are on *opposite* sides of the mean (if one is positive and the other negative), the area between them is given by the *sum* of the tabular values of the two $z$'s. For instance, the normal curve area

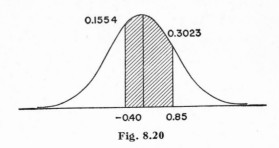

Fig. 8.20

between $z = -0.40$ and $z = 0.85$ is $0.1554 + 0.3023 = 0.4577$ (see Figure 8.20).

It can also happen that we will be given areas under the normal curve and then asked to find the corresponding values of $z$. For

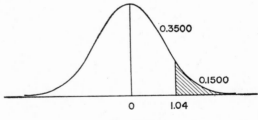

Fig. 8.21

instance, if we want to find a $z$ which is such that the area to its right is 0.1500, it is apparent from Figure 8.21 that this $z$ will have to correspond to an entry of 0.3500. Referring again to Table I, we find that the closest value is $z = 1.04$.

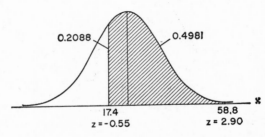

Fig. 8.22

To give an example in which we must first convert to standard units, let us suppose that a normal curve has $\mu = 24$, $\sigma = 12$, and that we want to find the area between $x_1 = 17.4$ and $x_2 = 58.8$ (see Figure 8.22). Writing

$$z_1 = \frac{17.4 - 24}{12} = -0.55 \quad \text{and} \quad z_2 = \frac{58.8 - 24}{12} = 2.90$$

we find that the areas corresponding to these $z$'s are 0.2088 and 0.4981 and that the desired area between 17.4 and 58.8 is 0.2088 + 0.4981 = 0.7069.

## EXERCISES

1. If the mean and standard deviation of a normal distribution are $\mu = 35.7$ and $\sigma = 2.8$ inches, change each of the following into standard units (round answer to two decimals):

   (a) 38.7 in.                    (c) 53.9 in.
   (b) 31.5 in.                    (d) 29.6 in.

2. Find the area under the standard normal curve which lies
   (a) to the right of $z = 2.68$
   (b) to the left of $z = 1.73$
   (c) to the right of $z = -0.66$
   (d) to the left of $z = -1.88$
   (e) between $z = 1.25$ and $z = 1.67$
   (f) between $z = -0.90$ and $z = -1.85$
   (g) between $z = -1.45$ and $z = 1.45$
   (h) between $z = -0.90$ and $z = 1.58$

3. Find $z$ if
   (a) the normal curve area between 0 and $z$ is 0.4515
   (b) the normal curve area to the right of $z$ is 0.3121
   (c) the normal curve area to the right of $z$ is 0.8023
   (d) the normal curve area to the left of $z$ is 0.4562
   (e) the normal curve area between $-z$ and $z$ is 0.7436

4. Given a normal curve with $\mu = 25.3$ and $\sigma = 8.1$, find the area under the curve between 20.6 and 29.1.

5. Given a normal curve with $\mu = 17.2$ and $\sigma = 3.5$, find (a) the area under the curve to the right of 20.0, (b) the area to the left of 19.4, and (c) the area between 9.3 and 11.7.

### 8.6 / Some Applications

When we discussed applications of the standard deviation in Chapter 4, we mentioned that in practice one often meets distributions in which certain fixed percentages of the cases fall within *one* standard deviation of the mean, within *two* standard deviations of the mean, and so forth. The kind of distributions we were referring to were normal curves or, at least, distributions of observed data that can be approximated very closely with normal curves. *With the use of the normal curve areas of Table I we are now in the position to verify the percentages given on page 92.*

If a measurement is one standard deviation above or below the mean, its $z$-value is $+1$ or $-1$ (see Figure 8.12) and according to Table I the area under the normal curve between $z = -1$ and $z = 1$ is $0.3413 + 0.3413 = 0.6828$. *This means that if a distribution is closely approximated by a normal curve, roughly 68 per cent of the cases will fall within one standard deviation of the mean.* Similarly, it can be shown that the normal curve area between $z = -2$ and $z = +2$ is $0.9546$ and that the normal curve area between $z = -3$ and $z = +3$ is $0.9973$. In other words, *if a distribution can be approximated closely with a normal curve, about 95 per cent of the cases will fall within two standard deviations of the mean and more than 99 per cent within three standard deviations of the mean.* The interval that covers one

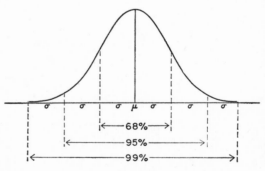

**Fig. 8.23**

standard deviation on either side of the mean is often called the *one-sigma range*. The terms *two-sigma range* and *three-sigma range* are similarly used to refer to the corresponding intervals shown in Figure 8.23.

In the examples that follow, we shall always assume that we are dealing with data whose distribution can be approximated very closely with normal curves. Obviously, there would otherwise be no justification for using the table of normal curve areas.

> **Example 1.** It is known from past experience that the number of telephone calls made daily in a certain community between 3 P.M. and 4 P.M. have a mean of 352 and a standard deviation of 31. What percentage of the time will there be more than 400 telephone calls made in this community between 3 P.M. and 4 P.M.?

Since the number of telephone calls is a *discrete* variable, we shall have to look for the area under the normal curve to the right of 400.5, namely, the shaded area of Figure 8.24. (400 is represented by the interval from 399.5 to 400.5.) Substituting $x = 400.5$ into (8.5.1), we get

$$z = \frac{400.5 - 352}{31} = 1.56$$

and the corresponding entry in Table I is 0.4406. Hence, the shaded area of Figure 8.24 is $0.5000 - 0.4406 = 0.0594$ and we can say that *roughly 6 per cent of the time there will be more than 400 telephone calls*

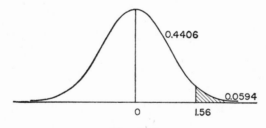

**Fig. 8.24**

*made in this community between 3 P.M. and 4 P.M.* We could also say that the *probability* that there will be more than 400 calls made during that period of time is 0.06. Information like this is important in planning sufficient numbers of lines, switchboards, etc.

> **Example 2.** The average density of a certain kind of glass brick is 2.480, with a standard deviation of 0.03. If the distribution of the densities of these bricks can be approximated closely with a normal curve, below what density can we expect to find the lightest 20 per cent of the bricks?

This problem differs from Example 1 inasmuch as we are now given the percentage and are asked to find the corresponding $z$ and $x$. As is apparent from Figure 8.25, we must first find the $z$ that corresponds to an area of 0.3000, and Table I shows that the nearest value is

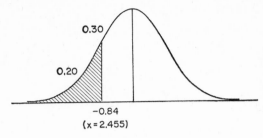

**Fig. 8.25**

$z = 0.84$. Substituting into (8.5.1), not forgetting, of course, to use a minus sign, we get

$$-0.84 = \frac{x - 2.480}{0.03}$$

Solving this equation for $x$, we find that the lightest 20 per cent of these glass bricks have densities below 2.455.

**Example 3.** The grades obtained by a large group of students in a final examination in statistics have a mean of 66 and a standard deviation of 7.8. Assuming that these grades are approximately normally distributed, what percentage of the students can be expected to have obtained grades from 60 to 69, inclusive?

Assuming that the individual grades are whole numbers, we shall again have to account for the continuity of the normal curve by

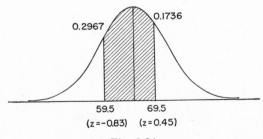

**Fig. 8.26**

looking for the area between 59.5 and 69.5, namely, the shaded area of Figure 8.26. (It should be noted that we did not have to make such an adjustment in Example 2 since the densities were supposedly measured on a continuous scale.) The $z$'s corresponding to the end-points of the desired interval are

$$z_1 = \frac{59.5 - 66}{7.8} = -0.83 \quad \text{and} \quad z_2 = \frac{69.5 - 66}{7.8} = 0.45$$

The corresponding entries in Table I are 0.2967 and 0.1736, and the percentage asked for in this example is $0.2967 + 0.1736 = 0.4703$ or, roughly, 47 per cent.

### EXERCISES

1. Suppose that the lengths of full-grown scorpions of a certain variety have a mean of 1.96 inches and a standard deviation of 0.32 inches. Considering these lengths to be measured on a continuous scale and assuming that the distribution of the lengths can be approximated closely with a normal curve, find
   (a) what percentage of these scorpions have a length of 2.50 inches or more,
   (b) what percentage have lengths from 1.80 to 2.20 inches,
   (c) above what value will we find the longest 10 per cent of these scorpions.

2. The lifetimes of certain kinds of electronic devices have a mean of 270 hours and a standard deviation of 26 hours. Assuming that the distribution of these lifetimes, which are measured to the nearest hour, can be approximated closely with a normal curve, find
   (a) the probability that any one of these electronic devices will have a lifetime of more than 300 hours,
   (b) what percentage will have lifetimes of 250 hours or less,
   (c) what percentage will have lifetimes from 260 to 280 hours, inclusive,
   (d) the value below which we will find the lowest 8 per cent of the lifetimes of these electronic devices.

3. A large set of (continuous) measurements is closely approximated by a normal curve with a mean of 26.6 cm and a standard deviation of 3.3 cm. Find
   (a) what percentage of these measurements can be expected to lie on the interval from 20.4 to 30.4 cm,
   (b) the probability that one of these measurements will differ from the mean by 4.5 cm or more,
   (c) the first and third quartiles of this distribution.

4. A large set of final examination grades in Freshman English has a mean of 62, a standard deviation of 15, and it can be approximated closely

with a normal curve. If the lowest 15 per cent of the students are to get F's, which score would be the highest F? If the highest 10 per cent are to get A's, which score would be the lowest A? (The grades are given as whole numbers.)

5. In 1945, after World War II, all service men were given point scores based on length of service, number of purple hearts, number of decorations, campaigns, etc. Assuming that the distribution of these point scores can be approximated closely with a normal curve whose mean and standard deviation are 63 and 20, respectively, how many men from an army of 8,000,000 would be discharged if the army discharged all men with more than 79 points? (Courtesy, Department of Mathematics, U.S. Military Academy.)

## 8.7 / The Binomial Distribution and the Normal Curve

In Section 8.5 we pointed out that when $p$ equals $\frac{1}{2}$ and $n$ is large, the binomial distribution can be approximated closely with a normal curve, and we illustrated this in Figure 8.9. In fact, normal curve areas can be used to approximate binomial probabilities even when $n$ is "not too large" and $p$ differs from $\frac{1}{2}$. To illustrate this *normal curve approximation of the binomial distribution*, let us first consider the probability of getting 5 heads in 12 tosses of a balanced coin. Substituting $n = 12$, $x = 5$, and $p = \frac{1}{2}$ into formula (8.2.1), we get

$$P(5;12,\tfrac{1}{2}) = (\tbinom{12}{5})(\tfrac{1}{2})^5(\tfrac{1}{2})^7 = \frac{792}{4096}$$

or approximately 0.1934. To determine the normal curve approximation of this binomial probability, we shall have to find the shaded area of Figure 8.27, namely, the area between 4.5 and 5.5. Since $\mu = 12(\frac{1}{2}) = 6$ and $\sigma = \sqrt{np(1-p)} = \sqrt{12(\frac{1}{2})(\frac{1}{2})} = 1.732$, we find that

$$z_1 = \frac{4.5 - 6}{1.732} = -0.87$$

$$z_2 = \frac{5.5 - 6}{1.732} = -0.29$$

The corresponding areas in Table I are 0.3078 and 0.1141, and the desired probability is $0.3078 - 0.1141 = 0.1937$. *Clearly, the difference between this value and the one obtained with (8.2.1) is negligible.* When $p$ is not $\frac{1}{2}$ and $n$ is less than 100, it is usually advisable to

obtain binomial probabilities from special tables such as those referred to in the Bibliography on page 190.  However, even if $n$ is less

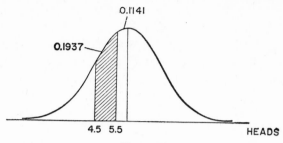

Fig. 8.27

than 100 and $p$ is *not too close* to 0 or 1, and the value in which we are
interested does *not lie too far away from the mean,* the normal curve
approximation will provide fairly good results.  To give an example
in which $p$ is not equal to $\frac{1}{2}$, let us find the probability of getting "6

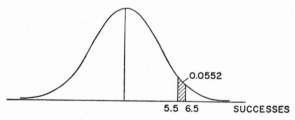

Fig. 8.28

successes in 16 trials" when the probability of an individual success is
$\frac{1}{5}$.  Using the normal curve approximation, we shall have to find the
shaded area of Figure 8.28, namely, that between 5.5 and 6.5.

Since $\mu = np = 16(\frac{1}{5}) = 3.2$ and $\sigma = \sqrt{16(\frac{1}{5})(\frac{4}{5})} = 1.6$, we get

$$z_1 = \frac{5.5 - 3.2}{1.6} = 1.44$$

$$z_2 = \frac{6.5 - 3.2}{1.6} = 2.06$$

the corresponding entries in Table I are 0.4521 and 0.4803, and the
desired probability is $0.4803 - 0.4251 = 0.0552$.  *This result agrees
very closely with the value of 0.0550 given in the National Bureau of
Standards Table referred to in the Bibliography on page 190.*  (We

might add that we were lucky inasmuch as rounding the $z$'s to two decimals made our answer look slightly better than it should.)

The normal curve approximation of the binomial distribution is of tremendous value in problems in which the use of formula (8.2.1) would involve a prohibitive amount of work. Suppose, for example, that the probability that a certain kind of tulip bulb will bloom is 0.80 and that we want to know the probability that among 100 such bulbs at least 85 will bloom. (In other words, we need the probability of "at least 85 successes in 100 trials" when the probability of a success is 0.80.) If we tried to solve this problem by using the formula for the binomial distribution, we would have to find the sum of the probabilities for $x = 85, 86, \ldots,$ and 100, and this would obviously involve an enormous amount of work. Using instead the normal curve approximation, we have only to find the shaded area of Figure 8.29, namely, the area to the right of 84.5. Since $\mu = 100(0.8) = 80$ and $\sigma = \sqrt{100(0.8)(0.2)} = 4$, we find that the $z$ corresponding to 84.5 is

$$z = \frac{84.5 - 80}{4} = 1.12$$

and the desired probability is $0.5000 - 0.3686 = 0.1314$ or, roughly, 0.13. *This means that about 13 per cent of the time 85 or more among 100 of these tulips will bloom.*

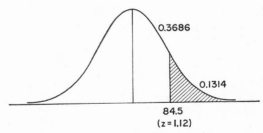

**Fig. 8.29**

To give another example in which it is impractical to use formula (8.2.1), let us determine the probability that there will be anywhere from 25 to 40 failures among 180 students taking a certain test, if it is known that on the average $\frac{1}{6}$ of all students fail the test. By using the normal curve approximation, we have only to find the shaded area of Figure 8.30, namely, the area between 24.5 and 40.5. (Note that in all these examples we made the necessary adjustment to account for the fact that the "number of successes" is a discrete variable while the normal curve is continuous.) Since the mean and standard deviation of a binomial distribution with $n = 180$ and

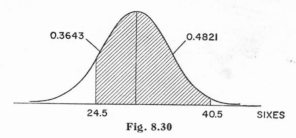

**Fig. 8.30**

$p = \frac{1}{6}$ are $\mu = 180(\frac{1}{6}) = 30$ and $\sigma = \sqrt{180(\frac{1}{6})(\frac{5}{6})} = 5$, we find that the $z$'s corresponding to 24.5 and 40.5 are

$$z_1 = \frac{24.5 - 30}{5} = -1.10$$

$$z_2 = \frac{40.5 - 30}{5} = 2.10$$

and the probability that there will be anywhere from 25 to 40 failures among the 180 students is $0.3643 + 0.4821 = 0.8464$.

While on the subject of approximations to the binomial distribution, let us also point out that _when n is very large, p is close to 0, and μ is less than 5_, the binomial distribution can be approximated closely with another theoretical distribution called the _Poisson distribution_. A reference to this approximation is given in the Bibliography on page 191.

### EXERCISES

**1.** Find the probability of getting 6 heads in 10 tosses of a balanced coin by using (a) formula (8.2.1), and (b) the normal curve approximation.

**2.** Find the probability of getting 1 six in 8 rolls of a balanced die using (a) formula (8.2.1), and (b) the normal curve approximation.

**3.** Use the normal curve approximation to find the probability of getting _more than_ 210 heads in 400 flips of a balanced coin.

**4.** Use the normal curve approximation to find the probability of getting anywhere from 185 to 215 heads, inclusive, in 400 flips of a balanced coin.

**5.** If the favorite color of 65 per cent of all people is red, find the probability that in a sample of 800 people fewer than 500 will prefer red. Use the normal curve approximation.

6. If 60 per cent of all visitors to a certain historical site come from the East, what is the probability that among 100 visitors to this site 70 or more come from the East?

7. Given that on the average 1 per cent of certain fuzes delivered to an army arsenal are duds, what is the probability that in a sample of 100 three or more are duds?

8. If a true-false test consists of 200 questions, what is the probability that a student who answers each question by flipping a coin (heads is "true" and tails is "false") will get 110 or more correct answers?

9. With reference to Exercise 8, what is the probability that the student will get anywhere from 95 to 105 correct answers?

## 8.8 / Fitting a Normal Curve to Observed Data

There are several ways in which one can test whether an observed distribution fits the pattern of a normal curve. A relatively crude yet simple method is based on a special kind of graph paper, called *probability graph paper* or *normal curve paper*.* Given the cumulative "less than" percentage distribution of a set of data that fits closely to a normal curve, the points which we obtain by plotting the cumulative frequencies on this kind of paper *will lie on a straight line* (or reasonably close to a straight line).

To illustrate this method, let us consider the following distribution of the weights of 300 army recruits:

| Weights (in pounds) | Frequency |
|---|---|
| 150 – 158 | 9 |
| 159 – 167 | 24 |
| 168 – 176 | 51 |
| 177 – 185 | 66 |
| 186 – 194 | 72 |
| 195 – 203 | 48 |
| 204 – 212 | 21 |
| 213 – 221 | 6 |
| 222 – 230 | 3 |
| | 300 |

*Probability graph paper may be purchased at most college bookstores or from dealers in art supplies. Instructions for "do it yourself" probability paper may be found on page 176 of A. E. Waugh, *Elements of Statistical Method*, 3rd ed. New York: McGraw-Hill, 1952.

Converting this distribution into a *cumulative percentage distribution* (see page 23), we get:

| Weights (in pounds) | Cumulative Percentage |
|---|---|
| less than 149.5 | 0 |
| 158.5 | 3 |
| 167.5 | 11 |
| 176.5 | 28 |
| 185.5 | 50 |
| 194.5 | 74 |
| 203.5 | 90 |
| 212.5 | 97 |
| 221.5 | 99 |
| 230.5 | 100 |

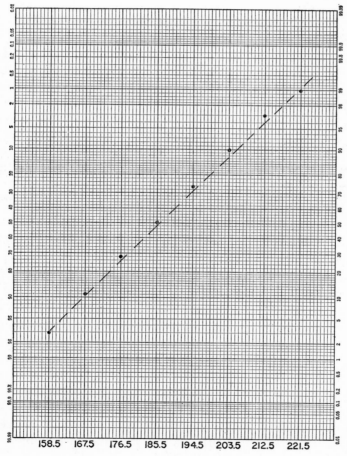

*Cum %*

*class boundaries*

**Fig. 8.31.** Probability graph paper.

*plot cum. "less than" percentage dist.*

Before we plot this cumulative percentage distribution on probability graph paper, let us investigate, briefly, the scales of this special kind of graph paper as shown in Figure 8.31. As can be seen from this figure, the cumulative percentage scale (the vertical scale) is already printed in the irregular pattern that makes it suitable for our particular purpose. The other scale (the horizontal scale) consists of equal subdivisions which, in Figure 8.31, are used to indicate the class boundaries of the distribution of the weights of the 300 recruits.

If we now plot a point corresponding to the cumulative percentage at each class boundary, we obtain the points shown in Figure 8.31. It would seem reasonable to say, by inspection, that *the points lie very close to a straight line* and, hence, that *the original distribution can be approximated very closely with a normal curve*. It should be noted that we did not plot points corresponding to 149.5 and 230.5, the first and last class boundaries; as was pointed out on page 169, we never reach 0 or 100 per cent of the area under the normal curve, no matter how far we go in either direction.

A serious disadvantage of the method we have just discussed is that we have to decide *subjectively* whether the points fall "reasonably close" to a straight line. It is surprising how close such points may *seem* to a straight line even though the distribution is quite skewed.

A more rigorous way of testing whether an observed distribution fits the pattern of a normal curve consists of the following two steps:

(a) We calculate the proportions (and frequencies) we could *expect* to find in the various classes if we had a normal distribution with the *same mean* and the *same standard deviation* as the observed data.

(b) We compare the *expected normal curve frequencies* thus obtained with those of the original distribution.

Since tests of hypotheses will not be taken up until Chapter 11, we shall, for the time being, limit ourselves to step (a), namely, that of calculating the expected normal curve frequencies. Later, in Section 12.2, we shall put the comparison of step (b) on a precise basis.

To illustrate how expected normal curve frequencies are calculated, let us refer again to the weight distribution on page 184. As can easily be verified, the mean of this distribution is 184.3 and its standard deviation is 14.54. Beginning with one of the classes, say, the one going from 204 to 212, we find that its class boundaries are 203.5 and 212.5, and that

$$z_1 = \frac{203.5 - 184.3}{14.54} = 1.32$$

$$z_2 = \frac{212.5 - 184.3}{14.54} = 1.94$$

.4738
− .4066
.0672 = 6.72 %/oo of 3
= 20.16

The corresponding entries in Table I are 0.4066 and 0.4738, and the area under the normal curve between 203.5 and 212.5 is 0.4738 − 0.4066 = 0.0672. *This means that 6.72 per cent of the weights could be expected to fall into the chosen class if the distribution were really close to a normal curve having the same mean and standard deviation as the actual data.* Since 6.72 per cent of 300, the total frequency in our example, is 20.16, we can say that the *expected normal curve frequency* for the chosen class is approximately 20.2. It is interesting to note that this value is very close to the actual frequency of 21.

When applying this technique to the entire distribution, that is, to all of its classes, it is usually convenient to arrange the calculations in the following fashion:

| Class Limits (1) | L (2) | z (3) | (4) | (5) | Normal Curve Frequencies (6) | Observed Frequencies (7) |
|---|---|---|---|---|---|---|
| | 149.5 | −2.39 | 0.4916 | | | |
| 150 – 158 | | | | 0.0300 ×300= | 9.0 | 9 |
| | 158.5 | −1.77 | 0.4616 | | | |
| 159 – 167 | | | | 0.0846 | 25.4 | 24 |
| | 167.5 | −1.16 | 0.3770 | | | |
| 168 – 176 | | | | 0.1716 | 51.5 | 51 |
| | 176.5 | −0.54 | 0.2054 | | | |
| 177 – 185 | | | | 0.2373 | 71.2 | 66 |
| | 185.5 | 0.08 | 0.0319 | | | |
| 186 – 194 | | | | 0.2261 | 67.8 | 72 |
| | 194.5 | 0.70 | 0.2580 | | | |
| 195 – 203 | | | | 0.1486 | 44.6 | 48 |
| | 203.5 | 1.32 | 0.4066 | | | |
| 204 – 212 | | | | 0.0672 | 20.2 | 21 |
| | 212.5 | 1.94 | 0.4738 | | | |
| 213 – 221 | | | | 0.0210 | 6.3 | 6 |
| | 221.5 | 2.56 | 0.4948 | | | |
| 222 – 230 | | | | 0.0045 | 1.4 | 3 |
| | 230.5 | 3.18 | 0.4993 | | | |

Whereas column (1) contains the class limits, column (2) contains the class boundaries, and column (3) contains the corresponding $z$'s. Column (4) contains the normal curve areas (of Table I) corresponding to the $z$'s of column (3), and column (5) contains the *differences* between the successive entries of column (4), except for the fourth, which is the *sum* of 0.2054 and 0.0319. The reason for this exception is that this is the only area between $z$'s with opposite signs. The last step consists of multiplying each area (proportion or probability) of column (5) by the total frequency — 300 in our example — and the results are shown in column (6).

Once the expected normal curve frequencies have been calculated, they can be compared with the observed frequencies, given originally on page 184 and copied again in column (7). Since we will not be able to put this comparison on a precise basis until we come to Section 12.2, let us be satisfied here with presenting the superimposed histograms of the distributions of columns (6) and (7) for a visual comparison. It would seem reasonable to say on the basis of Figure 8.32 that there is a very close agreement between the two sets of frequencies and that, therefore, *the original distribution fits closely to the pattern of a normal curve.*

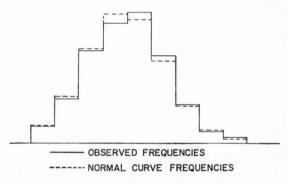

———— OBSERVED FREQUENCIES

------- NORMAL CURVE FREQUENCIES

**Fig. 8.32**

The method we have just discussed and to which we shall refer again in Section 12.2 is probably the most widely used in testing, or deciding, whether an observed distribution fits the pattern of a normal curve. An alternate test which at one time was widely used is based on $\alpha_3$ and $\alpha_4$, the measures of skewness and peakedness which we mentioned in Sections 5.2 and 5.3. It can be shown that for a normal curve $\alpha_3 = 0$ and $\alpha_4 = 3$, and the test is performed by checking whether the corresponding measures calculated on the basis of the observed distribution are sufficiently close to 0 and 3. An illustration of this method is referred to in the Bibliography on page 191.

### EXERCISES

1. Use probability graph paper to check whether the speed-check distribution given on page 17 fits reasonably well to a normal curve.

2. Plot the cumulative percentages of whichever data were grouped among Exercises 9, 11, 13, 14, and 15 on pages 25 through 28 on probability graph paper and decide whether the distribution fits reasonably well to a normal curve.

3. Plot the cumulative percentages of the distribution of the time lapses between eruptions of Old Faithful (obtained in Exercise 17 on page 28) on probability graph paper and check whether the distribution fits reasonably well to a normal curve.

4. Probability graph paper can be used to obtain a crude estimate of the standard deviation of a distribution, provided that this distribution fits closely to the pattern of a normal curve. We saw on page 176 that the normal curve area corresponding to $z = 1$ is roughly 0.34 and, hence, approximately 84 per cent of the cases fall below $z = +1$ and 16 per cent fall below $z = -1$. Checking 16 and 84 per cent on the vertical scale, we can judge by the straight line which we have drawn what points on the horizontal scale correspond to $z = -1$ and $z = +1$. Since the interval between these two points covers 2 standard deviations, division by 2 provides an estimate of the standard deviation. Use this method and Figure 8.31 to obtain an estimate of the standard deviation of the weight distribution. Compare your result with the actual value given on page 186.

5. Use the method indicated in Exercise 4 and the results of Exercise 1 to obtain an estimate of the standard deviation of the speed-check distribution.

6. Find the expected normal curve frequencies for the speed-check distribution on page 17, whose mean and standard deviation are 52.5 and 6.65 mph, respectively. Also draw superimposed histograms showing the observed frequencies and the expected normal curve frequencies.

7. Find the expected normal curve frequencies for whichever data were grouped among Exercises 11, 13, 14, and 15 on pages 25 through 28. (The mean was found among the exercises on page 54 and the standard deviation was found in Exercise 11 on page 94.) Also plot superimposed histograms showing the observed frequencies as well as the expected normal curve frequencies.

**8.** Find the expected normal curve frequencies for the distribution of time lapses between eruptions of Old Faithful of Exercise 17 on page 28. (The mean and the standard deviation were already found in part (a) of Exercise 16 on page 54 and Exercise 12 on page 94, respectively.)

## 8.9 / Other Theoretical Distributions

The fact that most of this chapter was devoted to the binomial and normal distributions may have given the erroneous impression that they are the only distributions that matter in statistical theory. Although it is true that the binomial and normal distributions play important roles in many applications, their indiscriminate use can lead to very misleading results. As was pointed out on page 159, the binomial distribution must be replaced with another distribution whenever the trials are not independent or the probability of success varies from trial to trial. Similarly, there are situations in which we have good reasons to expect continuous distributions other than normal curves. We shall see later in Chapters 10 through 13 that other continuous distributions, among them the $t$-distributions, the chi-square distribution, and the $F$-distribution, play very important roles in problems of estimation, prediction, and testing hypotheses.

### BIBLIOGRAPHY

Binomial probabilities for $n = 2$ to $n = 49$ may be found in

> *Tables of the Binomial Probability Distribution*, National Bureau of Standards Applied Mathematics Series No. 6. Washington, D. C.: U.S. Government Printing Office, 1950.

> Romig, H. G., 50–100 *Binomial Tables*. New York: John Wiley, 1953.

Derivations of the formulas for $\mu$ and $\sigma$ of the binomial distribution may be found in

> Kenney, J. F., and Keeping, E. S., *Mathematics of Statistics, Part II*. New York: Van Nostrand, 1951, p. 29.

The definition of the mean and standard deviation of a *continuous* distribution is given in

> Wilks, S. S., *Elementary Statistical Analysis*. Princeton, N. J.: Princeton University Press, 1951, pp. 116–117.

Proofs showing that the binomial distribution approaches the normal curve when $p$ is fixed and $n$ goes to infinity may be found in the book by Kenney and Keeping mentioned above (pp. 33–35) and in most other textbooks of mathematical statistics. A discussion of the *Poisson* approximation of the binomial distribution is given in

Hoel, P. G., *Introduction to Mathematical Statistics*, 2nd ed. New York: John Wiley, 1954, p. 68.

The method which employs $\alpha_3$ and $\alpha_4$ to test whether an observed distribution fits the pattern of a normal curve is illustrated in

Waugh, A. E., *Elements of Statistical Method*, 3rd ed. New York: McGraw-Hill, 1952, p. 246.

# Chapter 9

# Sampling and Sampling
# Distributions

### 9.1 / Random Sampling

In Chapter 3 we distinguished between *populations* and *samples*, saying that a population consists of all conceivably (or hypothetically) possible observations relating to a certain phenomenon and that a sample is simply part of a population. Since statistical inference, or inductive statistics, consists of making generalizations about populations on the basis of samples, let us investigate briefly under what conditions this may or may not be possible. Suppose, for example, that we want to study how much money the average American spends on his summer vacation and that the only information we have at our disposal pertains to visitors to a very swanky resort in Carmel, California. It would hardly seem reasonable to suppose that we can use this very limited and very special information to make sweeping generalizations. Similarly, we can hardly expect to arrive at reasonable generalizations about retail prices of farm products in general being supplied only with retail prices of eggs, *or* use information about traffic on the Pennsylvania Turnpike on the 4th of July to arrive at general conclusions about traffic on this highway throughout the year. These examples are perhaps somewhat extreme, but they serve to illustrate the fact that we must be very careful whenever we want to generalize on the basis of a sample.

The whole problem of when and under what conditions samples permit "reasonable" generalizations is not easily answered. In the methods which we shall develop in the next few chapters we will always assume that we have *random samples* — special kinds of samples to be defined below. Other kinds of sampling procedures will be mentioned only very briefly in Section 9.2.

Having defined populations and samples, let us distinguish further between populations that are *finite* and those that are *infinite*. A population is said to be *finite* if it consists of a finite number, that is, a fixed number of elements. For example, the population consisting of all drug stores in Cleveland, Ohio, is finite and so is that consisting of the I.Q.'s of all students currently enrolled in the schools of Richmond, Virginia, or that consisting of the current judges of the U.S. Supreme Court. The last of these finite populations has a fixed number, that is, 9 members. In contrast to finite populations, a population is said to be *infinite* if there is no limit to the number of elements that it contains. For instance, the population consisting of all hypothetically possible flips of a coin is an infinite population and so is that consisting of all hypothetically possible measurements of the length of a certain metal bar.

When sampling from _finite_ populations, we shall say that *a finite sample is random if every element of the population has an equal chance of being included in the sample*. This definition implies that the selection of random samples should, in some way, be left to chance, and it is, indeed, common practice to base random sampling on some form of gambling device.

If we wanted to study the merchandising practices of 723 retail food stores in a certain community, we *could* select a random sample of, say, 10 of these stores by writing their names on slips of paper, mixing the slips thoroughly, and then drawing 10. We said that it *could* be done in this fashion because, in actual practice, there are much less laborious ways. Whenever the construction of appropriate gambling devices, slips of paper, dice, roulette wheels, etc., becomes too tedious, it is preferable to select random samples with the use of specially designed tables of so-called *random numbers*. The sample page shown in Table VII on page 391 comes from a table of random numbers which, itself, was constructed with the use of some gambling device supposedly giving each digit an equal probability of being 0, 1, 3, . . ., or 9.

To demonstrate how random numbers (or *random digits*, as they are also called) are used in the selection of a sample, let us refer again to the example of the 723 retail stores from which we wanted to select a sample of *size* 10. (A sample is said to be of *size n* if it contains *n* measurements or observations.) Numbering the stores from 1 to 723 or, better, numbering them 001, 002, 003, . . ., and 723, we arbitrarily pick a page of a table of random numbers, three consecutive columns, and a row from which to start. Supposing that we pick columns 25, 26, and 27 of the page of random numbers given in Table VII and that we start with row 16, it can easily be verified that we will select the stores numbered

> 97   467   290   425   350   121   335   420   657   16

It should be noted that in the selection of this sample we ignored three-digit numbers exceeding 723. If, by chance, the same number had come up more than once, we would have included it only once.

In addition to the table of random numbers from which we reproduced Table VII there are others published commercially and suitable references are given in the Bibliography on page 210. Incidentally, if we had wanted to be "even more random" in our example, we could have left the selection of the page, columns, and row to chance by using some gambling device or, perhaps, another page of random numbers.

Having defined random samples for *finite* populations, let us add a few words about the more difficult to define concept of a random sample from an *infinite* population. To give a simple illustration, let us consider 5 flips of a balanced coin as a sample from the (hypothetically) infinite population which consists of all possible flips of this coin. *These 5 flips are looked upon as a random sample if the probability of getting heads is the same for each flip and if the 5 flips are, furthermore, independent.* Thus, the selection of each item, or value, to be included in a random sample from an infinite population must be controlled by the same probabilities and successive selections must be independent.

## 9.2 / Sample Designs

Having explained what is meant by random samples and having demonstrated (at least for finite populations) how random samples may be obtained with the use of random numbers, we might add that all this is very often easier said than done. If we were asked to estimate the average diameter of 1,000,000 ball bearings on the basis of a sample of 50, it would hardly be practical to number these ball bearings and then proceed as in our example dealing with the 723 stores. Similarly, it would be virtually impossible to sample trees in the Rockies by assigning a number to each tree *or* housewives in Chicago by giving a number to each, and then proceed with the use of random numbers. In situations like these we really have no choice but to proceed in some other way, using special *sample designs* or, perhaps, experience and judgment. In the latter case we might well keep our fingers crossed that the samples we get will be such that statistical theory otherwise reserved for random samples can be applied. This is true, particularly, in situations where we have little control over the selection of our data; for example, in medical studies where we often have to be satisfied with whatever cases happen to be available.

*A sample design is a definite plan, specified before any data are collected, of obtaining a sample from a given population.* Since the subject of sample designs is very extensive (many books have been written on this subject) we shall merely mention some of the most widely used schemes such as *stratified sampling, cluster sampling,* and *systematic sampling.* More detailed treatments of this important part of statistics are listed in the Bibliography on page 210.

In *stratified sampling* we divide the population into sub-populations, *strata,* to which we then allocate certain portions of the total sample. For example, let us suppose that income level has an important bearing on public opinion concerning an election and that 40 per cent of the voters have low incomes, 50 per cent have medium incomes, and 10 per cent have high incomes. If we then select corresponding proportions of our sample from these three income groups, for example 160 of 400 from the low income group, 200 from the medium income group, and 40 from the high income group, we are using what is called *proportional stratified sampling.*

To examine another kind of sampling, let us suppose that we want to study family expenditures in the San Francisco area and that we have decided to interview 1000 families. An economical way of handling this might be to divide the total area in which we are interested into smaller areas, say, city blocks, and then interview all (or samples of) families in a number of randomly selected city blocks.

Such sampling is called _cluster sampling_. If the clusters are geographical subdivisions like the city blocks of our example, such sampling is also referred to as _area sampling_.

If samples are obtained by taking, say, every 10th name in a telephone directory, every 20th voucher in a file, every 12th house on one side of a street, or every 5th item coming off an assembly line, we call this _systematic sampling_. Although systematic samples are not random samples in accordance with the definition given in Section 9.1, it is often possible to treat them as if they were random samples. Of course, there are certain dangers — we might arrive at very misleading results if we inspect every 5th piece coming off an assembly line and it so happened that owing to a defect in the machine every 5th piece has imperfections. We would also be in trouble if we interviewed the residents of every 12th house along a certain route and it so happened that each 12th house is in a choice location, say, a corner lot. The above are but a few examples of sample designs used in the collection of statistical data. In practice it is often necessary to combine several such plans or resort to much more complicated schemes.

### EXERCISES

1. Use random numbers to select a restaurant from the yellow pages of your local telephone directory.

2. Suppose that a research organization wishes to interview samples of voters in 10 states. Using random numbers and the 50 states in their alphabetic order, select a random sample of 10 states.

3. Random numbers can also be used to simulate various games of chance. For example, we might play "heads or tails" by letting 0, 2, 4, 6, and 8 represent _heads_, and 1, 3, 5, 7, and 9 stand for _tails_. Considering four successive random digits (in rows or columns) as tosses of four balanced coins, use Table VII to simulate an experiment consisting of 160 tosses of four balanced coins. Draw superimposed histograms of the distribution thus obtained and the corresponding expected distribution found in Exercise 1 on page 153.

4. Describe in detail how random numbers might be used to simulate an experiment consisting of 120 rolls of a balanced die.

### 9.3 / Sampling Distributions

To illustrate one of the most basic concepts of statistical inference, that of a _sampling distribution_, let us consider the following concrete (though fictitious) example of *estimating* the average height of the adult male residents of a certain community. Let us suppose that if we actually made a complete survey, that is, if we actually measured the height of each male resident of this community, we would obtain the following distribution:

| Height (in inches) | Frequency |
|:---:|:---:|
| 55 – 57 | 7 |
| 58 – 60 | 116 |
| 61 – 63 | 761 |
| 64 – 66 | 2379 |
| 67 – 69 | 3472 |
| 70 – 72 | 2379 |
| 73 – 75 | 761 |
| 76 – 78 | 116 |
| 79 – 81 | 7 |
|  | 9998 |

As can easily be verified, the mean of this population of heights is $\mu = 68$ inches and its standard deviation is $\sigma = 3.44$ inches.

Once an entire population is known, that is, if our sampling is *exhaustive*, finding the mean does not entail any generalizations it does not involve a statistical inference. *In actual practice, complete or exhaustive sampling is not only at times impossible or unfeasible, but it is usually impractical and unnecessary.* It is *impossible* if we sample from an infinite population and it is *unfeasible* if the sampling is destructive. A sampling procedure (or a method of obtaining data) is said to be *destructive* if it necessitates damaging or destroying the products or objects that are being measured. If we wanted to determine the true average lifetime of all TV tubes made by a given firm, we could not very well test them all. If we did, the firm would have none left to sell.

Even if we do not damage or destroy the objects with which we are concerned, there is seldom any need to resort to exhaustive sampling. In the example dealing with the heights of the 9998 male residents of a certain community, exhaustive sampling would be very *impractical* since the cost of locating, visiting, and measuring all 9998 would be prohibitive. However, even if we were willing to spend the money, it could well be an unnecessary waste because *it is generally possible to get information that is adequate for most purposes from relatively small random samples.* Why measure the height of 9998 individuals if the heights of 25, 50, or perhaps 100 give us whatever information we need?  Considerations like this are important, for we shall see later that *gains in the accuracy of estimates and reductions in the risks involved in making decisions are generally not proportional to increases in the size of our samples.*

Let us now return to the problem of estimating the average height of the adult male residents of the given community and *let us forget about the complete (exhaustive) survey which yielded the distribution shown on page 197*.  Instead, let us take a random sample of size 5 and use the mean of the 5 heights thus obtained as an estimate of $\mu$.  (We are limiting ourselves to only 5 observations to simplify the arithmetic of our example.  If this were not a fictitious example, we would probably take a sample of 25, 50, or more.)  Let us assume then that we obtain the following 5 measurements rounded to the nearest inch:

$$70 \quad 66 \quad 68 \quad 61 \quad 66$$

Since the mean of this sample is

$$\bar{x} = \frac{70 + 66 + 68 + 61 + 66}{5} = 66.2$$

we arrive at an *estimate* of 66.2 inches for $\mu$, the mean of the entire population with which we are concerned.  In other words, we generalize on the basis of this sample that the average height of all adult male residents of the given community is 66.2 inches.

Having made this inference about the heights of several thousand persons after measuring as few as 5, we may well be asked any one of the following questions:

1. Can we really expect a sample mean based on relatively few observations to be "reasonably close" to the mean of the population from which the sample was obtained?

2. How "sure" are we that the sample mean which we get for the heights does not differ from $\mu$, the quantity we want to estimate, by more than 1 inch, 2 inches, or, say, 3.4 inches?

3. If we were to repeat this experiment and take several random samples of 5 measurements each, how closely could we expect their means to be clustered around $\mu$?

Since these questions are very important, let us try to find answers by first conducting a further experiment, in fact, the one suggested in question 3.

It must be evident that we cannot reasonably expect every sample mean to coincide with the mean of the population from which the sample is obtained.  As a matter of fact, looking back on page 197, we find that $\mu = 68$ and that our estimate was 66.2 and, thus, off by 1.8 inches. Had the sample mean been 67.4, our estimate of $\mu$ would have been closer and had $\bar{x}$ been 61.8, it would have been worse.

In order to see how sample means fluctuate from sample to sample, let us now take 50 *separate* random samples of 5 measurements each from the given population which, as the reader will recall, consists of the heights of the 9998 adult male residents of a certain community. The following are 50 such random samples obtained with the use of random numbers from the distribution on page 197:

| | |
|---|---|
| Sample 1: 68, 66, 67, 71, 72 | Sample 26: 68, 68, 67, 59, 68 |
| Sample 2: 72, 69, 67, 64, 64 | Sample 27: 68, 74, 63, 70, 64 |
| Sample 3: 73, 70, 64, 69, 66 | Sample 28: 65, 70, 72, 71, 67 |
| Sample 4: 69, 68, 73, 71, 69 | Sample 29: 71, 68, 65, 68, 69 |
| Sample 5: 66, 61, 66, 70, 68 | Sample 30: 68, 65, 66, 70, 68 |
| Sample 6: 68, 67, 66, 65, 66 | Sample 31: 70, 56, 68, 75, 71 |
| Sample 7: 68, 73, 66, 65, 65 | Sample 32: 64, 72, 68, 70, 68 |
| Sample 8: 60, 68, 72, 69, 78 | Sample 33: 63, 70, 74, 73, 80 |
| Sample 9: 65, 70, 70, 63, 73 | Sample 34: 68, 70, 69, 67, 73 |
| Sample 10: 66, 73, 66, 65, 65 | Sample 35: 68, 68, 70, 66, 76 |
| Sample 11: 74, 67, 71, 70, 68 | Sample 36: 71, 70, 68, 62, 68 |
| Sample 12: 65, 70, 69, 68, 74 | Sample 37: 64, 69, 66, 66, 63 |
| Sample 13: 67, 64, 70, 69, 63 | Sample 38: 71, 74, 65, 62, 72 |
| Sample 14: 77, 70, 70, 69, 70 | Sample 39: 68, 70, 66, 67, 69 |
| Sample 15: 67, 69, 73, 69, 62 | Sample 40: 72, 68, 71, 65, 67 |
| Sample 16: 61, 67, 67, 67, 67 | Sample 41: 62, 72, 67, 67, 71 |
| Sample 17: 70, 64, 66, 67, 64 | Sample 42: 65, 68, 63, 65, 76 |
| Sample 18: 68, 69, 71, 66, 74 | Sample 43: 66, 73, 70, 70, 73 |
| Sample 19: 67, 68, 72, 75, 63 | Sample 44: 66, 70, 69, 71, 64 |
| Sample 20: 71, 70, 67, 65, 70 | Sample 45: 64, 64, 64, 70, 64 |
| Sample 21: 73, 66, 68, 66, 69 | Sample 46: 73, 70, 65, 69, 67 |
| Sample 22: 66, 69, 67, 65, 69 | Sample 47: 70, 66, 72, 73, 69 |
| Sample 23: 59, 69, 66, 70, 70 | Sample 48: 67, 69, 64, 66, 68 |
| Sample 24: 67, 65, 64, 61, 66 | Sample 49: 67, 66, 69, 69, 67 |
| Sample 25: 64, 70, 69, 72, 68 | Sample 50: 68, 67, 70, 67, 69 |

$M = 68$

Having obtained these 50 samples, our next step is to calculate the corresponding 50 means and study their distribution. Adding the five values in each sample and dividing by 5, we find that the 50 means are

| | | | | | | | | | |
|---|---|---|---|---|---|---|---|---|---|
| 68.8 | 67.2 | 68.4 | 70.0 | 66.2 | 66.4 | 65.4 | 69.4 | 68.2 | 67.0 |
| 70.0 | 69.2 | 66.6 | 71.2 | 68.0 | 65.8 | 66.2 | 69.6 | 69.0 | 68.6 |
| 68.4 | 67.2 | 66.8 | 64.6 | 68.6 | 66.0 | 67.8 | 69.0 | 68.2 | 67.4 |
| 68.0 | 68.4 | 72.0 | 69.4 | 69.6 | 67.8 | 65.6 | 68.8 | 68.0 | 68.6 |
| 67.8 | 67.4 | 70.4 | 68.0 | 65.2 | 68.8 | 70.0 | 66.8 | 67.6 | 68.2 |

and as can easily be checked with formulas (3.3.1) and (4.4.3), the mean of these 50 $\bar{x}$'s is 68.03 and their standard deviation is 1.55. Symbolically, we shall write

$$\bar{x}_{\bar{x}} = 68.03 \quad \text{and} \quad s_{\bar{x}} = 1.55$$

using the subscript $\bar{x}$ to indicate that we are referring to the mean and the standard deviation of the $\bar{x}$'s.

To get an over-all picture of the 50 sample means, let us group them into the following distribution, called an *experimental sampling distribution of means:*

| $\bar{x}$ | Frequency |
|---|---|
| 64.5 – 65.4 | 3 |
| 65.5 – 66.4 | 6 |
| 66.5 – 67.4 | 8 |
| 67.5 – 68.4 | 14 |
| 68.5 – 69.4 | 11 |
| 69.5 – 70.4 | 6 |
| 70.5 – 71.4 | 1 |
| 71.5 – 72.4 | 1 |

It goes by this name because it consists of means obtained in a sampling experiment in which we took repeated samples from the same population.

Although we have not used the term "experimental sampling distribution" before, we already met such distributions in Chapter 8. If 4 balanced coins are tossed 160 times (see Exercise 1 on page 153, the resulting distribution showing with what frequencies 0, 1, 2, 3, and 4 heads occurred is an experimental sampling distribution. Similarly, if a balanced die is rolled 120 times (see Exercise 6 on page 153), the resulting distribution showing with what frequencies the six faces appeared is an experimental sampling distribution. In the first case there are 160 samples, each consisting of tossing 4 balanced coins, and in the second there are 120 samples, each consisting of a roll of a balanced die.

We introduced these experimental sampling distributions in Chapter 8 to provide support for the corresponding expected distributions (or probability distributions). Such a comparison can also be made in the sampling experiment we have been discussing in this section. Corresponding to the experimental sampling distribution shown above, we might ask how many of the 50 means might be *expected* to fall between 64.5 and 65.4, between 65.5 and 67.4, between 67.5 and 68.4, . . . , or for the *probabilities* of obtaining a sample of 5 observations whose mean falls between 64.5 and 65.4, between 65.5 and 66.4, and so forth.

A distribution which gives the probabilities of obtaining given values of $\bar{x}$ when sampling from a certain population is called a *theoretical sampling distribution of $\bar{x}$.* (In the continuous case it provides the probabilities that $\bar{x}$ will fall into any given interval.) Thus, the distribution of Figure 8.2 on page 154 is a theoretical sampling distribution showing the probabilities of getting 0, 1, 2, and 3 *sixes* in a sample consisting of three rolls of a balanced die. To give another illustration involving means, let us suppose that we take 6 slips of paper on which we write the numbers 1, 3, 5, 7, 9, and 11. If we draw a sample of 2 of these slips we can get

| | | | | |
|---|---|---|---|---|
| 1 and 3 | 1 and 5 | 1 and 7 | 1 and 9 | 1 and 11 |
| 3 and 5 | 3 and 7 | 3 and 9 | 3 and 11 | 5 and 7 |
| 5 and 9 | 5 and 11 | 7 and 9 | 7 and 11 | 9 and 11 |

Calculating the means of these 15 samples and considering them as *equally likely,* we can construct the following *theoretical sampling distribution,* shown also in Figure 9.1:

| $\bar{x}$ | Probability |
|:---:|:---:|
| 2 | $\frac{1}{15}$ |
| 3 | $\frac{1}{15}$ |
| 4 | $\frac{2}{15}$ |
| 5 | $\frac{2}{15}$ |
| 6 | $\frac{3}{15}$ |
| 7 | $\frac{2}{15}$ |
| 8 | $\frac{2}{15}$ |
| 9 | $\frac{1}{15}$ |
| 10 | $\frac{1}{15}$ |

This distribution tells us that if we draw two of the slips, without replacement, the probability that the numbers we draw have a mean of 2 is $\frac{1}{15}$, the probability that they have a mean of 3 is $\frac{1}{15}$, the probability that they have a mean of 4 is $\frac{2}{15}$, etc.

Returning now to the problem dealing with the heights of the 9998 persons mentioned on page 197, we *could* duplicate what we have done in the last example by enumerating all possible samples of size 5, calculating their means, and constructing the theoretical sampling distribution of $\bar{x}$ by assigning each sample an equal chance of being selected. This would be an enormous job, but it would give us the probabilities of getting various values of $\bar{x}$ in a random sample of size 5 from the given population.

Fortunately, we can obtain information about theoretical

sampling distributions of $\bar{x}$ without having to perform the steps outlined in the preceding paragraph. Instead we can refer to two very

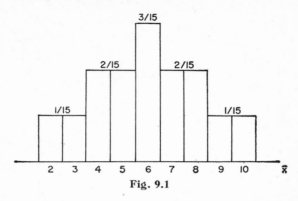

Fig. 9.1

basic theorems of statistics, the first concerning *the mean and standard deviation of the theoretical sampling distribution of $\bar{x}$:\**

> **THEOREM 9.1:**
>
> *If random samples of size n are taken from a population with the mean $\mu$ and the standard deviation $\sigma$, the theoretical sampling distribution of $\bar{x}$ has the mean $\mu$ and the standard deviation $\sigma/\sqrt{n}$.*

One aspect of this theorem which should not be surprising is that the mean of the theoretical sampling distribution *equals* that of the population. In our example of the 50 $\bar{x}$'s the mean of the (experimental) sampling distribution was 68.03, while that of the population was 68 (see pages 200 and 197). The reader may wish to verify that in the example dealing with the 6 slips of paper, the mean of the population, namely, the mean of 1, 3, 5, 7, 9, and 11, as well as the mean of the theoretical sampling distribution of $\bar{x}$ are equal to 6.

A very important feature of Theorem 9.1 is that the standard deviation of the theoretical sampling distribution of $\bar{x}$ is obtained by dividing $\sigma$ by the square root of $n$. Following customary symbolism and terminology, we shall write this standard deviation as $\sigma_{\bar{x}}$ and refer to it as the *standard error of the mean.* We thus have

$$\sigma_{\bar{x}} = \frac{\sigma}{\sqrt{n}}$$

(9.3.1)▲

*This theorem applies only for samples taken from *very large populations* so that a sample of size $n$ constitutes but a minute fraction of the population. If each sample constitutes an appreciable portion (more than 5 per cent) of the population, the theorem will have to be modified as explained in Section 10.6.

where $\sigma$ is the standard deviation of the population and $n$ the size of the sample. The standard error of the mean plays a very important role in statistical inference, as it measures *how much sample means fluctuate, or vary, owing to chance.*

Let us now check how the theoretical value for the standard error of the mean compares in our example with the value which we actually obtain for the 50 $\bar{x}$'s. Since the population had a standard deviation of 3.44 (see page 197) and the sample size was 5, formula (9.3.1) gives

$$\sigma_{\bar{x}} = \frac{3.44}{\sqrt{5}} = 1.54$$

and this is very close, indeed, to the value of $s_{\bar{x}} = 1.55$, which we obtained on page 200. We might thus say that the experiment in which we took the 50 samples provides very strong support for formula (9.3.1). This is important because Theorem 9.1 cannot be *proved* without using mathematics more advanced than we assumed for this book.

Formula (9.3.1), in which $\sigma$ is divided by $\sqrt{n}$, shows by inspection that the standard error of the mean *decreases* when the sample size is *increased*. This means that *when n becomes larger and we actually have more information, sample means can be expected to be closer to $\mu$, the true population mean they are supposed to estimate.* To illustrate how the variability of the $\bar{x}$'s thus decreases with increasing $n$, let us convert the 50 samples on page 199 into 25 samples of size 10 by combining Samples 1 and 2, Samples 3 and 4, Samples 5 and 6, and so forth. Calculating the means of these 25 samples we get

| | | | | |
|------|------|------|------|------|
| 68.0 | 69.2 | 66.3 | 67.4 | 67.4 |
| 69.6 | 68.9 | 66.9 | 67.9 | 68.8 |
| 67.8 | 65.7 | 67.3 | 68.4 | 67.8 |
| 68.2 | 70.7 | 68.7 | 67.2 | 68.3 |
| 67.6 | 69.2 | 67.0 | 68.4 | 67.9 |

and these values may be grouped into the following distribution:

| $\bar{x}$ | Frequency |
|-----------|-----------|
| 65.5 – 66.4 | 2 |
| 66.5 – 67.4 | 5 |
| 67.5 – 68.4 | 11 |
| 68.5 – 69.4 | 5 |
| 69.5 – 70.4 | 1 |
| 70.5 – 71.4 | 1 |

As can easily be checked with formulas (3.3.1) and (4.4.3), the mean and standard deviation of the 25 $\bar{x}$'s are 68.03 and 1.07, respectively. The value which we obtained for this standard deviation agrees very closely with what we should have *expected* according to Theorem 9.1. Substituting $\sigma = 3.44$ and $n = 10$ into the formula for $\sigma_{\bar{x}}$, we obtain $3.44/\sqrt{10} = 1.09$.

Clearly, there is less variability between the 25 means based on samples of size 10 than there is between the 50 means based on samples of size 5. The standard deviations of the corresponding

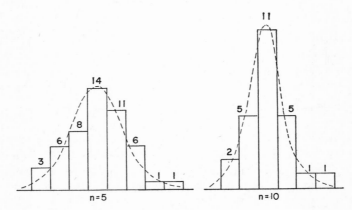

**Fig. 9.2.**   Experimental sampling distributions of the means.

sampling distributions (see Figure 9.2) are 1.07 and 1.55, respectively. Had we conducted our experiment by taking repeated samples of size 25, the standard deviation of our experimental sampling distribution should have been even less, namely, close to $3.44/\sqrt{25} = 0.69$ (see Exercise 1 on page 208).

Although it may be important to know the mean and standard deviation of a theoretical sampling distribution of $\bar{x}$, knowledge of these two values alone will not enable us to answer all the questions asked on page 198. To be able to calculate probabilities of $x$ falling into given intervals, for example, those asked for in Question 2 on page 198, we shall have to refer to a second theorem — the so-called *Central Limit Theorem:**

---

*It is difficult to make any precise statement as to how large $n$ must be before this theorem applies. Unless the distribution of the population has a very unusual shape, the approximation will be good even if $n$ is relatively small, say, not less than 30.

*central limit theorem*

THEOREM 9.2:

*If n is large, the theoretical sampling distribution of $\bar{x}$ can be approximated very closely with a normal curve having the mean $\mu$ and the standard deviation $\sigma/\sqrt{n}$.*

Since the $n$ which we used in our original sampling experiment was very small ($n$ equalled 5), let us add that Theorem 9.2 applies also when $n$ is smaller than the 30 mentioned in the footnote *provided that the distribution of the population can be approximated closely with a normal curve.* As can easily be verified, the distribution of the 9998 heights on page 197 is very close to a normal curve, and this — as well as a good deal of luck — explains why our experimental sampling distributions (see Figure 9.2) can be approximated closely with normal curves. The diagrams of Figure 9.2 give the experimental sampling distributions as well as the normal curves (the dotted curves) which approximate the corresponding theoretical sampling distributions.

Let us now show how Theorems 9.1 and 9.2 may be used to calculate probabilities related to the sampling distribution of $\bar{x}$. For instance, let us find the probability of getting a random sample of size 5 (from the population consisting of the 9998 heights) for which $\bar{x}$ lies between 68.5 and 69.5. Assuming that the sampling distribution of $\bar{x}$ can in this instance be approximated by a normal curve, we have only to find the shaded area of Figure 9.3 using the

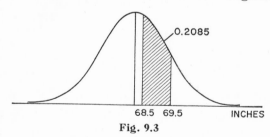

Fig. 9.3

methods of Section 8.6. Since $\mu = 68$ and $\sigma_{\bar{x}} = 1.54$ (see page 203), the $z$'s corresponding to 68.5 and 69.5 are

$$z_1 = \frac{68.5 - 68}{1.54} = 0.32$$

$$z_2 = \frac{69.5 - 68}{1.54} = 0.97$$

and the desired probability is $0.3340 - 0.1255 = 0.2085$ or approx-

$$\sqrt{\frac{N-n}{N-1}}$$

imately 0.21. Using the identical technique we could also calculate the probability of getting an $\bar{x}$ from this population which lies between 69.5 and 72.1, an $\bar{x}$ which lies between 60.5 and 67.3, etc. More generally, we can now calculate all probabilities that relate to the theoretical sampling distribution of $\bar{x}$ for sufficiently large random samples provided, of course, that we know $\mu$ and $\sigma$ of the population.

The concepts which we introduced in this section are not limited to sample means. If we were interested in the *medians* instead of the means, we could find the medians of the 50 samples on page 199 and study their distribution in order to get some idea how much medians vary from sample to sample. Actually doing this, we find that the 50 medians are

| | | | | | | | | | |
|----|----|----|----|----|----|----|----|----|----|
| 68 | 67 | 69 | 69 | 66 | 66 | 65 | 69 | 70 | 66 |
| 70 | 69 | 67 | 70 | 69 | 67 | 66 | 69 | 68 | 70 |
| 68 | 67 | 69 | 65 | 69 | 68 | 68 | 70 | 68 | 68 |
| 70 | 68 | 73 | 69 | 68 | 68 | 66 | 71 | 68 | 68 |
| 67 | 65 | 70 | 69 | 64 | 69 | 70 | 67 | 67 | 68 |

and that they fall into the following distribution:

| Median | Frequency |
|---------|-----------|
| 63.5 – 64.4 | 1 |
| 64.5 – 65.4 | 3 |
| 65.5 – 66.4 | 5 |
| 66.5 – 67.4 | 7 |
| 67.5 – 68.4 | 13 |
| 68.5 – 69.4 | 11 |
| 69.5 – 70.4 | 8 |
| 70.5 – 71.4 | 1 |
| 71.5 – 72.4 | 0 |
| 72.5 – 73.4 | 1 |

Comparing the experimental sampling distribution of the medians with that of the 50 means, it is apparent that the distribution of the medians is more "spread out" than that of the means. Whereas $s_{\bar{x}} = 1.55$ (we calculated this value on page 200) it can easily be shown that the standard deviation of the distribution of the 50 medians is $s_M = 1.73$. This bears out what we said on page 60, where we pointed out that *sample means are generally more reliable than sample medians* or, in other words, that *sample means generally do not fluctuate so much from sample to sample as the corresponding medians.*

Analogous to Theorems 9.1 and 9.2, there also exists theory pertaining to the theoretical sampling distribution of the median. As we shall formulate it here, it applies only to samples from popula-

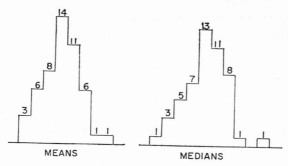

MEANS    MEDIANS

**Fig. 9.4.** Experimental sampling distributions of the means and medians.

tions whose distribution can be approximated closely with normal curves. If this is the case, *the theoretical sampling distribution of the median can be approximated closely with a normal curve whose mean is* $\mu$ *and whose standard deviation, the "standard error of the median," is*

$$\sigma_M = 1.25 \frac{\sigma}{\sqrt{n}} \qquad (9.3.2) \blacktriangle$$

Here $\mu$ and $\sigma$ are again the mean and standard deviation of the population and 1.25 is a constant rounded to two decimals. Some texts give it as 1.2533. Let us also add that, as before, this theory applies only if the sample constitutes but a very small part of the population. (See footnote on page 202.)

Since the standard deviation of the population from which we took the 50 samples was 3.44, we could have *expected* the standard deviation of the 50 medians to be

$$\sigma_M = 1.25 \frac{3.44}{\sqrt{5}} = 1.92$$

This is somewhat more than the value of $s_M = 1.73$ which we obtained on page 206, but if we had continued the experiment and taken more than 50 samples, the standard deviation of the medians should before long have come close to the theoretical value of 1.92.

We could continue our study of sampling distributions by calculating the standard deviations, the ranges, the modes, the geo-metric means, etc., of the 50 samples and construct the corresponding experimental sampling distributions. Then we could calculate the standard deviation of each sampling distribution to get an idea how much the respective statistic varies from sample to sample. (A *statistic* is a quantity that is calculated from a sample.) We could also check how closely each of the standard deviations agrees with the corresponding *standard error*, that is, with the standard deviation we could have *expected* according to appropriate theory.

Our discussion of sampling distributions was motivated by the three questions asked on page 198. Although we have not yet explained in so many words *how sure we can be that the error, which we make when using $\bar{x}$ as an estimate of $\mu$, does not exceed, say, 1 or 2,* we now have the necessary tools to find suitable answers. Reserving this task for the next chapter, let us conclude our discussion of sampling distributions with the following observation:

*In actual applied problems we do not have 50 samples or 100 sam-ples, but we generally have only 1 sample on which to base whatever generalizations or inferences we want to make. Hence, we must learn how to justify generalizations made on the basis of 1 sample mean, 1 sample median, 1. sample standard deviation, . . . . In practical situations we cannot repeat an experiment 50 times to see how much a mean or some other statistic varies from sample to sample; we did so in this chapter only to give concrete illustrations of sampling distributions.*

### EXERCISES

1. If we take the 50 samples given on page 199 and combine Samples 1 to 5, Samples 6 to 10, and so on, we obtain 10 samples of size 25 whose means are

$$68.12 \quad 67.28 \quad 69.00 \quad 67.84 \quad 67.12$$
$$67.68 \quad 69.48 \quad 67.76 \quad 67.76 \quad 68.28$$

Use formula (4.4.3) to find the standard deviation of these 10 means and compare it with the value which we could *expect* according to (9.3.1).

2. Take 100 milk-bottle tops, metal-rim tags, or other small symmetrical objects and record on them the numbers from 1 to 11 with the following frequencies

| Number to be Written on Tag | Frequency |
|:---:|:---:|
| 1 | 1 |
| 2 | 3 |
| 3 | 7 |
| 4 | 12 |
| 5 | 17 |
| 6 | 20 |
| 7 | 17 |
| 8 | 12 |
| 9 | 7 |
| 10 | 3 |
| 11 | 1 |

This provides a population whose mean and standard deviation are $\mu = 6$ and $\sigma = 2$, and which can be approximated closely with a normal curve. Take 50 samples of size 4, *replacing each tag before the next one is drawn,* and calculate the mean as well as the median of each of these 50 samples. Then use formula (4.4.3) to calculate the standard deviations of the 50 means and the 50 medians and compare them with the values which we should *expect* according to the theorems of this section. (*Hint:* The quantities to be substituted into the formulas for the standard errors are $\sigma = 2$ and $n = 4$.)

3. Repeat the experiment of Exercise 2 with the use of random numbers (use any two columns of Table VII) employing the following scheme

| Number to be Recorded | Random Numbers |
|:---:|:---:|
| 1 | 00 |
| 2 | 01 to 03 |
| 3 | 04 to 10 |
| 4 | 11 to 22 |
| 5 | 23 to 39 |
| 6 | 40 to 59 |
| 7 | 60 to 76 |
| 8 | 77 to 88 |
| 9 | 89 to 95 |
| 10 | 96 to 98 |
| 11 | 99 |

For instance, if we obtained the random numbers 23, 74, 41, and 81, we would record the numbers 5, 7, 6, and 8; if we obtained the random numbers 42, 97, 09, and 53, we would record the numbers 6, 10, 3, and 6.

4. What happens to the standard error of the mean if the sample size is changed from 100 to 400?

5. What happens to the standard error of the mean if the sample size is changed from 32 to 288?

**6.** Verify that a *median* based on a random sample of size 100 and a *mean* based on a random sample of size 64 are about *equally reliable* estimates of a population mean.

**7.** A random sample of size 36 is to be taken from a very large population whose mean and standard deviation are $\mu = 43.2$ and $\sigma = 6.3$. Find the probability that the mean of this sample will lie between 42.0 and 45.0. Treat the variable under consideration as a *continuous* variable.

**8.** Referring to the sample of Exercise 7 and assuming that the population from which it is obtained can be approximated closely with a normal curve, what is the probability that the sample *median* will lie between 42.0 and 45.0?

**9.** A random sample of size 64 is taken from a very large population whose mean and standard deviation are $\mu = 112$ and $\sigma = 16$. What is the probability that the mean of this sample will be less than 109 or greater than 115? (Treat the variable under consideration as a *continuous* variable, that is, find the normal curve area to the left of 109 plus that to the right of 115.)

**10.** Referring to the sample of Exercise 9 and assuming that the population from which it is obtained can be closely approximated with a normal curve, what is the probability that the sample *median* will be less than 109 or greater than 115?

## BIBLIOGRAPHY

The following are some of the most widely used tables of random numbers:

Kendall, M. G. and Smith, B. B., *Tables of Random Numbers, Tracts for Computers No. XXIV.* Cambridge: Cambridge University Press, 1939.

*Table of 105,000 Random Decimal Digits.* Interstate Commerce Commission, Bureau of Transport Economics and Statistics, Washington, D. C., 1949.

The Rand Corporation, *A Million Random Digits with 100,000 Normal Deviates.* Glencoe, Illinois: The Free Press, 1955.

Tippett, L. H. C., *Random Sampling Numbers, Tracts for Computers No. XV.* Cambridge: Cambridge University Press, 1927.

Introductions to the subject of sample design may be found in many introductory texts. See, for example

McCarthy, P. J., *Introduction to Statistical Reasoning.* New York: McGraw-Hill, 1957, Chap. 10.

More advanced treatments are given in

Cochran, W. G., *Sampling Techniques.* New York: John Wiley, 1953.

Deming, W. E., *Some Theory of Sampling.* New York: John Wiley, 1950.

Proofs of the two theorems concerning the theoretical sampling distribution of $\bar{x}$ may be found in most textbooks on mathematical statistics, for instance, in

Hoel, P. G., *Introduction to Mathematical Statistics,* 2nd ed. New York: John Wiley, 1954, Chap. 6.

A proof of the theorem dealing with the sampling distribution of the median is given in

Kendall, M. G., *The Advanced Theory of Statistics, Vol. I.* London: Charles Griffin, 1943, pp. 211–213.

Chapter **10**

# Problems of Estimation

## 10.1 / Introduction

Many problems of statistics deal with the estimation of unknown quantities such as means, standard deviations, and percentages. To mention a few examples, a scientist may wish to *estimate* the average nicotine content of certain cigarettes, a manufacturer of electronic missile components may wish to *estimate* how much variability there is in the performance of his product, and a television producer may wish to *estimate* what percentage of the total viewing audience is dialed to his show.

To give a concrete example, let us consider a study in which a psychologist wants to estimate the average time it takes an adult person to react to a certain visual stimulus. (Investigations like this are important, for example, in the study of driving habits and accident prevention.) Let us suppose then that an experiment in which a random sample of 40 adults were timed in their reaction to the given stimulus (say, changing lights) yielded the following results in seconds

| .12 | .15 | .13 | .15 | .13 | .09 | .13 | .14 | .16 | .12 |
|-----|-----|-----|-----|-----|-----|-----|-----|-----|-----|
| .13 | .14 | .12 | .15 | .18 | .15 | .14 | .13 | .11 | .13 |
| .19 | .17 | .08 | .11 | .12 | .13 | .16 | .14 | .12 | .11 |
| .10 | .13 | .12 | .14 | .14 | .12 | .16 | .09 | .12 | .13 |

The mean of this sample is $\bar{x} = 0.132$ seconds and, in the absence of other information, we may have to *estimate μ, the true average time that it takes an adult to react to the given stimulus,* as 0.132 seconds.

We now find ourselves in the same position as on page 197, where we tried to estimate the actual average height of a large group of persons by using the mean of a random sample. In order to avoid questions like those asked on page 198, namely, questions concerning the possible accuracy of our results, let us investigate how we might formulate our results so that such questions are automatically answered. To consider several possibilities, let us take a look at the following alternatives

**Alternative 1:** The average time that it takes an adult to react to the given stimulus is estimated as 0.132 seconds. This figure is the mean of a random sample of 40 observations.

**Alternative 2:** The average time that it takes an adult to react to the given stimulus is estimated as 0.132 seconds. This figure is the mean of a random sample of 40 observations whose standard deviation is 0.0232 seconds.

**Alternative 3:** The average time that it takes an adult to react to the given stimulus is estimated as 0.132 seconds. We are 95 per cent "sure" (we can assert with a probability of 0.95) that the error of this estimate is less than 0.007 seconds.

**Alternative 4:** We are 95 per cent "sure" (we can assert with a probability of 0.95) that the interval from 0.125 seconds to 0.139 seconds contains the true average time it takes an adult to react to the given stimulus.

Inasmuch as Alternative 1 mentions the size of the sample, it presents an improvement over merely stating that the estimate is 0.132 seconds. Although it is true that we are apt to have more confidence in an estimate based on 40 observations than on an estimate based on 5 or 10, knowledge of the sample size alone is not sufficient to answer questions about the accuracy of an estimate or the "reasonableness" of our generalization.

Although Alternative 2 provides all the information needed to answer the first two questions raised on page 198, it has the disadvantage that it requires a knowledge of statistics to translate the given values of $n$, $\bar{x}$, and $s$ into an evaluation of the accuracy or "reasonableness" of our generalization.

Alternative 3 gives the estimate together with an appraisal of its accuracy. It presents the generalization in terms that are easy to understand and in a form that is easy to use for further calculations. The only question that might arise is what we mean by "being 95 per cent sure." Of course, we did not explain how we arrived at the figure 0.007; this will be taken care of later on.

In the first three alternatives we estimated the true average time that it takes an adult to react to the given stimulus as 0.132 seconds. In the language of statistics this is referred to as a *point estimate;* the estimate consists of a single number or, in other words, a single point of the scale. The main disadvantage of *point estimation*, that is, giving an estimate as a single number, is that we would have to be exceedingly optimistic to suppose that such a number actually *equals* the quantity it is supposed to estimate. As we saw in Chapter 9, most of the sample means did not equal the population mean and this is why *a point estimate must always be supplemented with some statement about the possible size of the error.*

Since we cannot expect each $\bar{x}$ to equal the mean of the population from which the sample was obtained, it would seem only reasonable to give ourselves leeway by estimating $\mu$ to lie on some *interval*. Whereas we can be *practically certain* in our example that $\mu$, the true average time it takes a person to react to the stimulus, is *not exactly* 0.132 seconds, there are methods which enable us to assert with appropriate probabilities that it is covered by a certain interval, say, the interval from 0.125 seconds to 0.139 seconds. Estimating the mean of a population in this fashion is called *interval estimation;* the interval, itself, is called an *interval estimate*.

In Alternative 4 we gave an interval estimate for the average time it takes an adult to react to the given stimulus. What remains to be explained is how such an interval is obtained and what is meant by being "95 per cent sure" that the interval covers the true mean. *After all, the interval either does or does not contain the quantity we are trying to estimate.*

The foregoing discussion is not limited to the estimation of *means*. We can, similarly, use point estimates and interval estimates to estimate population *standard deviations*, *proportions*, and in general any *parameter* (description) of a population.

## 10.2 / The Estimation of Means (Large Samples) or if $\sigma$ is Known

Let us now show how we calculated the interval estimate going from 0.125 to 0.139 in Alternative 4 on page 213 and the maximum error of

0.007 accompanying the point estimate of 0.132 of Alternative 3. According to the first two theorems of Section 9.3 (see pages 202 and 205), we know that *if x is the mean of a random sample of size n, the theoretical sampling distribution of $\bar{x}$ has the mean $\mu$ and the standard deviation $\sigma_{\bar{x}} = \sigma/\sqrt{n}$, where $\mu$ and $\sigma$ are the mean and standard deviation of the population from which the sample was obtained; if n is large, the theoretical sampling distribution of $\bar{x}$ can, furthermore, be approximated closely with a normal curve.* )*

Let us suppose that the normal curve of Figure 10.1 represents a theoretical sampling distribution of $\bar{x}$ and that the indicated z is such that 95 per cent of the area under the curve lies between $-z$ and z. As can easily be verified in Table I, this z is 1.96. Since the theoretical sampling distribution of $\bar{x}$ provides the probabilities of getting $\bar{x}$'s which lie in a given interval, we can say with reference to the normal curve of Figure 10.1 that *if a sample mean is converted into standard*

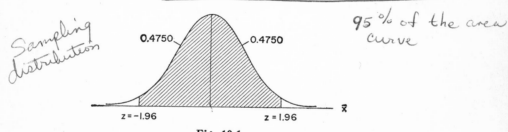

*Sampling distribution*     0.4750     0.4750     95 % of the area curve

z = -1.96          z = 1.96          $\bar{x}$

**Fig. 10.1**

*units, the probability that the corresponding z will lie between $-1.96$ and 1.96 is 0.95.*

As we saw on page 93, a measurement is converted into standard units by subtracting the mean of the distribution to which it belongs and then dividing by the standard deviation of this distribution. Since we are now talking about the sampling distribution of $\bar{x}$, whose mean and standard deviation are $\mu$ and $\sigma/\sqrt{n}$, the formula for z becomes

$$z = \frac{\bar{x} - \mu}{\sigma/\sqrt{n}} \qquad (10.2.1)$$

*As we pointed out on page 202, the formula $\sigma/\sqrt{n}$ applies only to samples taken from very large populations, so that the sample constitutes but a small fraction of the population. *The methods which we shall treat in this section apply, thus, only when n constitutes but a small portion of the population.* When n constitutes an appreciable portion of the population, say 5 per cent or more, these methods will have to be modified as indicated in Section 10.6.

In view of what we said above, we can now assert with a probability of 0.95 that if $\bar{x}$ is the mean of a random sample of size $n$ and $n$ *is large*, $z$ as calculated by means of (10.2.1) will lie between $-1.96$ and 1.96. In other words, *we can assert with a probability of 0.95 that the following inequality will hold*

$$-1.96 < \frac{\bar{x} - \mu}{\sigma/\sqrt{n}} < 1.96 \tag{10.2.2}$$

(In case the reader is not familiar with inequality signs, let us briefly explain that $a < b$ means "$a$ is less than $b$," while $a > b$ means "$a$ is greater than $b$." Also, $a \leq b$ means "$a$ is less than or equal to $b$," while $a \geq b$ means "$a$ is greater than or equal to $b$.")

Multiplying each term in (10.2.2) by $\sigma/\sqrt{n}$, it becomes

$$-1.96\frac{\sigma}{\sqrt{n}} < \bar{x} - \mu < 1.96\frac{\sigma}{\sqrt{n}} \tag{10.2.3}$$

and after subtracting $\bar{x}$ from each term and then multiplying by $-1$, we finally get

$$\bar{x} - 1.96\frac{\sigma}{\sqrt{n}} < \mu < \bar{x} + 1.96\frac{\sigma}{\sqrt{n}} \tag{10.2.4}$$

We can now claim with a probability of 0.95 that the interval from $\bar{x} - 1.96\dfrac{\sigma}{\sqrt{n}}$ to $\bar{x} + 1.96\dfrac{\sigma}{\sqrt{n}}$ contains $\mu$ and we shall refer to this interval as a *confidence interval*. We are 95 per cent confident, that is, we can assert with a probability of 0.95 that the interval contains the population mean $\mu$. The endpoints of a confidence interval, in this case $\bar{x} - 1.96\dfrac{\sigma}{\sqrt{n}}$ and $\bar{x} + 1.96\dfrac{\sigma}{\sqrt{n}}$, are referred to as the *lower and upper confidence limits* or, simply, as the *confidence limits*. Also, 0.95 (95 per cent) is called the *confidence coefficient.*

The confidence interval given by (10.2.4) has the unfortunate feature that it is of no use unless $\sigma$ is known. Since this is seldom the case in actual practice, it suggests itself that we replace $\sigma$ with an *estimate*, namely, with the sample standard deviation $s$. Since $s$ cannot be expected to provide a close estimate of $\sigma$ unless $n$ is large, we shall make the reservation that this substitution is permissible only for *large samples*. In this connection it is customary to refer to a sample as "large" when $n$ is 30 or more and as "small" when $n$ is less than 30.

Substituting $s$ for $\sigma$ in (10.2.4), we now have the following *large sample 95 per cent confidence interval for $\mu$.*

S may approx. σ when n > 30,

$$\bar{x} - 1.96\frac{s}{\sqrt{n}} < \mu < \bar{x} + 1.96\frac{s}{\sqrt{n}} \qquad (10.2.5)\blacktriangle$$

Returning now to the reaction-time example described on page 212, we find that $n = 40$, $\bar{x} = 0.132$, and as can easily be checked $s = 0.0232$. Substituting these values into (10.2.5), we get

$$0.132 - 1.96\frac{0.0232}{\sqrt{40}} < \mu < 0.132 + 1.96\frac{0.0232}{\sqrt{40}}$$

or
$$0.125 < \mu < 0.139$$

and we can assert with a probability of 0.95 that the interval from 0.125 to 0.139 seconds contains the true average time that it takes an adult person to react to the given stimulus. This is precisely the interval which we gave in Alternative 4 on page 213.

The fact that the confidence interval of (10.2.5) can be asserted with a probability of 0.95 should be interpreted as follows: *In a given problem, the quantity we want to estimate either does or does not lie in the interval which we calculate according to (10.2.5). However, if we calculate 95 per cent confidence intervals in many different problems, our intervals will in the long run "do their job" about 95 per cent of the time. In other words, we can expect 95 per cent of the confidence intervals we calculate with (10.2.5) to contain the population means they are supposed to estimate.*

If someone were to ask us whether we are *certain* that the interval from 0.125 to 0.139, which we calculated for our illustration, contains the true average reaction time to the given stimulus, our answer would, of course, have to be "NO." However, in view of the fact that we are using a method which, in the long run, works 95 per cent of the time, we should be willing to give pretty good odds that it does. As a matter of fact, *fair* odds would be 19 to 1 (95 to 5) that the interval does contain the true mean.

Throughout the preceding discussion we employed a confidence coefficient of 0.95. However, since there are situations in which we might be reluctant to use a method that works only 95 per cent of the time, (10.2.5) can be modified to apply also to other degrees of confidence.

The reader will recall that $z = 1.96$ was obtained by looking for a $z$ which is such that 95 per cent of the area under the normal curve lies between $-z$ and $z$ (see Figure 10.1). If we want to change the confidence coefficient to 0.98 (or 0.99), we have only to substitute for 1.96 a $z$-value which is such that 98 per cent (or 99 per cent) of the area under the normal curve lies between $-z$ and $z$. As can easily be verified with the use of Table I, 98 per cent of the area lies between $z = -2.33$ and $z = 2.33$, while 99 per cent of the area lies between $z = -2.58$ and $z = 2.58$. Substituting these values into (10.2.5) in place of 1.96, we can write the corresponding *large sample 98 per cent confidence interval for $\mu$* as

$$\bar{x} - 2.33\frac{s}{\sqrt{n}} < \mu < \bar{x} + 2.33\frac{s}{\sqrt{n}} \qquad (10.2.6)\blacktriangle$$

and the corresponding *large sample 99 per cent confidence interval for $\mu$* as

$$\bar{x} - 2.58\frac{s}{\sqrt{n}} < \mu < \bar{x} + 2.58\frac{s}{\sqrt{n}} \qquad (10.2.7)\blacktriangle$$

Had we wanted to calculate a 98 per cent confidence interval in the reaction-time example, substitution into (10.2.6) would have yielded

$$0.132 - 2.33\frac{0.0232}{\sqrt{40}} < \mu < 0.132 + 2.33\frac{0.0232}{\sqrt{40}}$$

or
$$0.122 < \mu < 0.141$$

We could, thus, have asserted with a probability of 0.98 that the interval from 0.122 to 0.141 seconds contains the true average time it takes an adult to react to the given stimulus. *This illustrates the very important fact that the surer we want to be, the less we have to be sure of. If we increase the degree of certainty, that is, the degree of confidence, the confidence interval becomes wider and tells us correspondingly less about the quantity we are trying to estimate.*

If $\bar{x}$ is used as a *point estimate* of $\mu$, the error we make is the difference between the estimate and the quantity it is supposed to estimate, namely, $\bar{x} - \mu$. Since this is the middle term of (10.2.3), we can write

$$-1.96\frac{\sigma}{\sqrt{n}} < \text{error} < 1.96\frac{\sigma}{\sqrt{n}} \qquad (10.2.8)$$

and this means that *we can assert with a probability of 0.95 that the error will be numerically less than* $1.96\frac{\sigma}{\sqrt{n}}$. ("Numerically less" means that we are referring to the magnitude of the error and not its sign.)

When $\sigma$ is not known and $n$ is 30 or more, we shall again substitute for $\sigma$ the sample standard deviation $s$. *We can then assert with a probability of 0.95 that $\bar{x}$, our estimate of $\mu$, is "off" by less than*

$s$ approx $\sigma$
when $n > 30$

$$\text{error} < 1.96\frac{s}{\sqrt{n}}$$

(10.2.9) ▲

Returning again to the reaction-time example, we find that for $n = 40$ and $s = 0.0232$ we get

$$1.96\frac{s}{\sqrt{n}} = 1.96\frac{0.0232}{\sqrt{40}} = 0.007$$

Using $\bar{x} = 0.132$ seconds as an estimate of the true average reaction time to the given stimulus, we can thus assert with a probability of 0.95 that our error is less than 0.007 seconds. *This is precisely what we said in Alternative 3 on page 213.* (Using the same argument as on page 218, we could change the probability with which we assert such statements about the error to 0.98 or 0.99 by substituting 2.33 or 2.58 for 1.96.)

The method we have just discussed can also be used to determine what sample size is needed to attain a desired degree of accuracy. To give an example, let us suppose that we want to estimate the current average annual income of secondary school teachers who received their **B.A.** degrees in 1950 and that we want to be able to assert with a probability of 0.95 that our estimate will be within $100 of the correct value. *The question is, how large a sample do we need to attain this degree of accuracy?*

According to what we said above, if $\bar{x}$ is used as a point estimate of $\mu$, we can assert with a probability of 0.95 that our error is less than $1.96\frac{\sigma}{\sqrt{n}}$. Since this quantity is supposed to equal $100, we can write

$$1.96\frac{\sigma}{\sqrt{n}} = 100$$

(10.2.10)

and we have an equation that can be solved for $n$. Unfortunately, (10.2.10) involves $\sigma$, which is usually unknown, and we shall thus have to make some assumption about $\sigma$ or, perhaps, substitute an estimate based on previous studies of a similar nature. Assuming that in our example (perhaps, on the basis of similar studies) $\sigma$ can be expected to be in the neighborhood of $1,000, equation (10.2.10) becomes

$$1.96\frac{1000}{\sqrt{n}} = 100$$

and solving for $n$ we get 384.2. *This means that a random sample of size 385 will suffice to give us the desired degree of accuracy.*

To formulate this method in a more general fashion, let us suppose that we want to use the mean of a random sample as an estimate of the mean of a population *and* that we want to be able to assert with a probability of 0.95 that our error will be less than some quantity $E$. Proceeding as in the numerical example, we can write

$$1.96\frac{\sigma}{\sqrt{n}} = E$$

and upon solving for $n$ this becomes

$$n = \left(\frac{1.96\sigma}{E}\right)^2 \qquad\qquad (10.2.11)\blacktriangle$$

If we want to be 98 or 99 per cent "sure" that our error is less than $E$, we have only to modify (10.2.11) by substituting 2.33 or 2.58 for 1.96. Had we wanted to be 99 per cent sure that the error is less than $100 in the above example dealing with the incomes of secondary school teachers, we would have had

$$n = \left[\frac{(2.58)(1000)}{100}\right]^2$$

and solving for $n$ we find that a sample of size 666 would have been required to attain this higher probability concerning the maximum error.

### EXERCISES

1. A study made by a staff officer of an armored division showed that in a random sample of 60 days the division had on the average 2114 vehicles in operating condition with a standard deviation of 225. Construct a 95 per cent confidence interval for the true daily average number of vehicles this armored division has in operating condition.

2. A random sample of 100 tractor-trailer trucks weighed at a check-point on U.S. 80 near Yuma, Arizona, had an average gross weight of 43,500 pounds with a standard deviation of 3500 pounds. Find a 95 per cent

confidence interval for the true average gross weight of tractor-trailer trucks passing this check-point.

**3.** The I.Q.'s of a random sample of 200 high school students living in a large city have a mean of 107 and a standard deviation of 12.4. Find a 95 per cent confidence interval for the true average I.Q. of all the high school students in the given city.

**4.** With reference to Exercise 3, what can we assert with a probability of 0.99 about the possible size of our error if we estimate this average I.Q. as 107?

**5.** If 50 measurements of the specific gravity of aluminum had a mean of 2.693 and a standard deviation of 0.038, construct a 98 per cent confidence interval for the true specific gravity of aluminum.

**6.** With reference to Exercise 5, what can we assert with a probability of 0.95 about the possible size of our error if we estimate the true specific gravity as 2.693?

**7.** A random sample of 50 delinquent charge accounts at a certain department store has a mean of $62.18 and a standard deviation of $24.57. Construct a 99 per cent confidence interval for the actual average size of all delinquent charge accounts at this store.

**8.** In an experiment conducted to determine the average lifetime of a certain kind of electronic tube, a random sample of 36 tubes lasted on the average 625 hours with a standard deviation of 53 hours. If we estimate the average lifetime of *all* the tubes from which this sample was obtained as 625 hours, with what probability can we assert that our error is less than 12 hours? (*Hint:* Find a $z$-value which is such that $z\dfrac{53}{\sqrt{36}} = 12$.)

**9.** With what probability can we assert in Exercise 2 that our estimate, namely, $\bar{x} = 43{,}500$ pounds, is within 1000 pounds of the actual average gross weight of tractor-trailers passing the given check-point?

**10.** If we wanted to determine the average clerical aptitude of a large group of people, how large a random sample would we need to be able to assert with a probability of 0.95 that our sample mean will be within 2 points of the true mean? Assume that it is known from previous studies that $\sigma = 14$.

**11.** What sample size would be needed in Exercise 10 if we wanted to be 99 per cent sure that our error will be less than 2?

12. An efficiency expert wants to determine the average time that it takes a housewife to iron a pair of pajamas. How large a sample will he need to be able to assert with a probability of 0.98 that his sample mean will differ from the true mean by less than $\frac{1}{5}$ of a minute? Assume that it is known from other studies that measurements of this kind can be expected to have a standard deviation of $\sigma = 2$ minutes.

## 10.3 / The Estimation of Means (Small Samples)

In the preceding section we stressed the fact that the methods we introduced apply only to *large* samples or else when $\sigma$ is known. To develop corresponding methods for *small* samples, when $n$ is less than 30, let us consider the sampling distribution of the statistic

$$t = \frac{\bar{x} - \mu}{s/\sqrt{n}} \tag{10.3.1}$$

where $\bar{x}$ and $s$ are the mean and standard deviation of a random sample of size $n$ from a population which has the mean $\mu$, the standard deviation $\sigma$, and *which can be* approximated closely with a normal curve.

If wanted to, we could calculate $\bar{x}$ and $s$ for each of the 50 samples on page 199 and (using the fact that $\mu = 68$) calculate the corresponding values of $t$. These 50 $t$'s could then be grouped into an *experimental sampling distribution of the statistic t* analogous to the ones we constructed for the 50 medians and means (see Figure 9.4). The problem of finding the corresponding *theoretical sampling distribution* was first investigated by W. S. Gosset who, in a paper published in 1908, derived its equation. Nowadays it is referred to as the *Student-t distribution* or, simply, the *t-distribution*. At the time, Gosset was employed by a well-known Irish brewery which did not permit the publication of research done by its staff. Gosset chose the pen name "Student," and hence the name "Student-t distribution."

The *t*-distribution, an illustration of which is shown in Figure 10.2, is a *symmetrical* distribution and, as in the case of the normal curve, it will suffice to tabulate its areas for positive values of $t$. Unfortunately, there is the complication that the equation of the *t*-distribution depends on a quantity called the "number of degrees of freedom." With reference to the application to be discussed in this section, this is *the sample size minus one*, that is, the quantity $n - 1$ to which we already referred as the number of degrees of freedom on page 97.

Since the formula for the $t$-distribution and, hence, the areas under the curve, depend on the number of degrees of freedom, it would be impractical to tabulate areas under this theoretical dis-

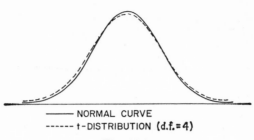

*depends on # df.*

NORMAL CURVE
------ t-DISTRIBUTION **(d.f.=4)**

Fig. 10.2

tribution as we tabulated areas under the normal curve. Instead of giving a complete table for each value of $n - 1$, we shall list only the values of $t$ above which we find 10, 5, $2\frac{1}{2}$, 1, and $\frac{1}{2}$ per cent of the area under the curve. Symbolically, we shall write $t_{.025}$ for the value of $t$ to the right of which we find 2.5 per cent of the area under the curve (see Figure 10.3), $t_{.01}$ for the value of $t$ to the right of which we find 1 per cent of the area under the curve, and so forth. Table II on page 385 contains the values of $t_{.10}$, $t_{.05}$, $t_{.025}$, $t_{.01}$, and $t_{.005}$ for $d.f.$, the number of degrees of freedom, from 1 to 29.

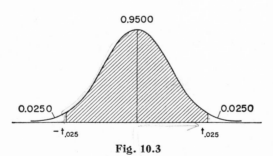

Fig. 10.3

If we now duplicate the argument presented on pages 215 and 216, using the $t$-distribution and Figure 10.3 instead of the normal curve of Figure 10.1, and

$$t = \frac{\bar{x} - \mu}{s/\sqrt{n}} \quad \text{instead of} \quad z = \frac{\bar{x} - \mu}{\sigma/\sqrt{n}}$$

we arrive at a 95 per cent confidence interval which differs from (10.2.4) only insofar as $\sigma$ is replaced with $s$ and the normal curve value of 1.96 is replaced with $t_{.025}$. [Since $\sigma$ is already replaced with $s$, there is no need now to make the approximation which led from (10.2.4) to (10.2.5).] Without actually going through all these steps, let us write the resulting confidence interval as

$$\bar{x} - t_{.025}\frac{s}{\sqrt{n}} < \mu < \bar{x} + t_{.025}\frac{s}{\sqrt{n}} \qquad (10.3.2)\blacktriangle$$

*We now have a 95 per cent confidence interval for $\mu$ which can be used when n is less than 30, that is, for small samples. The appropriate value of $t_{.025}$ is to be looked up in Table II with the number of degrees of freedom equal to n − 1.* If we want to change the degree of confidence to 0.98 or 0.99, we have only to substitute $t_{.01}$ or $t_{.005}$ for $t_{.025}$.

To illustrate the use of (10.3.2), let us return to the study mentioned on page 61, the one dealing with the problem of estimating the true average length of full-grown scorpions of the newly discovered variety. Taking the results of Biologist A, who obtained lengths of 1.43, 2.06, and 2.21 inches (on page 61 these figures were rounded to one decimal) it can easily be shown that for these three numbers $\bar{x} = 1.90$ and $s = 0.41$. Since $n = 3$, the number of degrees of freedom is $3 - 1 = 2$, and according to Table II the appropriate value of $t_{.025}$ is 4.303. Substituting all these values into (10.3.2) gives

$$1.90 - 4.303\frac{0.41}{\sqrt{3}} < \mu < 1.90 + 4.303\frac{0.41}{\sqrt{3}}$$

or

$$0.88 < \mu < 2.92$$

and we can thus assert with a probability of 0.95 that the interval from 0.88 inches to 2.92 inches contains the true average length of full-grown members of the given variety of scorpions. (We are tacitly assuming that Biologist A's measurements constitute a random sample and that the population consisting of the lengths of all scorpions of the given kind can be approximated closely with a normal curve.)

*The above example illustrates the important fact that although we can make logically valid inferences on the basis of very small samples, our results are apt to be very vague that is, the confidence intervals are apt to be very wide; perhaps too wide to be of much practical use.*

The method which we employed on page 219 to indicate the possible size of our error can easily be adapted to small samples. The only change needed is to replace 1.96, 2.33, and 2.58, respectively, by $t_{.025}$, $t_{.01}$, and $t_{.005}$. To give an example, let us consider the following measurements of compressive strength, constituting a random sample of the strength of the steel produced by a certain mill (figures in pounds per square inch)

$$43,500 \quad 46,750 \quad 71,900 \quad 72,500 \quad 82,850$$

The mean and standard deviation of this sample are $\bar{x} = 63,500$ and $s = 17,350$, and since for $5 - 1 = 4$ degrees of freedom $t_{.025} = 2.776$, we find that

$$t_{.025}\frac{s}{\sqrt{n}} = 2.776\frac{17,350}{\sqrt{5}} = 21,540$$

If we estimate the average compressive strength of *all* the steel from which this sample was obtained as being $\bar{x} = 63,500$, we can assert with a probability of 0.95 that our error is less than 21,540 pounds per square inch.

### EXERCISES

1. A chemist who took 16 measurements of the percentage of manganese in ferromanganese, an alloy of manganese and iron, obtained a mean of 81.15 per cent and a standard deviation of 0.40 per cent. Construct a 95 per cent confidence interval for the true average per cent of manganese in the alloy from which the sample was obtained.

2. Using the data of Exercise 1, construct a 98 per cent confidence interval for the average per cent of manganese in the alloy from which the sample was obtained.

3. A random sample of 25 delegates spent an average of $238.50 (with a standard deviation of $17.58) while attending a national political convention. Assuming that the method of this section can be used, construct a 98 per cent confidence interval for the actual average amount spent by delegates attending this convention.

4. Using the data of Exercise 3, construct a 99 per cent confidence interval for the average amount of money spent by delegates attending the given convention.

5. What can we assert with a probability of 0.95 about the possible size of our error if in Exercise 3 we estimate the average amount spent by a delegate attending the convention as $238.50?

6. Experimenting with a new cake mix, home economists found that cakes prepared with a sample of 5 packages of this mix had heights of 1.8, 2.3, 2.4, 1.7, and 1.9 inches. Find $\bar{x}$ and $s$ for this sample and then construct a 95 per cent confidence interval for the true average height of *all* cakes baked with this mix.

7. What can we assert with a probability of 0.98 about the possible size of our error if we use the mean of the sample of Exercise 6 as a point estimate of the height of *all* cakes baked with the mix?

8. Use the first of the 50 samples on page 199 to construct a 99 per cent confidence interval for the true average height of the male residents of the given community.

## 10.4 / The Estimation of Proportions  *optional*

Many applications of statistics deal with the estimation of percentages, proportions, and probabilities. To mention a few examples, a market research organization may wish to estimate what *percentage* of American housewives prefer Soap A to Soap B, an air line executive may wish to know what *proportion* of vacationists traveling between New York City and Florida go by air, and an investor may wish to estimate the *probability* that a certain business venture will succeed. In principle, these problems are all the same since a percentage is merely a proportion multiplied by 100 and a probability is a proportion "in the long run."

The information that is usually available for the estimation of a proportion is the *relative frequency* with which an appropriate event has occurred. If an event occurs $x$ *times out of* $n$, the relative frequency of its occurrence is $x/n$ and we generally use this *sample proportion* as an estimate of $p$, the true proportion with which we are concerned. For example, if in a random sample of 500 housewives, 310 prefer Soap A while 190 prefer Soap B, then $x/n = 310/500 = 0.62$ and we might claim that 62 per cent of *all* housewives prefer Soap A to Soap B.

Strictly speaking, the binomial distribution of Section 8.2 provides the probabilities of events occurring $x$ times out of $n$ *only when the probability of a success remains the same from trial to trial and the trials are independent.* (See discussion on page 159.) In actual practice, however, the binomial distribution is often used when these conditions are met only in an approximate sense. Let us consider, for example, the problem dealing with housewives' preferences for two kinds of soap and let us suppose that the population from which we are sampling consists of 50,000 housewives, with 30,000 preferring Soap A and 20,000 preferring Soap B.   Then, the probability that the first randomly selected housewife perfers Soap A is 30,000/50,000 = 0.60, but the probability that the second housewife included in the sample prefers Soap A *depends on the preference of the housewife selected first.*   If the first housewife preferred Soap A the probability that the second housewive will prefer Soap A is 29,999/49,999 = 0.599992, and if the first housewife preferred Soap B the probability that the second will prefer Soap A is 30,000/49,999 = 0.600012.   Clearly, these two probabilities are so close to 0.60 that we can, for all practical purposes, assume that they are equal and that there is *no dependence.*   In the remainder of this section we shall thus assume that the populations from which we are sampling are so large that we can calculate (approximate) probabilities of getting $x$ successes in $n$ trials with the binomial distribution.   If the population from which we are sampling is small and (or) the sample constitutes more than 5 per cent of the population, it will be necessary to make the modification suggested in Section 10.6.

Using the normal curve approximation of the binomial distribution and duplicating the argument presented on page 216, we can say that if $x$, the number of successes observed in $n$ trials, is converted into *standard units*, the probability of its $z$-value lying between $-1.96$ and $1.96$ is $0.95$.   Since this $z$-value is obtained by subtracting from $x$ the mean of its probability distribution, as given by (8.3.3), and then dividing by the standard deviation, formula (8.3.5), we get

$$z = \frac{x - np}{\sqrt{np(1 - p)}}$$

*and we can assert with a probability of 0.95 that the following inequality holds*

$$-1.96 < \frac{x - np}{\sqrt{np(1 - p)}} < 1.96$$

Multiplying all terms by $\sqrt{np(1 - p)}$ and then dividing by $n$, this can be written as

$$-1.96\sqrt{\frac{p(1 - p)}{n}} < \frac{x}{n} - p < 1.96\sqrt{\frac{p(1 - p)}{n}} \qquad (10.4.1)$$

or as
$$\frac{x}{n} - 1.96\sqrt{\frac{p(1 - p)}{n}} < p < \frac{x}{n} + 1.96\sqrt{\frac{p(1 - p)}{n}} \qquad (10.4.2)$$

If we manipulated inequalities (10.4.1) or (10.4.2) so that the middle term is $p$ and the other two terms consist of expressions that can be calculated *without* knowledge of $p$, we would obtain *a 95 per cent confidence interval for p.* Since this would involve a considerable amount of algebra and, subsequently, rather messy calculations, we shall leave this work to others and use instead tables constructed for this special purpose. Table V on page 389 provides 95 per cent confidence limits for $p$, *the probability or proportion we want to estimate*, for random samples of size 10, 15, 20, 30, 50, 100, 250, and 1000. For other values of $n$ we will literally have to read between the lines. (Similar tables for 98 and 99 per cent confidence intervals are referred to in the Bibliography on page 238.)

To illustrate the use of Table V, let us suppose that in a random sample of 250 cigarette smokers there were 60 who preferred Brand X while 190 preferred some other brand. Our problem is to estimate the true proportion of smokers preferring Brand X. The sample proportion of smokers preferring Brand X being $60/250 = 0.24$, we begin by marking this value on the *horizontal scale* (the $x/n$ scale)

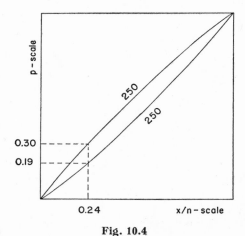

**Fig. 10.4**

of Table V (see Figure 10.4). Since $n = 250$, we then go up *vertically* from this point until we reach the two curves labeled 250. The values on the *vertical scale* that correspond to the points at which we cut these two curves, finally, give the desired confidence limits for $p$. In our example these values are approximately 0.19 and 0.30 and *we can now assert with a probability of 0.95 that the interval from 19 to 30 per cent contains the true percentage of smokers preferring Brand X to all other brands of cigarettes.*

In Section 9.3 we referred to the standard deviation of the sampling distribution of $\bar{x}$ as the *standard error of the mean* and wrote it as $\sigma_{\bar{x}}$. Using the same terminology and symbolism, let us now refer to the standard deviation of the sampling distribution of $x/n$ as the *standard error of a proportion* and write it as $\sigma_{x/n}$. The formula for this standard error is easy to obtain. The sampling distribution of $x$, the *number of successes* in $n$ trials, can be converted into the sampling distribution of $x/n$, the *proportion of successes* in $n$ trials, by leaving the distribution as is and performing the change of scale indicated in Figure 10.5. Since this change of scale merely involves division

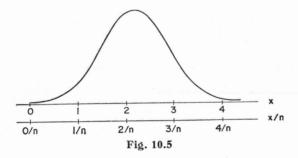

Fig. 10.5

by $n$, the standard deviation for $x/n$ is obtained by dividing the standard deviation for $x$, namely, $\sqrt{np(1-p)}$, by $n$. We thus find that the formula for the *standard error of a proportion* becomes

$$\sigma_{x/n} = \sqrt{\frac{p(1-p)}{n}} \qquad (10.4.3)\,\blacktriangle$$

In order to avoid confusion, let us reiterate that $\sqrt{\dfrac{p(1-p)}{n}}$

measures how much the *proportion* of successes varies from sample to sample, and $\sqrt{np(1-p)}$ measures how much the *number* of successes varies from sample to sample.

In Section 10.2 we approximated the standard error of the mean by writing $s/\sqrt{n}$ instead of $\sigma/\sqrt{n}$ and we were thus able to construct (large sample) 95 per cent confidence intervals for $\mu$. Similarly, approximating $\sigma_{x/n}$ by substituting $x/n$ for $p$ in (10.4.2), we find that

$$\frac{x}{n} - 1.96\sqrt{\frac{\frac{x}{n}\left(1 - \frac{x}{n}\right)}{n}} < p < \frac{x}{n} + 1.96\sqrt{\frac{\frac{x}{n}\left(1 - \frac{x}{n}\right)}{n}} \qquad (10.4.4)\,\blacktriangle$$

is an *approximate 95 per cent confidence interval for p.* To change the degree of confidence to 0.98 or 0.99, we have only to substitute 2.33 or 2.58 for 1.96.

Had we used (10.4.4) in the illustration given above, we would have obtained the following confidence interval for the true proportion of smokers preferring Brand X to all other brands of cigarettes

$$0.24 - 1.96\sqrt{\frac{(0.24)(0.76)}{250}} < p < 0.24 + 1.96\sqrt{\frac{(0.24)(0.76)}{250}}$$

or
$$0.187 < p < 0.293$$

It is interesting to note that this is very close to the values of 0.19 and 0.30 obtained previously with the use of Table V.

Duplicating the arguments of Section 9.2, the theory presented here can also be used to say something about the *error* we might make when using $x/n$ as a point estimate of $p$ *and* to determine the sample size needed to assure a required degree of accuracy when using $x/n$ as an estimate of $p$.

If $x/n$ is used as an estimate of $p$, the *error* is their difference, namely, $\frac{x}{n} - p$, and (10.4.1) may be rewritten

$$-1.96\sigma_{x/n} < \text{error} < 1.96\sigma_{x/n}$$

Substituting $x/n$ for $p$ in the formula for $\sigma_{x/n}$, we can thus say that *if $x/n$ is used as an estimate of $p$, we can assert with a probability of 0.95 that our error is numerically less than*

$$\text{error} < 1.96\sqrt{\frac{\frac{x}{n}\left(1 - \frac{x}{n}\right)}{n}} \tag{10.4.5} \blacktriangle$$

In view of the approximations involved in (10.4.4) and (10.4.5), it is preferable that these formulas *not* be used unless $n$ is, say, 100 or more.

To illustrate the use of (10.4.5), let us suppose that a random sample of 600 eligible voters included 330 votes for Candidate X and 270 for Candidate Y. If on the basis of this sample we claim that Candidate X will receive $330/600 = 0.55$ (or 55 per cent) of the vote, we should add that we can only be 95 per cent sure that the error of this estimate is within

$$1.96\sqrt{\frac{(0.55)(0.45)}{600}} = 0.04 \quad \text{(or 4 per cent)}$$

Without substituting $x/n$ for $p$, (10.4.1) enables us to assert with a probability of 0.95 that if $x/n$ is used as an estimate of $p$, the error is less than $1.96\sqrt{\dfrac{p(1-p)}{n}}$. Consequently, if we want to be 95 per cent sure that the error is less than some quantity $E$, we can write

$$1.96\sqrt{\frac{p(1-p)}{n}} = E$$

and, solving for $n$, this becomes

$$n = p(1-p)\left(\frac{1.96}{E}\right)^2 \qquad (10.4.6)\blacktriangle$$

Unfortunately, this formula can seldom be used as it stands; it requires knowledge of $p$ which, after all, is the quantity we are trying to estimate. However, $p$ must lie on the interval from 0 to 1 and it can be shown by completing the square or with the use of calculus that $p(1-p)$ is *at most* equal to $\frac{1}{4}$. It follows that the sample size required to give the desired degree of accuracy is *at most*

$$\frac{1}{4}\left(\frac{1.96}{E}\right)^2 \qquad \textit{is a proportion} (10.4.7)\blacktriangle$$

It is important to remember that here and in (10.4.6) the maximum error $E$ must be written as a *proportion* and not as a percentage.

To illustrate the use of (10.4.7), let us suppose that we want to estimate the proportion of teenagers (in a certain city) who go to the movies at least once a week and that we want to be 95 per cent sure that our estimate, the sample proportion, will not be off by more than 0.02. Substituting $E = 0.02$ into (10.4.7), we obtain

$$\frac{1}{4}\left(\frac{1.96}{0.02}\right)^2 = 2401$$

and if we base our estimate on a random sample of size 2401 we can be *at least* 95 per cent sure that the sample proportion we will get does not differ from the true proportion by more than 0.02. We are "at least" 95 per cent sure because the sample size of 2401 may be larger than required to assure the desired degree of accuracy.

We used (10.4.7) in this example, assuming that we had no knowledge about the possible value of $p$. Had we known from past experience (or other sources of information) that the proportion we want to estimate is in the neighborhood of 0.80, we could have substituted this value into (10.4.6), getting

$$n = (0.80)(0.20)\left(\frac{1.96}{0.02}\right)^2 = 1537$$

This illustrates the fact that information about the possible value of $p$ can reduce the required size of the sample.

## EXERCISES

1. A random sample of 100 peaches (taken from a very large shipment) contains 14 with imperfections. Use Table V to construct a 95 per cent confidence interval for the actual proportion of imperfect peaches in this shipment.

2. In a random sample of 250 students attending a large university, 90 stated that they own cars while 160 stated that they did not. Use Table V to construct a 95 per cent confidence interval for the actual proportion of students at this university who own cars.

3. If a medical study shows that 6 of 30 people died from a certain fever, use Table V to construct a 95 per cent confidence interval for the mortality rate of this fever. (Assume that the 30 cases may be looked upon as a random sample.)

4. In a random sample of 1000 families owning television sets in Los Angeles, California, 350 were tuned to Network A during the broadcast of a certain show.
   (a) Use Table V to construct a 95 per cent confidence interval for the actual percentage of families with television sets in this area who at the given time were tuned to Network A.
   (b) Use (10.4.4) to calculate a 95 per cent confidence interval for the desired percentage and compare your result with that obtained in (a).

5. In a random sample of 400 eligible voters, 240 were for a new issue of school bonds while 160 were against it.
   (a) Use Table V to construct a 95 per cent confidence interval for the actual proportion of voters who are for the new issue of bonds.
   (b) If we use the sample proportion of $240/400 = 0.60$ to estimate the actual proportion of voters who are for the new issue of bonds, what can we assert with a probability of 0.95 about the possible error of this estimate?

6. Use (10.4.4) and the sample of Exercise 5 to construct a 98 per cent confidence interval for the actual proportion of voters who are for the new issue of bonds.

7. In a random sample of 4000 consumers, 1800 expressed a preference for Product X while 2200 expressed a preference for Product Y.
   (a) Use (10.4.4) to construct a 95 per cent confidence interval for the actual proportion of consumers preferring Product X to Product Y.
   (b) If we used 0.45 as an estimate of the desired proportion, what could we assert with a probability of 0.99 about the possible size of our error?

8. Using (10.4.4) and the sample of Exercise 7, construct a 98 per cent confidence interval for the actual proportion of consumers preferring Product X over Product Y.

9. In a random sample of 10 doctors practicing in a certain city, 3 stated that they smoke pipes while 7 stated that they did not. Use Table V to construct a 95 per cent confidence interval for the true proportion of doctors practicing in this city who smoke pipes. *Note that the sample proportion of 0.30 does not lie in the middle of the confidence interval. This is explained by the fact that the binomial distribution is not necessarily symmetrical.*

10. What is the smallest random sample a public opinion poll will have to take in order to be able to assert with a probability of 0.95 that their estimate of the proportion of votes Candidate Jones will receive is "off" by less than 0.02?

11. What would be the required sample size in Exercise 10, if the probability were raised from 0.95 to 0.99?

12. Suppose we want to estimate what proportion of a very large shipment of ball bearings is defective. What is the smallest sample size needed so that we can assert with a probability of 0.95 that the sample proportion we get will not be "off" by more than 0.04?

13. What sample size would suffice in Exercise 12 if we knew from past experience that the proportion we are trying to estimate is in the neighborhood of 0.06?

14. Suppose we want to estimate what percentage of secretaries stay in their first job for more than one year. How large a random sample will we need to be able to assert with a probability of 0.98 that the error of our estimate will be "off" by less than 0.05? To what figure would this sample size be reduced if we knew that the proportion we want to estimate is in the neighborhood of 0.25?

## 10.5 / Standard Errors and Probable Errors *optional*

So far we have studied only the construction of confidence intervals for means and proportions and the evaluation of the accuracy of point estimates of these parameters. However, methods that are quite similar can be used to estimate other population parameters, that is, other descriptions of populations. By studying the sampling distributions of appropriate statistics, statisticians have developed formulas giving confidence intervals for population standard deviations, medians, quartiles, coefficients of variation, and the like. In principle, the concepts and methods are always the same, and the main problem is that some of these theoretical sampling distributions are of a rather complicated kind. Fortunately, this difficulty is resolved by the fact that *for large samples many of the theoretical sampling distributions needed in actual practice can be approximated closely with normal curves*.

The last statement implies that if $S$ is some statistic calculated on the basis of a *large* random sample, we can often write a 95 per cent confidence interval for the population parameter which $S$ is supposed to estimate as

$$S - 1.96\sigma_S < \text{population parameter} < S + 1.96\sigma_S \quad (10.5.1) \blacktriangle$$

Here $\sigma_S$ is the standard deviation of the sampling distribution of $S$ or, in other words, the *standard error of* $S$. If $S$ happened to be a sample mean, $\sigma_S$ would be $\sigma_{\bar{x}}$ and (10.5.1) would reduce to (10.2.4); if $S$ happened to be a sample proportion, $\sigma_S$ would be $\sigma_{x/n}$ and (10.5.1) would reduce to (10.4.2). Formulas for the standard errors of various other statistics are referred to in the Bibliography on page 238.

When we first studied *standard deviations* in Chapter 4, we indicated how important it can be to have some knowledge, that is, some estimate, of the size of the standard deviation of a population. Since for *large samples* the *standard error of s* may be written (approximated)

*standard error for large samples*

$$\sigma_s = \frac{\sigma}{\sqrt{2n}} \quad (10.5.2) \blacktriangle$$

where $s$ is as always the sample standard deviation, substitution into (10.5.1) and subsequent simplifications give the following *large sample 95 per cent confidence interval for σ*

$$\frac{s}{1 + 1.96/\sqrt{2n}} < \sigma < \frac{s}{1 - 1.96/\sqrt{2n}} \quad (10.5.3) \blacktriangle$$

Corresponding 98 and 99 per cent confidence intervals may be obtained by substituting 2.33 or 2.58, respectively, for 1.96. It is important to remember that this confidence interval for $\sigma$ is to be used only for *large* samples. An appropriate technique for *small* samples, when $n$ is less than 30, is explained in Exercise 3 on page 236.

Referring again to the reaction-time example of Section 10.1, let us substitute $n = 40$ and $s = 0.0232$ into (10.5.3). Getting

$$\frac{0.0232}{1 + 1.96/\sqrt{80}} < \sigma < \frac{0.0232}{1 - 1.96/\sqrt{80}}$$

or
$$0.0190 < \sigma < 0.0297$$

we can, thus, assert with a probability of 0.95 that the interval from 0.0190 seconds to 0.0297 seconds contains $\sigma$, the true standard deviation of the reaction times of adults to the given stimulus.

In the methods presented in this chapter we (more or less arbitrarily) chose 0.95, 0.98, and 0.99 as our confidence coefficients and as the probabilities in terms of which we appraised the possible size of our error. Had we wanted to use a probability of 0.50, we would only have had to substitute 0.6745 in our formulas for 1.96, at least, whenever we used normal distributions. (It can easily be checked in a table of normal curve areas more detailed than Table I that 50 per cent of the area under the normal curve lies between $z = -0.6745$ and $z = 0.6745$. (Our table shows only that this $z$ must lie between 0.67 and 0.68.)

If we had used 0.6745 instead of 1.96 in (10.2.8) and (10.4.5) to evaluate the possible size of our errors, we would have had a *fifty-fifty chance* of making errors less than the quantities given by these formulas. If there is a fifty-fifty chance that the error of an estimate is less than some quantity, it is customary to refer to this quantity as the *probable error* of the estimate. When estimating a population mean with a sample mean $\bar{x}$, we can assert with a probability of 0.50 that our error is less than

$$0.6745\frac{\sigma}{\sqrt{n}}$$

and this quantity is referred to as the *probable error of the mean*. Similarly, the *probable error of a proportion* is

$$0.6745\sqrt{\frac{p(1 - p)}{n}}$$

the *probable error of a sample standard deviation s* is (for large samples)

$$0.6745\frac{\sigma}{\sqrt{2n}}$$

and, in general, probable errors are obtained by multiplying the corresponding standard errors by 0.6745. Nowadays, probable errors are used mainly in military applications, where they are employed in connection with problems of gunnery and bombardment.

## EXERCISES

**1.** Use the data of Exercise 3 on page 221 to construct a 95 per cent confidence interval for $\sigma$, the standard deviation of the I.Q.'s of all the high school students in the given city.

**2.** Use the sample of Exercise 2 on page 220 to construct a 95 per cent confidence interval for $\sigma$, the standard deviation of the gross weights of all tractor-trailer trucks passing the given check-point.

**3.** As we pointed out in the text, (10.5.3) cannot be used to construct 95 per cent confidence intervals for $\sigma$ for *small* samples. Instead we refer to a theoretical distribution called the $\chi^2$ distribution (chi-square distribution), which will be discussed in more detail in Section 12.1. Thus, a 98 per cent confidence interval for $\sigma$ may be written as

$$\sqrt{\frac{(n-1)s^2}{\chi^2_{.01}}} < \sigma < \sqrt{\frac{(n-1)s^2}{\chi^2_{.99}}} \qquad (10.5.4)▲$$

provided that the sample comes from a population which can be closely approximated with a normal curve. Here $s^2$ is the sample variance calculated according to (4.4.3), $n$ is the sample size, and $\chi^2_{.01}$ and $\chi^2_{.99}$ are quantities which must be looked up in Table III on page 386. The *number of degrees of freedom* (see page 97) is $n-1$. (Had we wanted to use a confidence coefficient of 0.95, we would have had to write $\chi^2_{.250}$ and $\chi^2_{.975}$ instead of $\chi^2_{.01}$ and $\chi^2_{.99}$. These values are not given in Table III, but they may be found in more extensive tables of the $\chi^2$ distribution.)

Use (10.5.4) and the data of the example on page 224 (where $n$ was 3 and $s$ equalled 0.41) to construct a 98 per cent confidence interval for $\sigma$, the standard deviation of the lengths of *all* full-grown members of the given variety of scorpions.

**4.** Use the method outlined in Exercise 3 and the data of Exercise 6 on page 226 to construct a 98 per cent confidence interval for $\sigma$, the standard deviation of the heights of all cakes baked with the new mix.

## 10.6 / Sampling from Small Populations

The methods which we discussed in this chapter were based on several assumptions. Foremost, we always assumed that our samples were *random* and that we sampled from *very large populations*. To illustrate why the latter assumption is necessary, let us suppose that we want to determine what proportion of the doctors living in a certain community smoke cigars. Let us suppose, furthermore, that there are 10 doctors in this community and that among the 9 that could be reached, 3 smoke cigars and 6 do not. If we used the "standard technique" of Section 10.4, we would find that for $n = 9$ and $x/n = \frac{3}{9}$ Table V yields 95 per cent confidence limits of 0.07 and 0.69. Aside from the fact that the sample was not really random, it is easy to see that what we have done here does not make much sense. *If the 10th doctor smokes cigars,* $p = \frac{4}{10} = 0.40$, *and if he does not,* $p = \frac{3}{10} = 0.30$. Since $p$ must equal 0.30 or 0.40, it would seem rather silly to say that we are 95 per cent "sure" that $p$ lies between 0.07 and 0.69. As a matter of fact, we can be 100 per cent sure that this is the case.

Whenever a sample constitutes an appreciable portion of a population, 5 per cent or more, this fact may be accounted for by making a suitable modification in the formula for the standard error of the statistic with which we are concerned. When dealing with means and proportions, this modification consists of multiplying the expression for the standard error by

$$\sqrt{\frac{N - n}{N - 1}}$$

where $N$ is the size of the population and $n$, as always, the size of the sample. Thus, the formula for $\sigma_{\bar{x}}$, the *standard error of the mean*, becomes

$$\frac{\sigma}{\sqrt{n}}\sqrt{\frac{N - n}{N - 1}} \text{ or } \frac{S}{\sqrt{n}}\sqrt{\frac{N - n}{N - 1}} \qquad (10.6.1)▲$$

and the formula for $\sigma_{x/n}$, the *standard error of a proportion*, becomes

$$\sqrt{\frac{p(1 - p)}{n}}\sqrt{\frac{N - n}{N - 1}} \qquad (10.6.2)▲$$

To demonstrate that this refinement need not be used when $n$ is small compared to $N$, let us evaluate the adjustment factor for

$n = 100$ and $N = 10,000$, when the sample constitutes 1 per cent of the population. Clearly

$$\sqrt{\frac{N-n}{N-1}} = \sqrt{\frac{10,000-100}{10,000-1}} = 0.995$$

is so close to 1 that it might just as well be put equal to 1. Generally speaking, it is recommended that the adjustment factor be used when the sample constitutes 5 per cent or more of a population.

## BIBLIOGRAPHY

An informal treatment of interval estimation is given under the heading of "How to be precise though vague," in

> Moroney, M. J., *Facts from Figures*. London: Penguin Books, 1951, Chap. 14.

Formulas for the *standard errors* of various statistics, for instance, medians, quartiles, coefficients of variation, etc., may be found in

> Waugh, A. E., *Elements of Statistical Method*, 3rd ed. New York: McGraw-Hill, 1952, Chap. 9.

Tables for 98 and 99 per cent confidence intervals for $p$ (analogous to Table V) are given in

> Clopper, C. J., and Pearson, E. S., "The Use of Confidence or Fiducial Limits Illustrated in the Case of the Binomial." *Biometrika*, Vol. 26, 1934, p. 404.

*Chapter* **11**

# Tests of Hypotheses

## 11.1 / Introduction

The most widely used term in modern statistics is the word "decision;" it is used so much because *statistical theory and statistical methods play an ever increasing role in the construction and analysis of criteria on which decisions are based.* If we must decide whether to accept a shipment of steel or reject it, whether to invest in government bonds or real estate, whether to recommend one variety of corn or another, whether to give a student a D or an F, whether to buy a new car or have the old one repaired, we always face the possibility that the alternative which we choose turns out to be the least profitable one. No matter how we decide problems arising in science, in business, and in everyday life, we must always face the risk of making a wrong choice and suffer whatever consequences are involved. *A major task of modern statistics is to evaluate such risks and to provide criteria which minimize the chances of making wrong decisions, which minimize "penalties" or maximize "rewards."*

To give an example which is typical inasmuch as it illustrates the most important concepts underlying statistical decision criteria, let us suppose that a manufacturer of a new suntan lotion claims that his product is 75 per cent effective, namely, that 75 per cent of all people who use his product while spending a good deal of time out in the sun will not get sunburnt. To investigate this claim, a consumer testing service assigns one of its investigators to try the new lotion on a random sample of 100 persons, observe its effect, and then decide on the basis of this experiment whether to accept or reject the manufacturer's claim.

The investigator, having to draw the line somewhere, proposes that the following criterion be used:

*Accept the manufacturer's claim if 70 or more of the 100 persons in the sample get adequate protection from the sun; reject it if 69 or fewer get adequate protection.*

This provides a clear-cut criterion for deciding whether to accept or reject the manufacturer's claim but, unfortunately, it is not infallible. Could it not happen, purely by chance, that fewer than 70 of the persons in the sample get adequate protection *in spite of the fact that the lotion is as good as claimed?* If this happened the consumer testing service would make the mistake of discrediting a product which actually is as good as claimed. This may lead to legal action, the investigator may lose his job, and there may be all sorts of other consequences. In view of all this, it would seem wise for the investigator to calculate the *probability* that his criterion will, thus, lead him to a wrong decision.

In the language of probability, he will have to determine the probability of getting "69 or fewer successes in 100 trials" if the probability of an individual success is 0.75. Using the normal curve approximation to the binomial distribution (see Section 8.7), this probability may be found by determining the shaded area of Figure 11.1, namely, the area under this normal curve to the left of 69.5.

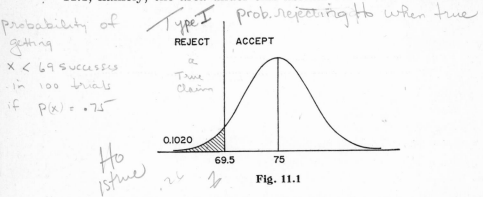

Fig. 11.1

Since the formulas for the mean and standard deviation of the binomial distribution are

$$\mu = np \quad \text{and} \quad \sigma = \sqrt{np(1 - p)}$$

see pages 161 and 162, substituting $n = 100$ and $p = 0.75$ yields

$$\mu = 100(0.75) = 75$$

and

$$\sigma = \sqrt{100(0.75)(0.25)} = 4.33$$

The $z$-value of the dividing line of the criterion (see Figure 11.1), is thus

$$z = \frac{69.5 - 75}{4.33} = -1.27$$

and the corresponding entry in Table I is 0.3980. *Hence, the probability that the criterion will erroneously lead to the rejection of the manufacturer's claim is* **0.5000** *− 0.3980 = 0.1020 or, roughly, 0.10.*

Offhand, this probability seems rather large, but whether or not it is an acceptable risk is a matter of "executive" decision, not of statistics. It would have to depend on whatever consequences there are to discrediting a good product. So far as statistics is concerned, we can easily change the criterion so that the above probability becomes as small as we want. All we have to do is to move the dividing line of Figure 11.1 to the left so that the manufacturer's claim is accepted if, say, *68 or more* (or *65 or more*) of the 100 persons in the sample receive adequate protection. It will be left to the reader (Exercises 1 and 2 on page 243) to calculate the probabilities with which these modified criteria will erroneously reject the manufacturer's claim.

Before moving the dividing line of Figure 11.1 to the left, there is really another question that should first be asked. It concerns the possibility of *accepting the manufacturer's claim when actually it is false.* Supposing, for example, that the suntan lotion is effective only 60 per cent of the time, *what is the probability that the investigator's criterion will nevertheless lead to the acceptance of the manufacturer's*

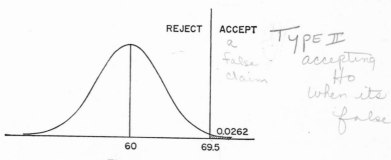

**Fig. 11.2**

*claim?* The probability of this happening is the probability of getting "70 or more successes in 100 trials" when the probability of an individual success is 0.60. Using again the normal curve approximation to the binomial distribution, this probability is given by the shaded area of Figure 11.2, namely, by the area under the curve to the right of 69.5. Substituting $n = 100$ and $p = 0.60$ into the formulas for the mean and standard deviation of the binomial distribution, we get

$$\mu = 100(0.60) = 60$$

and
$$\sigma = \sqrt{100(0.60)(0.40)} = 4.90$$

The $z$-value of the dividing line of the criterion is thus

$$z = \frac{69.5 - 60}{4.90} = 1.94$$

and the corresponding entry in Table I is 0.4738. *Hence, the probability that the criterion on page 240 leads to the error of accepting the manufacturer's claim even though the suntan lotion is effective only 60 per cent of the time is 0.5000 − 0.4738 = 0.0262 or, roughly, 0.03.*

If it is felt that this probability entails too high a risk, the criterion could be changed by moving the dividing line of Figure 11.2 to the right, for example, by modifying the criterion so that the manufacturer's claim is accepted only if 73 or more of the 100 persons receive adequate protection from the sun. Unfortunately, this change would automatically *increase* the probability of making the error which we discussed earlier, namely, the error of discrediting the new suntan lotion even though it is as good as claimed. This illustrates the fact that by moving the dividing line of the criterion to *reduce* the probability of making one kind of error, we automatically *increase* the probability of making another. (The probabilities of making either error can be reduced only by increasing the size of the sample.)

In the above we arbitrarily studied the case where the suntan lotion failed to meet the manufacturer's claim by being only 60 per cent effective. It will be left to the reader (Exercises 3 and 4 on page 243) to calculate the probabilities that the original criterion will erroneously *accept* the manufacturer's claim even though the suntan lotion is effective only 65 or 70 per cent of the time.

The purpose of the discussion of this section has been to illustrate informally how probabilities of making wrong decisions can be calculated. In Sections 11.2 and 11.3 we shall treat this problem in a more general and more rigorous fashion.

## EXERCISES

1. Suppose that in the example discussed in the text the criterion is changed so that the manufacturer's claim is accepted if 68 or more of the 100 persons in the sample receive adequate protection from the sun and that otherwise his claim is rejected.
   (a) Find the probability that this modified criterion will lead to the *rejection* of the manufacturer's claim even though the suntan lotion is as good as claimed, that is, even though the probability that the suntan lotion will protect a person using it is 0.75.
   (b) Find the probability that this modified criterion will lead to the *acceptance* of the manufacturer's claim even though the probability that the suntan lotion protects any one person using it is only 0.60.

2. Suppose that in the example discussed in the text the criterion is changed so that the manufacturer's claim is accepted if 65 or more of the 100 persons in the sample receive adequate protection from the sun and that otherwise his claim is rejected.
   (a) Find the probability that this modified criterion will lead to the *rejection* of the manufacturer's claim even though the suntan lotion is as good as claimed, that is, even though the probability that the suntan lotion will protect any one person using it is 0.75.
   (b) Find the probability that this modified criterion will lead to the *acceptance* of the manufacturer's claim even though the probability that the suntan lotion will protect any one person using it is only 0.60.

3. Referring to the original criterion on page 240, what is the probability that the manufacturer's claim will be *accepted* even though the probability that the suntan lotion will protect any one person is only 0.65?

4. Referring to the original criterion on page 240, what is the probability that the manufacturer's claim will be *accepted* even though the probability that the suntan lotion will protect any one person is only 0.70?

## 11.2 / Type I and Type II Errors

In order to treat the problem of Section 11.1 in a more rigorous fashion, let us refer to the hypothesis that the suntan lotion is as effective as claimed as *hypothesis H*. Since the manufacturer claimed that the suntan lotion is 75 per cent effective, we can write

$$hypothesis \ H: \quad p = 0.75$$

$H : P = .75$

where $p$ is the probability that any one person using the suntan lotion will receive adequate protection from the sun. Now, hypothesis $H$ is either true or false and it will be accepted or it will be rejected. If hypothesis $H$ is *true and accepted* or if it is *false and rejected* the decision is in either case the right one. If hypothesis $H$ is *true but rejected* the decision is in error and this rejection of a true hypothesis is referred to as a *Type I error*. Generally speaking, *a Type I error is committed when we reject a hypothesis which should have been accepted;* in our example, the error of rejecting the manufacturer's claim although it is true is a Type I error.

If hypothesis $H$ is *false but accepted* the decision is in error and we call this a *Type II error*. Thus, in general, *a Type II error is committed when we accept a hypothesis which should have been rejected;* in our example, the error of accepting the manufacturer's claim although the suntan lotion is actually not as effective as claimed is a Type II error.

We thus find ourselves in the situation which is described schematically in the following table

*Type I*
*true but rej.*

*Type II*
*false but accept.*

Probabilities
of
making wrong
decisions

|            | $H$ is true         | $H$ is false        |
|------------|---------------------|---------------------|
| Accept $H$ | correct decision    | Type II error       |
| Reject $H$ | Type I error        | correct decision    |

power

This is reminiscent of Section 7.5, where we looked upon decision problems as games between opponents having various moves. Analogous to the decision between an outdoor picnic and an indoor buffet supper (see page 141), we now have to decide whether to accept or reject hypothesis $H$ *and* analogous to Nature's decision between no rain and rain, Nature now has control over hypothesis $H$'s being true or false.

A big stumbling block in trying to carry this analogy further is that in actual practice there are very few problems of testing hypotheses where we can put "cash values" on all possible outcomes as we did on page 141. After all, how can we put "cash values" on someone's deciding to accept inferior steel for the construction of a bridge, someone's deciding against the use of a new drug which might save many lives, or someone's deciding to allocate special funds to School System A where they might do much more good for School System

B? In view of this difficulty, we shall devote most of our attention to the *probabilities* of making wrong decisions (Type I and Type II errors), worrying perhaps tacitly about the consequences that may be involved. Of course, the seriousness of these consequences will usually determine whether a risk is acceptable or not; for instance, whether 0.10, the probability of committing a Type I error which we calculated for the suntan lotion example, is acceptable or whether it is too high.

In Section 11.1 we evaluated the "goodness" of the decision criterion, the one given on page 240, by calculating the probabilities of committing Type I and Type II errors. We saw that the probability of committing the Type I error of erroneously rejecting the manufacturer's claim was, approximately, 0.10. This is a Type I error because we are rejecting a hypothesis which should be accepted, namely, hypothesis $H$ that $p = 0.75$.

We also saw that the probability of committing a Type II error, the error of accepting the manufacturer's claim when his product is actually less than 75 per cent effective, depended on the value of $p$. We showed on page 242 that for $p = 0.60$ the probability of committing a Type II error was, roughly, 0.03, and it was left to the reader to show that the corresponding probabilities for $p = 0.65$ and $p = 0.70$ are 0.17 and 0.54, respectively. Plotting these values as in Figure 11.3, we obtain a diagram which might reasonably be called a "performance chart" of the decision criterion. It shows the probabilities of committing Type II errors for various alternative values of $p$.

Since Figure 11.3 does not show *all* the risks to which we are exposed, it does not indicate the probability of committing a Type I error, let us modify it as follows: let us relabel the vertical scale of Figure 11.3 "probability of accepting $H$" instead of "probability of committing Type II error." This

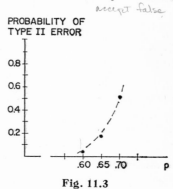

*accept false*

PROBABILITY OF
TYPE II ERROR

**Fig. 11.3**

does not change anything so far as the points of Figure 11.3 are concerned, but we can now add a point for $p = 0.75$. When $p = 0.75$ in our example, the probability of accepting $H$ is the probability of making the *right* decision and it equals 1 *minus* the probability of committing a Type I error. Since the probability of com-

$P(\text{right decision}) = 1 - \text{Type I error}$

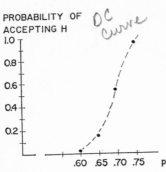

PROBABILITY OF
ACCEPTING H

**Fig. 11.4.** Operating characteristic curve.

mitting a Type I error was shown to be approximately 0.10, the probability of accepting $H$ when $H$ is *true* (when $p = 0.75$) is $1 - 0.10 = 0.90$. Plotting this value at $p = 0.75$, we obtain the curve shown in Figure 11.4.* It is called the *operating characteristic curve* of the criterion or, simply, its *OC-curve*. If we plotted the probabilities of *rejecting* $H$ instead of the probabilities of accepting $H$, we would obtain an analogous curve called the *power function* of the decision criterion.

An operating characteristic curve shows the probabilities of committing Type II errors for various values of the parameter (in our example, the parameter $p$) with one exception. For the value assumed under the hypothesis, hypothesis $H$, it gives the probability of making the *right* decision, namely, 1 *minus* the probability of committing a Type I error. An OC-curve, thus, provides a picture of the various risks to which we are exposed by the use of a decision criterion.

Since a thorough study of operating characteristic curves would go far beyond the scope of this text, the purpose of our example was mainly to provide an illustration of how statistical methods can be used to analyze and describe various risks connected with decision criteria. Of course, these methods are not limited to the special hypothesis which we formulated for the suntan lotion example. Hypothesis $H$ in the table on page 244 could be that the students in one school are as intelligent as those in another, it could be the hypothesis that tourists visiting a national park spend on the average $14.73 per day, it could be the hypothesis that a certain kind of tire lasts on the average 24,000 miles, or any one of countless other hypotheses.

### EXERCISES

1. Suppose that on the basis of a sample we want to test the hypothesis that *the average price charged for 3-bedroom homes in the Phoenix area is*

*To add two more points, it can easily be verified that for $p = 0.55$ the probability of accepting $H$ is *close to zero* and that for $p = 0.80$ it is very *close to 1*.

$13,000. - Explain under what conditions we would be committing a Type I error and under what conditions we would be committing a Type II error.

**2.** Suppose that a public opinion poll is asked to test the hypothesis that *the democratic candidate will win a certain gubernatorial election.* Explain under what conditions this poll would be committing a Type I error and under what conditions it would be committing a Type II error.

**3.** *Whether an error is a Type I error or a Type II error depends on how we formulate the hypothesis we want to test.* To illustrate this, suppose that Mr. Smith is being interviewed for a teaching position and that the principal of the school is concerned about his competence as a classroom teacher.

  (a) If the hypothesis is formulated as "Mr. Smith is a competent classroom teacher," explain under what conditions the principal would be committing Type I and Type II errors.

  (b) If the hypothesis is formulated as "Mr. Smith is not a competent classroom teacher," show that the Type I error of (a) is now a Type II error and vice versa.

**4.** Referring to the modified criterion of Exercise 1 on page 243, find the probabilities that the hypothesis ($p = 0.75$) is accepted when (a) $p = 0.55$, (b) $p = 0.65$, and (c) $p = 0.70$. Use these probabilities together with the results obtained in Exercise 1 on page 243 to draw a graph of the operating characteristic curve of this modified criterion.

## 11.3 / Null Hypotheses and Tests of Significance

In the suntan lotion example studied in the preceding section we had fewer difficulties with Type I errors than we had with Type II errors. This was due to the simple fact that we formulated our hypothesis in such a way that the probability of committing a Type I error could immediately be calculated. Had we formulated the hypothesis that *the suntan lotion is not as good as claimed,* that the probability (that the lotion protects any one person using it) is *less than 0.75,* we would not have been able to calculate the probability of committing a Type I error. At least, we could not have done so without specifying "how much less," that is, without specifying a definite value of $p$.

In choosing hypothesis $H$ for the suntan lotion example, we followed the widely accepted rule of *always formulating hypotheses in such a way that we know what to expect if they are true.* By formulating the hypothesis $p = 0.75$, as we did on page 243, we *know* that on the average we can expect 75 out of 100 persons to receive adequate protection, we *know* that for a sample of size 100 the sampling distribution of the number of persons receiving adequate protection has a standard deviation of $\sqrt{100(0.75)(0.25)} = 4.33$, and we *know* that this sampling distribution can be approximated closely with a normal curve. *Hence we have enough information to calculate the probability of committing a Type I error.* Had we formulated the original hypothesis as $p < 0.75$, we would *not* have known exactly what to expect and we would *not* have been able to calculate the probability of committing a Type I error.

Following the rule given in the preceding paragraph, we often have to assume the exact opposite of what we may be trying to prove. If we wanted to show that the students in School A have a higher average I.Q. than the students in School B, we would have to formulate the hypothesis that there is *no difference* in the average I.Q.'s. Similarly, if we wanted to show that a new drug reduces the mortality rate of a given disease, we would formulate the hypothesis that it does *not*, and if we wanted to show that one kind of ore has a higher percentage content of uranium than another kind of ore, we would formulate the hypothesis that the two percentages are the *same*. In view of the fact that we assumed that there is *no difference* between the average I.Q.'s, that there is *no difference* regardless of whether we use the new drug, and that there is *no difference* between the uranium contents of the two ores, hypotheses like these are referred to as *null hypotheses.*

Although we may be avoiding one kind of difficulty by always formulating hypotheses so that we can calculate the probability of committing a Type I error, this will not help so far as Type II errors are concerned. The only time that there will be no problem in calculating the probability of committing either kind of error is when we test a specific hypothesis against a specific alternative. For instance, if in the suntan lotion example we had wanted to test the hypothesis $p = 0.75$ against the specific alternative $p = 0.60$, it would have been easy to calculate the probabilities of committing either kind of error. As a matter of fact, this is precisely what we did in Section 11.1. Unfortunately, there are only few practical problems, mainly in industrial statistics, where we can thus limit the alternatives of whatever hypotheses we want to test.

A possible escape from the difficulties connected with calculating probabilities of committing Type II errors is to avoid Type II errors altogether. Although this may sound like an ostrich burying his head in the sand, let us see how it might be done. Let us suppose, for example, that we want to test the hypothesis that *a given coin is balanced* (that the probability for heads is 0.50), and that we want to base our decision on the number of heads obtained in 400 tosses of the coin. If we use the criterion

> *reject the hypothesis* ($p = 0.50$) *if the number of heads obtained in the 400 tosses exceeds 220 or is less than 180; reserve judgment if there are anywhere from 180 to 220 heads,*

*[handwritten: TO AVOID TYPE II ERROR]*

it can easily be verified that the probability of committing a Type I error is about 0.04. There is no need to calculate the probability of committing a Type II error; we never really accept the hypothesis and we, therefore, cannot possibly make the mistake of accepting a false hypothesis. If we obtained, say, 239 heads, we would *reject* the hypothesis that the coin is balanced. If we obtained 197, we would say that *the difference between what we expected and what we got, namely, the difference between 200 and 197, is not "statistically significant," meaning that it may reasonably be attributed to chance.*

*[handwritten: NOT SIGNIFICANT MEANS MAY BE DUE TO CHANCE]*

The procedure which we have outlined in this example is called a *test of significance.* If the difference between what we expect and what we get is *so large* that it cannot reasonably be ascribed to chance, we reject the hypothesis on which our expectation was based. If the difference between what we expect and what we get is *small enough* to be attributed to chance, we say that it is *not (statistically) significant.* We can then accept the hypothesis and expose ourselves to the possibility of committing a Type II error *or* we can reserve judgment. This choice will have to depend on whether a definite decision, a definite action one way or the other, is required.

To give an example in which "reserving judgment" would be appropriate, let us suppose that we want to test the effectiveness of a new drug in the treatment of a disease for which the mortality rate is 0.15. Formulating the *null hypothesis* that the new drug is *not* effective, that even with the new drug the mortality rate is still 0.15, let us consider the following criterion:

> *the new drug is to be given to 100 patients having the disease and the null hypothesis is to be rejected if fewer than 10 of these patients die.*

Suppose now that 12 of the patients die. On the basis of the given criterion the null hypothesis cannot be rejected, *we cannot decide that the drug is effective.* On the other hand, there were fewer deaths than expected and it would seem quite dangerous to rule out the possibility that the drug might nevertheless reduce the mortality rate to some extent. It would seem appropriate to report that, *statistically speaking, the difference between what we expected under the null hypothesis and what we got, namely, the difference between 15 and 12, is not significant.* We thus express our reluctance to decide on the basis of this experiment that the drug is *not* effective. (Perhaps a more reasonable criterion would be to *reject* the null hypothesis if fewer than 10 of the patients die, to *accept* it if 15 or more die, and to *reserve judgment* if the number of deaths is from 10 to 14.)

Referring again to the suntan lotion example, we can convert the criterion on page 240 into that of a *significance test* by writing

*reject the manufacturer's claim (the hypothesis that $p = 0.75$) if fewer than 70 of the 100 persons in the sample get adequate protection from the sun; reserve judgment if 70 or more get adequate protection.*

Comparing the two criteria, we find that the rule for rejecting the hypothesis is unchanged and the probability of committing a Type I error is still 0.10. However, so far as Type II errors are concerned, we are now *playing it safe* by reserving judgment. If it so happened that 73 of the 100 persons in the sample received adequate protection from the sun, the investigator might report that *his criterion did not enable him to reject the manufacturer's claim.* This is not a direct endorsement of the product, but merely a negative sort of statement that he could not find anything wrong.

Reserving judgment in the manner outlined above presents an escape from committing Type II errors, but it is a luxury we cannot always afford. If the nature of a problem demands a decision one way or the other, we have no choice but to expose ourselves to Type II errors. We then have to investigate probabilities of committing Type II errors and, preferably, construct the entire OC-curve.

Since the general problem of testing hypotheses and constructing decision criteria is fairly complicated, it will help to construct tests of significance using the following five steps

(1) *We formulate a hypothesis H in such a way that the probability of committing a Type I error can be calculated.*

(2) *We formulate an alternative hypothesis so that the rejection of hypothesis H is equivalent to the acceptance of the alternative.*

In the suntan lotion example $H$ was the hypothesis that $p = 0.75$, where $p$ is the probability that a person using the lotion will get adequate protection from the sun; the alternative hypothesis was $p < 0.75$. This is referred to as a *one-sided alternative* and we are using it here because we are interested in knowing whether the suntan lotion is inferior, not whether it is better than claimed. In the coin-tossing example on page 249, we assumed the hypothesis $H$ that the coin is balanced, namely, that $p = 0.50$; the alternative hypothesis was that the coin is not balanced, namely, that $p \neq 0.50$. This time the alternative is *two-sided* since a coin is considered off balance if the probability for heads is either too high or too low.

Beginners often find it difficult to decide between using one-sided and two-sided alternatives; the only help we can give is to stress the point that this can only be dictated by the nature of the problem.

(3) *We specify the probability of committing a Type I error.* This probability is also called the *level of significance* at which the test is being performed. Although the choice of a level of significance is essentially arbitrary, it depends on whatever consequences there may be to committing a Type I error, it is customary to use 0.05 or 0.01.

The probability of committing a Type I error, that is, the level of significance, is often represented by the Greek letter $\alpha$ (alpha). To indicate that a test is being conducted at a level of significance of, say, 0.05, we can simply write $\alpha = 0.05$. To distinguish between Type I and Type II errors, the probability of committing a Type II error is generally represented by the Greek letter $\beta$ (beta).

(4) *We use statistical theory to construct a criterion for testing the hypothesis formulated in (1) against the alternative formulated in (2) at the level of significance specified in (3).*

The construction of such criteria will have to depend on whatever *statistics* we may want to base our decision and their sampling distributions. A considerable part of the remainder of this book will be devoted to the problem of constructing suitable test criteria.

(5) *We specify whether the alternative to rejecting the hypothesis formulated in (1) is to reject it or to reserve judgment.*

As we saw in our example, this will have to depend on the nature of the problem, possible consequences or risks, and whether a decision one way or the other must be reached. It thus happens quite often that we are forced to *accept* a null hypothesis with the tacit hope that we are not exposing ourselves to too high a risk of committing a *serious* Type II error. Of course, if necessary, we can always calculate the probabilities of committing Type II errors for various alternate values of the parameter in question and study the resulting OC-curve.

Before going into the actual problem of constructing various kinds of test criteria, let us point out that the concepts discussed in this and the preceding sections are *not* limited to tests concerning proportions. The ideas which we have introduced apply equally well to hypotheses about means or standard deviations, about the randomness of samples, about the relationships between several variables, and so forth.

## 11.4 / Tests Concerning Proportions    OPTIONAL

To illustrate the steps outlined in the preceding section, let us suppose that someone has claimed that Mr. Jones, running for a local political office, will receive *at most* 60 per cent of the vote, and that we want to test this claim on the basis of a random sample of the electorate.

Letting $p$ stand for the probability that a person eligible to vote in this election is for candidate Jones, the hypothesis to be tested is

$$Hypothesis\ H: \quad p = 0.60$$

and the alternative hypothesis is

$$Alternative: \quad p > 0.60$$

This alternative is *one-sided* since the claim that Jones will receive at most 60 per cent of the vote is false only if he receives *more than 60 per cent of the vote.*

To take care of step (3), let us set the level of significance at 0.05, and we are now ready for step (4), that of constructing a suitable test criterion. It stands to reason that the acceptance or rejection of the hypothesis which we have formulated should be based on the number of votes Mr. Jones receives in the sample of the electorate — the only question that remains is *where are we going to draw the line?* In order to find an answer for this, let us consider Figure 11.5, which represents the sampling distribution of $x$, the number of persons in

the sample who are for candidate Jones. Since the level of significance was set at 0.05, the dividing line of the criterion must be such
that the shaded area of Figure 11.5 is 0.05. Using the normal curve
approximation to the binomial distribution and the fact that 5 per

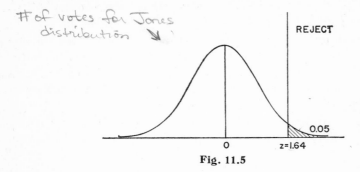

# of votes for Jones distribution

**Fig. 11.5**

cent of the area under a normal curve lies to the right of $z = 1.64$
(see Table I), we arrive at the following decision criterion:

*reject the hypothesis (and accept the alternative) if $z > 1.64$; accept
the hypothesis or reserve judgment if $z \leq 1.64$, where*

$$z = \frac{x - np}{\sqrt{np(1-p)}} \qquad (11.4.1)▲$$

This formula for $z$ is obtained by subtracting from $x$, the number of
"successes," the mean of its sampling distribution $\mu = np$, and then
dividing by the standard deviation $\sigma = \sqrt{np(1-p)}$. (Let us remind
the reader that $z > 1.64$ means that "$z$ is greater than 1.64," and
that $z \leq 1.64$ means that "$z$ is less than or equal to 1.64.")

If the study concerning Mr. Jones' chances is actually made, and
if a random sample of 400 eligible voters contains 258 votes for Jones
and 142 for his opponent, we get

$$z = \frac{258 - 400(0.60)}{\sqrt{400(0.60)(0.40)}} = 1.84$$

Since this *exceeds* the dividing line of the criterion of $z = 1.64$, we can
*reject* the original hypothesis and accept the alternative that *Jones
will receive more than 60 per cent of the vote.*

The criterion shown in Figure 11.5 is referred to as a *one-tail test.*
The hypothesis is rejected only if the $z$-value obtained from the
sample falls into *one* tail, in this case the *right-hand tail* of the distribution. It should be noted that *a one-tail test goes with a one-sided*

5.000
4.495
.0505

*alternative hypothesis.* Clearly, there would have been no sense in rejecting the claim that Jones will receive at most 60 per cent of the vote if he had received, say, only 30 per cent of the vote in the sample, and $z$ would have fallen into the left-hand tail of the distribution of Figure 11.5. The criterion on page 240 is also a *one-tail test*, rejecting the manufacturer's claim only if the number of persons receiving adequate protection with the new suntan lotion is too small. This one-tail criterion, according to which we reject the hypothesis if $z$ falls into the left-hand tail of the distribution, goes with the one-sided alternative $p < 0.75$, namely, the alternative that the suntan lotion is not as good as claimed.

To give an example in which it is appropriate to use a *two-tail test* and a *two-sided alternative hypothesis*, let us suppose that an advertising executive claims to a sponsor that 50 per cent of the people who saw a certain big "spectacular" television program will remember the name of the product advertised 24 hours after they saw the show. The problem is to test this claim (with $\alpha = 0.01$) if 24 hours after the show was on the air, 112 viewers in a sample of 200 remembered the name of the product advertised.

Having no idea whether 50 per cent might be correct, too high, or too low, we shall test the hypothesis that the correct figure is 50 per cent against the alternative that it is not. Formally,

$$Hypothesis: \quad p = 0.50$$
$$Alternative: \quad p \neq 0.50$$

TWO TAILED

where $p$ is the probability that a person who saw the show will remember the product advertised 24 hours later. The alternative is

Level of
Significance
is

.01

.005 in each
tail

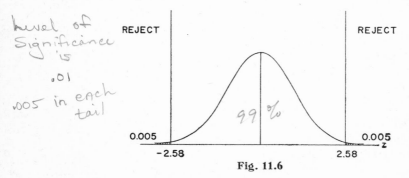

Fig. 11.6

*two-sided* since we shall want to reject the executive's claim if it is too low and also if it is too high.

Since we shall want to base our decision on the fact that 112 of 200 viewers remembered the name of the product, let us consider the normal curve shown in Figure 11.6 which approximates the sampling distribution of the number of "successes" in 200 trials with $p = 0.50$. The probability of committing a Type I error, the level of significance, is given by the shaded area of Figure 11.6 and, as was specified above, it equals 0.01. Putting half of this area into each tail of the distribution, the $z$'s of the dividing line of the criterion must be such that 99 per cent of the area lies between $-z$ and $z$. As we saw on page 218, 99 per cent of the area under a normal curve lies between $z = -2.58$ and $z = 2.58$, and we thus have the following criterion

*reject the hypothesis (and accept the alternative) if $z < -2.58$ or $z > 2.58$; accept the hypothesis or reserve judgment if $-2.58 \leq z \leq 2.58$, where*

$$z = \frac{x - np}{\sqrt{np(1 - p)}}$$

The formula for $z$ here is the same as in (11.4.1). Substituting $x = 112$, $n = 200$, and $p = 0.50$, we get

$$z = \frac{112 - 200(0.50)}{\sqrt{200(0.50)(0.50)}} = 1.70$$

Since this value lies between $-2.58$ and $2.58$, we shall have to accept the advertising executive's claim or reserve judgment. Assuming that a decision one way or the other must be made, we shall accept the claim that 50 per cent of the viewers of the "spectacular" remembered the name of the product 24 hours after they saw the show.

The best way to proceed with step (4) when testing hypotheses concerning proportions is to begin by drawing figures like 11.5 and 11.6. Such figures should indicate for what values of $z$ the hypothesis is to be rejected and the $z$-value (or $z$-values) of the dividing lines of the criterion. Thus, if a level of significance of 0.01 is used in a *one-tail test*, the dividing line of the criterion is $z = -2.33$ or $z = 2.33$, depending on whether the hypothesis is to be rejected for values falling into the left-hand tail or the right-hand tail of the distribution. Similarly, if a level of significance of 0.05 is to be used in a *two-tail test*, the dividing lines of the criterion are $z = -1.96$ and $z = 1.96$. Let us repeat that *a one-tail test is used when the alternative hypothesis is one-sided and a two-tail test is used when the alternative hypothesis is two-sided.*

## EXERCISES

1. It has been claimed that 30 per cent of all students entering college drop out during or right after the first year. Test this claim against the alternative that the percentage is greater if a random sample of 300 students, who entered college in 1956, contains 112 who dropped out during or right after the first year. Use a level of significance of 0.05.

2. It has been claimed that 50 per cent of all families move at least once every 3 years. Test this claim against the two-sided alternative that $p \neq 0.50$, if a sample survey showed that among 400 families interviewed 189 had moved at least once during the preceding 3 years. Use a level of significance of 0.05.

3. Among 100 businessmen interviewed in a certain city, 77 expressed dissatisfaction with their city administration. Assuming that this is a random sample, test the hypothesis that *at least* 80 per cent of the businessmen in this city are dissatisfied with the city administration. Use a level of significance of 0.05.

4. If 1000 flips of a coin produced 452 heads and 548 tails, test the hypothesis that the coin is balanced at a level of significance of 0.01.

5. An opinion research organization is asked to test the hypothesis that at least 65 per cent of all housewives prefer a certain product. Show that the hypothesis that $p = 0.65$ cannot be rejected at a level of significance of 0.05 if 311 of 500 housewives interviewed expressed a preference for the given product. How would you phrase this result so that you would not be exposed to the risk of committing a Type II error?

6. If a random sample of 250 electronic components contained 14 defectives, test the claim that at least 10 per cent of the components from which this sample was obtained are defective. Use a level of significance of 0.05.

7. A sample survey showed that 623 of 800 persons interviewed preferred to live in medium-sized towns. Using a two-sided alternative and a level of significance of 0.05, test the hypothesis that the true percentage of persons preferring to live in medium-sized towns is 0.75.

8. A personnel director claims that 55 per cent of all single women hired for clerical jobs get married and quit work within two years after they are hired. Test this hypothesis against the two-sided alternative that $p \neq 0.55$, given that in a random sample of 600 single women hired for clerical jobs 352 got married and quit work within two years. Use a level of significance of 0.05.

9. What would be the answer to Exercise 8 if the alternative hypothesis were changed to $p > 0.55$?

## 11.5 / Differences between Proportions    OPTIONAL

There are many problems in which we must decide whether an observed difference between two sample proportions, or percentages, is significant or whether it may reasonably be attributed to chance. For instance, if 81 per cent of a sample of one kind of seed germinates but only 77 per cent of a sample of another, we may have to decide whether the observed difference of 4 per cent may be attributed to chance or whether it implies that there is an actual difference between the two kinds of seeds. Similarly, if one manufacturing process produces 16 defective pieces in a sample of size 400 while another produces 24 defective pieces in a sample of 300, it may be of interest to know whether the difference between $16/400 = 0.04$ and $24/300 = 0.08$ may reasonably be attributed to chance.

Questions of this kind are usually decided on the basis of the following theory: *if $x_1$ and $x_2$ are the number of "successes" observed, respectively, in large independent random samples of size $n_1$ and $n_2$, and if $p_1$ and $p_2$ are the corresponding probabilities for success in individual trials, then the sampling distribution of the statistic*

$$\frac{x_1}{n_1} - \frac{x_2}{n_2} \tag{11.5.1}$$

*the difference between the two sample proportions, can be approximated closely with a normal curve whose mean is $p_1 - p_2$ and whose standard deviation is*

$$\sqrt{\frac{p_1(1-p_1)}{n_1} + \frac{p_2(1-p_2)}{n_2}} \tag{11.5.2}$$

STANDARD ERROR OF the difference of 2 proport.

(Derivations of these formulas for the mean and standard deviation of the sampling distribution of the difference between two proportions are referred to in the Bibliography on page 271.) In accordance with the terminology introduced in Chapter 9 we shall refer to the standard deviation given by (10.5.2) as the _standard error of the difference between two proportions;_ it is the standard deviation of the sampling distribution of differences between two proportions.

To illustrate what is meant by this sampling distribution, let us suppose that $p_1$ is the actual proportion of male voters in Detroit favoring a certain piece of legislation and that $p_2$ is the corresponding proportion for female voters in Detroit. If we sent out a large number of interviewers, telling each to interview random samples of $n_1$ male voters and $n_2$ female voters in Detroit, we would expect that the figures they get for $x_1$ and $x_2$, the number of male and female votes favoring the given piece of legislation, are not all the same, nor are the values they obtain for the difference between $x_1/n_1$ and $x_2/n_2$. If we then constructed a distribution of the differences obtained by the various interviewers, we would get an *experimental sampling distribution of the difference between two proportions*. The sampling distribution referred to above, namely, the one whose standard deviation is given by (11.5.2), is the corresponding *theoretical sampling distribution*.

The example of the preceding paragraph also serves to illustrate the fact that the two samples must be *independent*, that they must, so to speak, be selected separately. It stands to reason that we would probably get very misleading results if we interviewed married couples, whose political views are apt to be the same.

In problems dealing with differences between proportions we are usually interested in testing whether there actually is a difference between $p_1$ and $p_2$. We shall thus test the null hypothesis

$$Hypothesis: \quad p_1 = p_2 (= p)$$

against the *two-sided* alternative hypothesis

$$Alternative: \quad p_1 \neq p_2$$

Substituting $p$ for $p_1$ and $p_2$ in the formulas for the mean and standard deviation of the sampling distribution of the difference between two proportions, we find that under the null hypothesis the mean is 0 whereas (11.5.2), the standard deviation, becomes

$$\sqrt{p(1-p)\left(\frac{1}{n_1} + \frac{1}{n_2}\right)} \qquad (11.5.3) \blacktriangle$$

Since (11.5.3) cannot be used without knowledge of $p$, we shall approximate it by substituting for $p$ the proportion of successes in the two samples combined, namely,

$$p = \frac{x_1 + x_2}{n_1 + n_2} \qquad (11.5.4) \blacktriangle$$

*approx. for*

Aside from the fact that we are using a normal curve approximation, this is another reason why the method which we are developing must be used only for *large samples*.

To illustrate how the method works, let us refer again to the example on page 257, the one dealing with the number of defective pieces obtained in samples produced by two different machines.

Letting $p_1$ and $p_2$ stand for the probabilities that a piece produced by either manufacturing process is defective, we shall test the null hypothesis formulated above at a level of significance of 0.05.

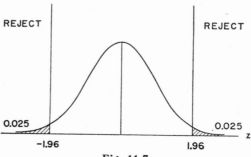

**Fig. 11.7**

If we consider the normal curve of Figure 11.7, representing the sampling distribution of the difference between two proportions, we can now formulate the following criterion

*reject the null hypothesis if $z < -1.96$ or $z > 1.96$; accept the null hypothesis or reserve judgment if $-1.96 \leq z \leq 1.96$, where*

$$z = \frac{\dfrac{x_1}{n_1} - \dfrac{x_2}{n_2}}{\sqrt{p(1-p)\left(\dfrac{1}{n_1} + \dfrac{1}{n_2}\right)}} \qquad (11.5.5) \blacktriangle$$

*and where $p$ is to be approximated with (11.5.4).*

This formula for $z$ was obtained by subtracting from the observed difference between the two sample proportions the *mean of its sampling distribution*, namely, **0**, and then dividing by the *standard deviation* given by (11.5.3).

Substituting the numerical values given on page 257, we find that for $x_1 = 16$, $n_1 = 400$, $x_2 = 24$, and $n_2 = 300$, formulas (11.5.4) and (11.5.5) yield

$$p = \frac{16 + 24}{400 + 300} = 0.057$$

and

$$z = \frac{\dfrac{16}{400} - \dfrac{24}{300}}{\sqrt{(0.057)(0.943)\left(\dfrac{1}{400} + \dfrac{1}{300}\right)}} = -0.71$$

Since this value falls between $-1.96$ and $1.96$, we shall *accept* the null hypothesis that $p_1 = p_2$, namely, *the hypothesis that the true proportions of defectives produced by the two processes is the same.* If we did not want to expose ourselves to the risk of committing a Type II error, we could merely state that *the difference between the two sample proportions* (*is* (*not statistically significant.*) could be gotten by chance )

The example we have given here is typical of tests concerning two proportions. A test which serves to compare more than two proportions will be discussed later in Section 12.1.

### EXERCISES

1. A marketing study conducted in San Francisco showed that in a random sample of 200 housewives 138 preferred Beverage A to Beverage B. In a similar study made in Los Angeles 162 of 200 housewives preferred Beverage A to Beverage B. Use a level of significance of 0.05 to test whether the difference between the two proportions of preferences is significant.

2. In a poll taken at the preview of a new movie 41 of 100 men said that they liked it, and 48 of 100 women also reacted favorably. Test at a level of significance of 0.05 whether there is a significant difference between the reactions of the two groups.

3. A test item in an objective test is *good* if it discriminates between good and poor students. Is a certain test item *good* if it is answered correctly by 182 of 250 good students and by 75 of 150 poor students? Use a level of significance of 0.05.

## 11.6 / Tests Concerning Means

Once the reader has grasped the basic ideas underlying tests of hypotheses, the various tests we shall study in this and in later section should not present any difficulties. In principle these tests are all the same; we assume a (null) hypothesis for which we can calculate the probability of committing a Type I error, an alternative hypothesis, and then we construct a decision criterion using the sampling distribution of an appropriate statistic.

In this section we shall study tests applying to problems in which we are interested in deciding on the basis of a sample whether the mean of a population equals some assumed value $\mu$. We may, thus, want to know whether the true average I.Q. of the students residing in a certain community is 108, whether the true average high temperature in a certain area is 84 degrees, or whether the actual average hourly wage paid to workers in a certain industry is $1.64.

To illustrate the general approach, let us test the hypothesis that *the average distance required to stop a car going 20 miles per hour is 25 feet.* Let us suppose, furthermore, that 100 drivers averaged $\bar{x} = 27.3$ feet (in stopping a car going 20 mph) with a standard deviation of $s = 2.1$ feet.

If $\mu$ is the true average braking distance required at the given speed, the hypothesis we want to test and the two-sided alternative are

*Hypothesis:*  $\mu = 25$ *feet*

*Alternative:*  $\mu \neq 25$ *feet*

The level of significance is set at 0.05.

Having already studied the sampling distribution of $\bar{x}$ in Chapters 9 and 10, we know that *for large n* it can be approximated closely with a normal curve having the mean $\mu$ and the standard deviation $\sigma/\sqrt{n}$, where $\mu$ and $\sigma$ are the mean and standard deviation of the

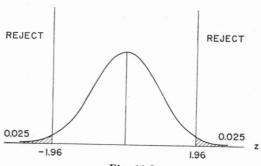

**Fig. 11.8**

population from which the sample is obtained. Considering the normal curve of Figure 11.8, which represents the sampling distribution of $\bar{x}$, we arrive at the following criterion

*reject the hypothesis if z < −1.96 or z > 1.96; accept the hypothesis (or reserve judgment) if −1.96 ≤ z ≤ 1.96, where*

$$z = \frac{\bar{x} - \mu}{s/\sqrt{n}} \qquad\qquad (11.6.1)\blacktriangle$$

*and where (in this example) $\mu = 25$.*

This formula for $z$ was obtained by subtracting from $\bar{x}$ the mean of

TWO
REASONS
WHY
$n > 30$

its sampling distribution and then dividing by its standard deviation. ①With reference to the latter we substituted $s$ for $\sigma$, and this is one reason why the above criterion should be used only for *large samples*, that is for $n$ greater than 30. Another reason is that we are approxi-②mating the sampling distribution of $\bar{x}$ with a normal curve.

Substituting the numerical values given in our example, namely, $\bar{x} = 27.3$, and $s = 2.1$, we get

$$z = \frac{27.3 - 25}{2.1/\sqrt{100}} = 10.95$$

Since this exceeds 1.96, we can reject the hypothesis that $\mu = 25$; *we can conclude that the average braking distance at the given speed is not 25 feet.* In fact, it must be considerably greater.

In the above example we used a *two-tail test* because we originally formulated the *two-sided alternative* $\mu \neq 25$. To consider an example in which it would be appropriate to use a *one-sided alternative* and, correspondingly, a *one-tail test*, let us suppose that some educator claims that the average I.Q. of American college students is *at most* 110, and that in a study made to test this claim 150 American college students, selected at random, had an average I.Q. of 111.2 with a standard deviation of 7.2.

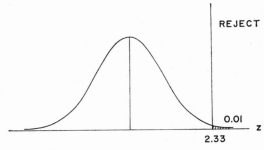

**Fig. 11.9**

As we have formulated this problem, we should really test the hypothesis $\mu \leq 110$ against the alternative that $\mu > 100$. However, this would not give us a unique value for the probability of committing a Type I error and we shall instead write

$Hypothesis:$   $\mu = 110$

$Alternative:$   $\mu > 110$

Considering Figure 11.9, it is apparent that the one-tail criterion for testing the given hypothesis at a level of significance of 0.01 is:

*reject the hypothesis if z > 2.33; accept the hypothesis (or reserve judgment) if z ≤ 2.33, where*

$$z = \frac{\bar{x} - \mu}{s/\sqrt{n}}$$

*and where (in this example) μ = 110.*

Substituting the data given in our example, namely $\bar{x} = 111.2$, $s = 7.2$, and $n = 150$, we get

$$z = \frac{111.2 - 110}{7.2/\sqrt{150}} = 2.03$$

It follows that we *cannot* reject the educator's claim that the average I.Q. of American college students is at most 110. Depending on whether a decision one way or the other is required, we shall have to accept the educator's claim *or* reserve judgment.

*It is important to note that if we had used a level of significance of 0.05 in this example, the dividing line of the criterion would have been z = 1.64, our result would have been significant, and we would have been able to reject the educator's claim. This illustrates the important point that the level of significance should be specified before any tests are made. This will save us from the temptation of later on choosing a level of significance that happens to suit our objectives.*

An important limitation of the method we have outlined so far in this section is that it applies only to *large* samples. If $n$ is small, less than 30, we shall have to proceed as in Section 10.3 and base our decision on the statistic

For Small Samples

$$t = \frac{\bar{x} - \mu}{s} \sqrt{n} \qquad\qquad (10.3.1)▲$$

whose sampling distribution is the Student-*t* distribution with $n - 1$ degrees of freedom, *provided that the population from which we are sampling can be approximated closely with a normal curve.* (If this assumption cannot be met, there is the possibility of using a so-called *nonparametric* method, like the one described in Exercise 3 on page 301.)

Since the above formula for $t$ is identical with that given for $z$ in (11.6.1), the only difference between the small-sample test and the large-sample test is that we must use $t_{.05}$, $t_{.025}$, $t_{.01}$, and $t_{.005}$ as given in Table II instead of the normal curve values of 1.64, 1.96, 2.33, and 2.58.

To illustrate the small-sample technique, let us suppose that a paint manufacturer claims that *on the average* a gallon of his paint will cover 600 square feet and that a random sample of 12 such cans covered on the average 572 square feet with a standard deviation of 26 square feet. Setting the level of significance at 0.05, the hypothesis we want to test and the alternative are

$$Hypothesis: \quad \mu = 600$$

$$Alternative: \quad \mu < 600$$

(This alternative is *one-sided* since we are interested only in testing whether the product is inferior, not whether it is better than claimed.)

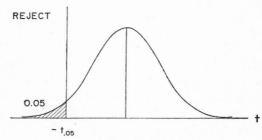

REJECT

0.05

$-t_{.05}$

**Fig. 11.10**

As can be seen from Figure 11.10, which represents the *t*-distribution with $n - 1 = 12 - 1 = 11$ degrees of freedom, the criterion for testing the given hypothesis against the given alternative can be written as

*reject the hypothesis if $t < -t_{.05}$; accept the hypothesis (or reserve judgment) if $t \geq -t_{.05}$, where*

$$t = \frac{\bar{x} - \mu}{s} \sqrt{n} \tag{11.6.2}▲$$

*and where (in this example) $\mu = 600$ and the number of degrees of freedom equals $n - 1 = 12 - 1 = 11$.*

Substituting the numerical values given in our example, namely, $\bar{x} = 572$, $s = 26$, and $n = 12$, we get

$$t = \frac{572 - 600}{26} \sqrt{12} = -3.73$$

Since this is less than $-1.796$, the value given in Table II for $t_{.05}$ with

11 degrees of freedom, *we can reject the manufacturer's claim*. His product is not as good as claimed.

Had we wanted to test the manufacturer's claim against the *two-sided* alternative $\mu \neq 600$, our criterion would have read

*reject the hypothesis if $t < -t_{.025}$ or $t > t_{.025}$; accept the hypothesis (or reserve judgment) if $-t_{.025} \leq t \leq t_{.025}$, where $t$ and the number of degrees of freedom are to be calculated as before.*

As can easily be verified, this modified criterion (whose level of significance is still 0.05) would also enable us to reject the manufacturer's claim.

## EXERCISES

1. Given $\bar{x} = 86$, $s = 12$, and $n = 100$, test the hypothesis $\mu = 80$ against the two-sided alternative $\mu \neq 80$ at a level of significance of 0.05.

2. Given $\bar{x} = 23.5$, $s = 1.2$, and $n = 23$, test the hypothesis $\mu = 22$ against the alternative $\mu \neq 22$ at a level of significance of 0.05.

3. An achievement test given to a random sample of 400 students produced the following results: $\bar{x} = 76$ and $s = 16$. Use this information to test the hypothesis $\mu = 74$ against the two-sided alternative $\mu \neq 74$ at a level of significance of 0.01.

4. A survey showed that a random sample of 100 private passenger cars were driven on the average 12,500 miles a year with a standard deviation of 2400 miles. Use this information to test the hypothesis that the average passenger car is driven 12,000 miles a year against the alternative that the average is higher. Use a level of significance of 0.05.

5. A random sample of boots worn by 40 combat soldiers in a desert region showed an average life of 1.08 years with a standard deviation of 0.5 years. Under standard conditions the boots are known to have an average life of 1.28 years. Is there reason to assert at a level of significance of 0.05 that use in the desert causes the mean life of such boots to decrease?

6. A random sample of 10 steel beams has an average compressive strength of 57,498 psi (pounds per square inch) with a standard deviation of 539 psi. Test the hypothesis that the true average compressive strength of the steel beams from which this sample was obtained is $\mu = 57,000$. Use the two-sided alternative $\mu \neq 57,000$ and a level of significance of 0.01.

**7.** A manufacturer of certain missile components claims that under standard operating conditions they will last on the average $\mu = 320$ hours. Test this claim against the alternative $\mu < 320$ if 15 pieces of this equipment lasted on the average 308 hours with a standard deviation of 29 hours. Use a level of significance of 0.05.

**8.** A study of 28 families in a certain large city showed that average family income during 1958 was \$6,548 with a standard deviation of \$952. Test the hypothesis that the true average income of families in this city during 1958 was \$6,000 against the alternative that it was not \$6,000. Use a level of significance of 0.05.

## 11.7 / Differences between Means

Another important test of significance concerns the question whether an observed difference between two sample means may be attributed to chance or whether it is indicative of the fact that the samples came from populations with unequal means. We may want to decide, for example, whether there actually is a difference in the speed with which men and women can perform a certain task if a random sample of 200 men took on the average 4 minutes 24 seconds while a random sample of 150 women took on the average 4 minutes 31 seconds. Similarly, we may want to decide whether the students of one school are actually superior to those of another if a random sample of 60 students from School A averaged 81 in a certain test while a sample of 40 students from School B averaged only 79.

The technique that is generally employed to test whether an observed difference $\bar{x}_1 - \bar{x}_2$ is significant is based on the following theory: *if $\bar{x}_1$ and $\bar{x}_2$ are the means of two large independent random samples of size $n_1$ and $n_2$, the theoretical sampling distribution of the statistic $\bar{x}_1 - \bar{x}_2$ can be approximated closely with a normal curve whose mean is*

$$\mu_1 - \mu_2 \qquad\qquad (11.7.1)\blacktriangle$$

*and whose standard deviation is*

$$\sqrt{\frac{\sigma_1^2}{n_1} + \frac{\sigma_1^2}{n_2}} \qquad\qquad (11.7.2)\blacktriangle$$

*where $\mu_1$ and $\mu_2$ are the means of the populations from which the two samples were obtained and $\sigma_1$ and $\sigma_2$ are their standard deviations.*

By "independent" samples we meant that the selection of one

sample is in no way affected by the selection of the other. The theory described above does *not* apply, therefore, to "before and after" kinds of comparisons. If $\bar{x}_1$ is the mean of the weights of certain persons before starting a given diet and $\bar{x}_2$ is the mean of their weights after the diet is completed, the two sets of data are clearly *not independent*. A special method for handling this kind of problem is referred to in Exercise 7 on page 270.

The sampling distribution referred to above is the distribution we could *expect* for values of $\bar{x}_1 - \bar{x}_2$ obtained from repeated samples from two populations. [Derivations of formulas (11.7.1) and (11.7.2) are referred to in the Bibliography on page 271.] Using the terminology of Chapter 9, the expression given in (11.7.2) is called the *standard error of the difference between two means*. Since $\sigma_1$ and $\sigma_2$ are usually unknown, we shall approximate this standard error formula by substituting the sample standard deviations $s_1$ and $s_2$ for the two $\sigma$'s. We shall thus write

ONLY FOR LARGE SAMPLES

$$\sqrt{\frac{s_1^2}{n_1} + \frac{s_2^2}{n_2}} \qquad\qquad (11.7.3)\blacktriangle$$

instead of (11.7.2), *with the understanding that this formula is to be used only for large samples*.

To illustrate how this theory is applied, let us return to the example referred to on page 266, the one in which we wanted to test whether the students of one school are actually superior to those of another. Giving the additional information that the standard deviations of the two samples are $s_1 = 4$ and $s_2 = 3$, the total information with which we are supplied is

$$n_1 = 60 \qquad \bar{x}_1 = 81 \qquad s_1 = 4$$

$$n_2 = 40 \qquad \bar{x}_2 = 79 \qquad s_2 = 3$$

Letting $\mu_1$ and $\mu_2$ stand for the true average scores (which we would obtain if the test were given to *all* the students in these schools), the null hypothesis to be tested and the two-sided alternative are

*Hypothesis:* $\mu_1 = \mu_2$

*Alternative:* $\mu_1 \neq \mu_2$

Let us also specify the level of significance as 0.05.

Basing our argument on the theory about the sampling distribution of $\bar{x}_1 - \bar{x}_2$ given above, we can now formulate the following criterion (see also Figure 11.11):

*reject the hypothesis if z < −1.96 or z > 1.96; accept the hypothesis (or reserve judgment) if −1.96 ≤ z ≤ 1.96, where*

$$z = \frac{\bar{x}_1 - \bar{x}_2}{\sqrt{\dfrac{s_1^2}{n_1} + \dfrac{s_2^2}{n_2}}} \qquad (11.7.4)\blacktriangle$$

This formula for $z$ was obtained by subtracting from $\bar{x}_1 - \bar{x}_2$ the mean of its sampling distribution which, under the null hypothesis, is $\mu_1 - \mu_2 = 0$, and then dividing by the standard deviation given by (11.7.3).

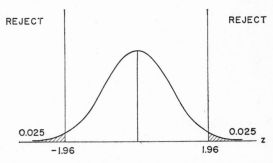

REJECT          REJECT

0.025          0.025

−1.96          1.96          z

**Fig. 11.11**

Substituting into (11.7.4) the numerical values of $n_1$, $\bar{x}_1$, $s_1$, $n_2$, $\bar{x}_2$, and $s_2$ given for our example, we get

$$z = \frac{81 - 79}{\sqrt{\dfrac{4^2}{60} + \dfrac{3^2}{40}}} = 2.85$$

Since this *exceeds* 1.96, we can conclude that the difference between $\bar{x}_1 = 81$ and $\bar{x}_2 = 79$ is *significant*. Rejecting the hypothesis that $\mu_1 = \mu_2$, we can conclude that the students of the first school are superior to those of the second.

We pointed out earlier that the method of this section can be used only if $n_1$ and $n_2$ are both large, that is, 30 or more. When dealing with *small samples* the method must be modified; as is indicated in Exercise 5 on page 269, we shall again use the Student-$t$ distribution instead of the normal curve. Another modification is required when our two samples are *dependent*, and this special technique is indicated in Exercise 7 on page 270.

There exist methods, so-called *nonparametric* methods, which can be used as alternates for the methods of this section and Exercises 5 and 7. Some of these will be taken up briefly in Chapter 13.

## EXERCISES

1. An investigation of the relative merits of two kinds of flashlight batteries showed that a random sample of 100 batteries of Brand X lasted on the average 36.5 hours with a standard deviation of 1.8 hours, while a random sample of 80 batteries of Brand Y lasted on the average 36.8 hours with a standard deviation of 1.5 hours. Use a level of significance of 0.05 to test whether the observed difference between the average lifetimes is significant.

2. Measurements of the heights of male adults living in two different countries produced the following results (in inches)

$$n_1 = 200 \qquad \bar{x}_1 = 69 \qquad s_1 = 2$$
$$n_2 = 150 \qquad \bar{x}_2 = 67 \qquad s_2 = 3$$

Test at a level of significance of 0.01 whether the difference between the two sample means is significant.

3. A study made to compare the nicotine content of two brands of cigarettes showed that 50 cigarettes of Brand A had an average nicotine content of 24.2 milligrams with a standard deviation of 1.3 milligrams, whereas 50 cigarettes of Brand B had an average nicotine content of 25.1 milligrams with a standard deviation of 1.5 milligrams. Test at a level of significance of 0.05 whether the difference between the means of these two samples is significant.

4. The same achievement test was given to samples of high school seniors in two different cities with the following results

$$n_1 = 100 \qquad \bar{x}_1 = 64 \qquad s_1 = 6$$
$$n_2 = 100 \qquad \bar{x}_2 = 59 \qquad s_2 = 5$$

Use a level of significance of 0.05 to test whether the difference between the means is significant. *Read.*

5. When dealing with small samples, tests of the significance of the difference between two sample means are based on the Student-*t* distribution instead of the normal curve. Specifically, they are based on the statistic

$$t = \frac{\bar{x}_1 - \bar{x}_2}{\sqrt{\dfrac{(n_1 - 1)s_1^2 + (n_2 - 1)s_2^2}{n_1 + n_2 - 2}} \cdot \sqrt{\dfrac{1}{n_1} + \dfrac{1}{n_2}}} \qquad (11.7.5) \blacktriangle$$

Making the assumption that the two samples come from populations that can be approximated closely with normal curves *and* the assumption that these two populations have equal standard deviations, the criterion with which we test the hypothesis $\mu_1 = \mu_2$ against the alternative $\mu_1 \neq \mu_2$ at a level of significance of 0.05 becomes

*reject the hypothesis if $t < -t_{.025}$ or $t > t_{.025}$; accept the hypothesis (or reserve judgment) if $-t_{.025} \le t \le t_{.025}$, where $t$ is to be calculated with formula (11.7.5) and the number of degrees of freedom is $n_1 + n_2 - 2$.*

Use this criterion to test the significance of the difference between the average yield of two varieties of corn, if 6 test plots planted with one variety yielded on the average 88.6 bushels per acre with a standard deviation of 5.7 bushels per acre, while 6 test plots planted with the other variety yielded on the average 96.0 bushels per acre with a standard deviation of 6.2 bushels per acre. Use a level of significance of 0.05.

6. A random sample of 12 families in one city showed an average weekly food expenditure of $38 with a standard deviation of $10, and a random sample of 15 families in another city showed an average weekly food expenditure of $32 with a standard deviation of $12. Using the criterion of Exercise 5 with $t_{.005}$ instead of $t_{.025}$, test whether the difference between the two means is significant at a level of significance of 0.01.

7. The method of Section 11.7 and, for that matter, the method of Exercise 5 above do not apply unless the two samples are *independent*. Suppose, then, that we want to study the effectiveness of a certain diet and that we are given the following information concerning the weights "before and after" of a random sample of 8 adult females in the age group from 35 to 40 (data in pounds).

|  | *Before* | *After* |
|---|---|---|
| Mrs. Jones | 137 | 132 |
| Mrs. Brown | 130 | 121 |
| Mrs. Smith | 124 | 126 |
| Mrs. Green | 138 | 130 |
| Mrs. Black | 149 | 147 |
| Mrs. White | 140 | 141 |
| Mrs. Taylor | 168 | 159 |
| Mrs. Doe | 152 | 147 |

The mean of the first column is 142.2, that of the second column is 137.9, and in order to test whether the difference between the means of these *dependent* samples is significant we proceed as follows: instead of working with the actual weights, we use the differences in weight (the increases or decreases in weight), which in this example are $-5$, $-9$, 2, $-8$, $-2$, 1, $-9$, and $-5$. *We then test the null hypothesis that these differences constitute a random sample from a population whose mean is* $\mu = 0$ *against the one-sided alternative that $\mu$ is less than 0, using the method of Section* 11.6. Since $n = 8$ in our example, use the small-sample technique of Section 11.6 to test whether the diet is effective. Use a level of significance of 0.05.

## BIBLIOGRAPHY

Informal discussions of the two types of errors, tests of significance, null hypotheses, operating characteristic curves, and the various tests treated in this chapter may be found in many elementary texts, including

Moroney, M. J., *Facts from Figures*. London: Penguin Books, 1951, Chap. 13.

Wallis, W. A., and Roberts, H. V., *Statistics: A New Approach*. Glencoe, Ill.: The Free Press, 1956, Chaps. 12 and 13.

Derivations of the formulas for the standard error of the difference between two proportions and the standard error of the difference between two means are given in

Hoel, P. G., *Introduction to Mathematical Statistics*, 2nd ed. New York: John Wiley, 1954, Chap. 6.

A discussion of the *small sample t-test* for the comparison of two means may also be found in the book by Hoel mentioned above (page 227). The test of the significance of the difference between the means of two *dependent* samples (see Exercise 7 above) is mentioned in

Croxton, F. E., and Cowden, D. J., *Applied General Statistics*, 2nd ed. Englewood Cliffs, N. J.: Prentice-Hall, 1955, p. 654.

# Chapter 12

# Further Tests of Hypotheses

## 12.1 / The Analysis of an *r* by *k* Table

A direct generalization of the work of Section 11.5, where we tested the significance of the difference between *two* proportions, is to consider differences among *more than two* proportions. For example, we may want to test whether a production process is "in control," whether the true proportion of defectives remains constant, if on 3 consecutive days there were 15 defectives in a sample of size 100, 24 defectives in a sample of size 120, and 36 defectives in a sample of size 200. We would thus be interested in testing whether the differences among $15/100 = 0.15$, $24/120 = 0.20$, and $36/200 = 0.18$ may be attributed to chance of whether they are indicative of a lack of control.

To consider another example, we may want to decide whether the members of four large labor unions really differ in opinion concerning a certain piece of legislation, if we are given the sample information contained in the following table.

|  | Union A | Union B | Union C | Union D | Totals |
|---|---|---|---|---|---|
| For the legislation | 83 | 67 | 114 | 95 | 359 |
| Against the legislation | 37 | 33 | 86 | 55 | 211 |
| Totals: | 120 | 100 | 200 | 150 | |

The technique that is used to decide questions of this kind applies also to the more general situation where each "trial" permits *more than two possible outcomes*. For example, in our illustration each union member might be asked whether he is for the legislation, against it, or undecided, and we might get the following 3 by 4 table (it contains 3 rows and 4 columns).

|  | Union A | Union B | Union C | Union D | Totals |
|---|---|---|---|---|---|
| For the legislation | 80 | 55 | 103 | 86 | 324 |
| Against the legislation | 30 | 21 | 68 | 42 | 161 |
| Undecided | 10 | 24 | 29 | 22 | 85 |
| Totals: | 120 | 100 | 200 | 150 | |

In both of these examples the *column totals* are fixed, they are the sizes of the samples taken from the four groups, but the *row totals* depend on chance. Since the statistical technique we shall presently discuss applies also to problems in which *the column totals as well as the row totals depend on chance*, let us consider an example of this type. Let us suppose, for instance, that we want to study whatever relationship there may exist between a family's dietary habits with regard to milk consumption and the amount of education received by the homemaker. If a survey constituting a random sample of 500 families produced the following result

ADEQUACY OF MILK CONSUMPTION

|  | Inadequate | Barely adequate | Very adequate | Totals |
|---|---|---|---|---|
| Did not finish high school | 75 | 54 | 12 | 141 |
| Finished high school | 64 | 106 | 28 | 198 |
| At least one year of college | 28 | 82 | 51 | 161 |
| Totals: | 167 | 242 | 91 | |

the totals of the rows as well as the columns are left to chance. Incidentally, the headings of the rows refer to the education of the homemaker.

In order to discuss the criterion used to analyze problems of this kind, let us begin by introducing a general notation. Writing the column headings as $A_1, A_2, \ldots, A_k$ and the row headings as $B_1, B_2,$

..., $B_r$, we shall refer to the entries of an *r by k table* and the various totals in the following fashion.

|  | $A_1$ | $A_2$ | $A_3$ |  | $A_k$ | Row totals |
|---|---|---|---|---|---|---|
| $B_1$ | $n_{11}$ | $n_{12}$ | $n_{13}$ | . | $n_{1k}$ | $n_{1.}$ |
| $B_2$ | $n_{21}$ | $n_{22}$ | $n_{23}$ | . | $n_{2k}$ | $n_{2.}$ |
| $B_3$ | $n_{31}$ | $n_{32}$ | $n_{33}$ | . | $n_{3k}$ | $n_{3.}$ |
|  | . | . | . | . | . |  |
| $B_r$ | $n_{r1}$ | $n_{r2}$ | $n_{r3}$ | . | $n_{rk}$ | $n_{r.}$ |
| Column totals: | $n_{.1}$ | $n_{.2}$ | $n_{.3}$ |  | $n_{.k}$ | $n$ |

The *observed cell frequencies*, as the entries in the individual cells are called, are written $n_{11}$, $n_{23}$, $n_{46}$, ..., and in general, $n_{ij}$, where the *first* subscript indicates the *row* while the *second* subscript indicates the *column* to which the respective cell belongs. Thus, the number of items falling into the cell which is in the second row and third column is written as $n_{23}$. The totals of the rows are referred to as $n_{1.}$, $n_{2.}$, ..., $n_{r.}$, and in general, as $n_{i.}$; the totals of the columns are correspondingly referred to as $n_{.1}$, $n_{.2}$, ..., $n_{.k}$, and in general, as $n_{.j}$. The *grand total*, that is, the total number of cases for the entire table, is given by the letter $n$.

To demonstrate what hypotheses we actually want to test, let us again refer to our three numerical examples. In the first, on page 272, we want to test *whether the actual proportions of union members for (or against) the legislation is the same for all four unions*. In the second, on page 273, we want to test *whether the true distribution of proportions of union members for the legislation, against it, or undecided is the same for all four unions*. In the third example, on page 273, we want to test *whether the true distribution of proportions of homemakers whose family's milk consumption is inadequate, barely adequate, or very adequate is the same regardless of the homemakers education*. To state matters more simply without introducing further symbolism, let us point out that we are in each case testing a hypothesis of *independence*. In the first example we are testing whether endorsement or opposition to the given piece of legislation is *independent* of membership in the given unions; in the second example we are testing whether preferences for the three categories are *independent* of membership in the given unions; and in the third example we are testing whether adequacy of milk consumption is *independent* of the education of the homemaker.*

As we pointed out in the preceding chapter, a statistical hypothesis can be accepted or rejected only *if we know what to expect if the hypothesis is true.* To proceed, we shall thus have to ask for the frequencies which we might *expect* in the various cells of an *r* by *k* table if the hypothesis of independence is true.

To illustrate the calculation of so-called *expected cell frequencies*, let us return to the example on page 273, namely, the one dealing with adequacy of milk consumption and the education of the homemaker. We might ask, for instance, *how many families can we expect in a sample of 500 whose milk consumption is inadequate and whose homemaker did not finish high school?* Using the word "expect" in the sense of a mathematical expectation, the expected frequency for this cell is obtained by multiplying 500 by the probability of getting a family fitting the description of this cell. Under the assumption of *independence* (see Section 7.2) the probability of getting a family whose milk consumption is inadequate *and* whose homemaker did not finish high school is the *product* of the two individual probabilities, that is, the probability of getting a family whose milk consumption is inadequate and the probability of getting a family whose homemaker did not finish high school. Since these probabilities are generally unknown, we have no choice but to estimate them from our data; thus, since 141 of the 500 families had homemakers who did not finish high school, we *estimate* the probability of getting a family whose homemaker did not finish high school as $141/500 = 0.282$. Similarly, since 167 of the 500 families were rated as not drinking enough milk, we *estimate* the probability of getting a family whose milk consumption is inadequate as $167/500 = 0.334$. Having obtained these two estimates, we can now say that, under the null hypothesis of independence, we could have expected

$$500(0.282)(0.334) = 47.1$$

of the 500 families to belong to the cell in the first row and first column of our table.

*More rigorous formulations of the hypotheses tested in the first two examples are given on pages 246 and 254 of the book by Freund and Williams referred to in the Bibliography on page 293. In the third example we might formulate the hypothesis to be tested as follows: writing $p_{ij}$ for the probabililty of getting an item falling into the $i$th row and $j$th column, $p_{i.}$ for the probability of getting an item falling into the $i$th row, and $p_{.j}$ for the probability of getting an item falling into the $j$th column, the null hypothesis becomes $p_{ij} = p_{i.} \cdot p_{.j}$ for all $i$ and $j$ [see formula (7.2.3)].

Similarly, the expected frequency for the cell belonging to the first row and second column can be obtained by multiplying 500 by the product of the probability of getting a family whose homemaker did not finish high school and the probability of getting a family whose milk consumption is barely adequate. Proceeding as before, we get

$$500(141/500)(242/500) = 68.2$$

rounding our result again to one decimal.

The remaining cell frequencies could be obtained in the same way, but the calculations may be simplified using the fact that *the sum of the expected cell frequencies of any row or column must equal the sum of the observed frequencies of that row or column.* The expected number of families whose milk consumption is very adequate and whose homemaker did not finish high school may, thus, be obtained by subtracting 47.1 and 68.2 from 141, getting $141 - 47.1 - 68.2 = 25.7$.

Calculating the expected frequency for the cell belonging to the second row and first column by the same method which we used above, we get

$$500(198/500)(167/500) = 66.1$$

and calculating that for the cell belonging to the second row and second column, we get

$$500(198/500)(242/500) = 95.8$$

All the remaining cell frequencies can now be obtained by subtraction from the row and column totals. The expected number of families whose milk consumption is inadequate and whose homemaker had at least one year of college is $167 - 47.1 - 66.1 = 53.8$; the expected number of families whose milk consumption is barely adequate and whose homemaker had at least one year of college is $242 - 68.2 - 95.8 = 78.0$; the expected number of families whose milk consumption is very adequate and whose homemaker finished high school is $198 - 66.1 - 95.8 = 36.1$; and the expected number of families whose milk consumption is very adequate and whose homemaker finished at least a year of college is $161 - 53.8 - 78.0 = 29.2$ *or* $91 - 25.7 - 36.1 = 29.2$.

What we have done here can easily be generalized to calculate the expected frequency for any cell of an $r$ by $k$ table. Letting $e_{ij}$ stand for the expected frequency for the cell belonging to the $i$th row and $j$th column, we can obtain this quantity by multiplying the total frequency $n$, the sum of the observed frequencies of all the cells, by the product of the probability of getting a case falling into the $i$th row and the probability of getting a case falling into the $j$th column. *Estimating* these two probabilities as before as $n_{i.}/n$ and $n_{.j}/n$ we get

$$e_{ij} = n\left(\frac{n_{i.}}{n}\right)\left(\frac{n_{.j}}{n}\right) = \frac{(n_{i.})(n_{.j})}{n} \qquad (12.1.1)\blacktriangle$$

*Under the hypothesis of independence, the expected frequency for any cell can thus be obtained by multiplying the total of the row to which the cell belongs by the total of the column to which it belongs and then dividing by the grand total.*

We arrived at this formula for $e_{ij}$ by referring to the illustration in which the row totals as well as the column totals were left to chance. However, formula (12.1.1) applies also to the other examples in which the column totals were fixed. With reference to these examples we would have to justify its derivation in a slightly different way.

We calculated the expected cell frequencies in our example in order to test the null hypothesis that there is *no relationship* between a family's milk consumption and the education of its homemaker. Any decision to accept or reject this hypothesis will have to depend on a comparison between the $n_{ij}$ and the $e_{ij}$, that is, a comparison between the frequencies which we observed and those which we could have expected if the null hypothesis is true. *If there is a very close agreement between the two sets of frequencies, this would be indicative of the fact that the null hypothesis should be accepted; if there are pronounced differences, this would be indicative of the fact that the null hypothesis should be rejected.* To facilitate this comparison, let us show the two sets of frequencies together as in the following table, with each expected frequency in parentheses below the corresponding observed frequency.

ADEQUACY OF MILK CONSUMPTION

|  | *Inadequate* | *Barely adequate* | *Very adequate* |
|---|---|---|---|
| Did not finish high school | 75 (47.1) | 54 (68.2) | 12 (25.7) |
| Finished high school | 64 (66.1) | 106 (95.8) | 28 (36.1) |
| At least one year of college | 28 (53.8) | 82 (78.0) | 51 (29.2) |

It should be noted that in calculating the expected cell frequencies we rounded to one decimal. It is customary to round such frequencies to one decimal or to the nearest whole number.

Looking at the above table it is apparent that there are considerable differences between the two sets of frequencies, *but it remains to be seen whether these differences may be attributed to chance or whether they are indicative of the fact that the null hypothesis is false, namely, that there is a dependence between a family's milk drinking habits and the education of its homemaker.*

The criterion which we shall use to put this decision on a precise basis employs the statistic

$$\chi^2 = \sum \frac{(n_{ij} - e_{ij})^2}{e_{ij}} \qquad (12.1.2)\blacktriangle$$

It is called "chi-square" and its symbol is the Greek letter *chi* with the exponent 2. It owes its name to the fact that (if the null hypothesis of independence is true) its sampling distribution can be approximated very closely with the theoretical distribution, called the *chi-square distribution*, which we met earlier in Exercise 3 on page 236.

The summation in (12.1.2) extends over all cells of the *r* by *k* table; in other words, we must calculate

$$\frac{(n_{ij} - e_{ij})^2}{e_{ij}}$$

separately for each cell of the table, in our illustration for each of the 9 cells of the 3 by 3 table, and then add the values obtained.

If there is a close agreement between the observed and expected frequencies, the differences $n_{ij} - e_{ij}$ and $\chi^2$ will be relatively small; if the agreement is poor, the differences and $\chi^2$ will be large. *Small values of $\chi^2$ thus support the null hypothesis while large values of $\chi^2$ lead to its rejection.* The actual decision whether $\chi^2$ is large enough to reject the null hypothesis of independence is based on the chi-square distribution (see Figure 12.1) whose areas are given in Table III in the same way in which areas under the *t*-distribution were given in Table II. Analogous to $t_{.05}$ and $t_{.01}$ we shall write $\chi^2_{.05}$ and $\chi^2_{.01}$ for values which are such that 5 and 1 per cent of the area under the chi-square distribution lies to their right.

The chi-square distribution, like the *t*-distribution, depends on a quantity called the *number of degrees of freedom. When $\chi^2$ is calculated for an r by k table, the formula for the number of degrees of freedom is*

$$(r - 1)(k - 1) \qquad (12.1.3)\blacktriangle$$

To justify this formula let us point out that in our numerical example we had to apply (12.1.1) only $(3 - 1)(3 - 1) = 4$ times to calculate the expected cell frequencies; we then obtained all the others by

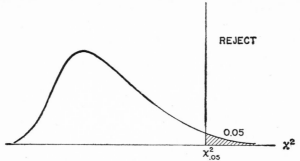

**Fig. 12.1.** A chi-square distribution.

subtraction from suitable row or column totals. More generally, it can be shown that if $(r - 1)(k - 1)$ of the expected cell frequencies of an $r$ by $k$ table are calculated with formula (12.1.1), all of the remaining $e_{ij}$ may be obtained by subtraction from the totals of rows or columns.

Using the statistic $x^2$, we can now test the null hypothesis of independence as formulated with reference to our examples on pages 272 and 273 with the following criterion (see Figure 12.1)

*reject the hypothesis if $x^2 > x^2_{.05}$; accept the hypothesis (or reserve judgment) if $x^2 \leq x^2_{.05}$, where $x^2$ is to be calculated with (12.1.2) and the number of degrees of freedom equals $(r - 1)(k - 1)$.*

If we wanted to use a level of significance of 0.01 instead of 0.05, we would only have to substitute $x^2_{.01}$ for $x^2_{.05}$.

To illustrate the use of the chi-square criterion, let us now continue with the example in which we wanted to decide whether there is a dependence between a family's milk drinking habits and the education of its homemaker. Substituting the observed and expected frequencies shown in the table on page 277, we get

$$x^2 = \frac{(75 - 47.1)^2}{47.1} + \frac{(54 - 68.2)^2}{68.2} + \frac{(12 - 25.7)^2}{25.7} + \frac{(64 - 66.1)^2}{66.1}$$

$$+ \frac{(106 - 95.8)^2}{95.8} + \frac{(28 - 36.1)^2}{36.1} + \frac{(28 - 53.8)^2}{53.8}$$

$$+ \frac{(82 - 78.0)^2}{78.0} + \frac{(51 - 29.2)^2}{29.2}$$

$$= 58.63$$

Since this exceeds 9.4888, the value given in Table III for $\chi^2_{.05}$ with $(3 - 1)(3 - 1) = 4$ degrees of freedom, *the null hypothesis must be rejected.* The discrepancies between the observed and expected frequencies are too big to be attributed to chance and we conclude that there is a relationship, that is, a dependence, between a family's milk drinking habits and the education of its homemaker.

To give another illustration of the method presented in this section, let us consider the first example mentioned on page 272, the one dealing with the opinions (pro and con) expressed by the members of 4 unions with regard to a certain piece of legislation. Calculating the expected frequencies for the first three cells of the first row with (12.1.1), we get

$$\frac{(359)(120)}{570} = 75.6$$

$$\frac{(359)(100)}{570} = 63.0$$

$$\frac{(359)(200)}{570} = 126.0$$

and subtracting these values from appropriate row and column totals we get the expected frequencies shown in parentheses in the following table.

|  | *Union A* | *Union B* | *Union C* | *Union D* |
|---|---|---|---|---|
| For the legislation | 83 (75.6) | 67 (63.0) | 114 (126.0) | 95 (94.4) |
| Against the legislation | 37 (44.4) | 33 (37.0) | 86 (74.0) | 55 (55.6) |

If we now substitute these observed and expected frequencies into formula (12.1.2), we get

$$\chi^2 = \frac{(83 - 75.6)^2}{75.6} + \frac{(67 - 63.0)^2}{63.0} + \frac{(114 - 126.0)^2}{126.0} + \frac{(95 - 94.4)^2}{94.4}$$

$$+ \frac{(37 - 44.4)^2}{44.4} + \frac{(33 - 37.0)^2}{37.0} + \frac{(86 - 74.0)^2}{74.0} + \frac{(55 - 55.6)^2}{55.6}$$

$$= 5.72$$

Using again a level of significance of 0.05, we find that $\chi^2_{.05}$ for $(2 - 1)(4 - 1) = 3$ degrees of freedom is 7.815 (see Table III on page 386). Since the value which we calculated for our 2 by 4 table is less than this tabular value of $\chi^2_{.05}$ *the null hypothesis cannot be rejected.* The discrepancies between the observed and expected frequencies may be attributed to chance and *we can reserve judgment or conclude that the proportion of members favoring the given piece of legislation is the same for each of the four unions.*

As we have pointed out earlier, it is customary to round the expected cell frequencies of an r by k table to one decimal or to the nearest whole number. Most of the entries of Table III are given to three decimals, but there is seldom any need to carry more than two decimals when calculating $\chi^2$ by means of formula (12.1.2).

Since the sampling distribution of $\chi^2$, as defined by means of formula (12.1.2), is only *approximately* the theoretical distribution on which Table III is based, the criterion on page 279 should not be used when the expected cell frequencies are very small. *A relatively safe rule followed by many statisticians is to use the chi-square criterion only when none of the expected cell frequencies is less than 5. If one or more of the cells have expected frequencies less than 5, the criterion can still be used by combining some of the cells. This is done, for example, in the numerical illustration of Section 12.2. If 2 cells are thus treated as one, it will also be necessary to subtract 1 from the number of degrees of freedom.*

Although we have used the term "r by k table" in all our examples, the term "contingency table" is frequently used when items are classified in a two-way table and the row as well as column totals are left to chance.

## EXERCISES

1. In a random sample of 100 registered voters *with low incomes* 65 are for Candidate X and 35 are for Candidate Y; in a random sample of 100 registered voters *with average incomes* 50 are for Candidate X and 50 are for Candidate Y; and in a random sample of 100 registered voters *with high incomes* 45 are for Candidate X and 55 are for Candidate Y. Test at a level of significance of 0.05 whether the differences of opinion concerning Candidates X and Y are significant.

2. A research organization, interested in testing whether the proportions of sons taking up the occupations of their fathers are equal for a selected group of occupations, took random samples of size 200, 150, 180, and 100, respectively, in which the fathers are doctors, bankers, teachers, and lawyers, and obtained the following results:

| | Doctors | Bankers | Teachers | Lawyers |
|---|---|---|---|---|
| Same Occupation | 37 | 22 | 26 | 23 |
| Different occupation | 163 | 128 | 154 | 77 |

Use a level of significance of 0.05 to test the hypothesis that the true proportions of sons taking up the occupations of their fathers is the same for the given occupations.

3. Samples of three kinds of materials, subjected to extreme temperature changes, produced the results shown in the following table.

| | Material A | Material B | Material C |
|---|---|---|---|
| Broke completely | 25 | 45 | 40 |
| Showed slight defects | 40 | 35 | 35 |
| Remained perfect | 35 | 20 | 25 |

Test, at a level of significance of 0.05, whether the true proportions of items falling into the three categories are the same for all three materials.

4. Decide on the basis of the information given in the following table whether students' interest in statistics is *independent* of their ability in mathematics (use a level of significance of 0.01):

| | | ABILITY IN MATHEMATICS | | |
|---|---|---|---|---|
| | | Low | Average | High |
| | Low | 32 | 23 | 11 |
| INTEREST IN STATISTICS | Average | 29 | 31 | 24 |
| | High | 8 | 25 | 47 |

5. A study to determine whether salesmanship (as measured by volume of sales) is *independent* of a salesman's sense of humor (as measured by a certain objective test) produced the results shown in the following table.

| | | SENSE OF HUMOR | | |
|---|---|---|---|---|
| | | Low | Average | High |
| | Low | 65 | 51 | 42 |
| VOLUME OF SALES | Average | 113 | 178 | 93 |
| | High | 38 | 57 | 67 |

Test at a level of significance of 0.05 whether the hypothesis of *independence* is to be accepted or rejected.

**6.** (*Theoretical Exercise*)  If random samples of size $n_1$ and $n_2$ yield $x_1$ and $x_2$ successes, show that $\chi^2$, calculated according to (12.1.2), gives

$$\chi^2 = \frac{(n_1 + n_2)(n_2 x_1 - n_1 x_2)^2}{n_1 n_2 (x_1 + x_2)[(n_1 + n_2) - (x_1 + x_2)]}$$

**7.** (*Theoretical Exercise*)  Show that the *square* of the expression given for $z$ in (11.5.5) equals the expression given for $\chi^2$ in Exercise 6.

## 12.2 / Tests of Goodness of Fit

The chi-square criterion introduced in the preceding section was used to compare two sets of frequencies, those which were observed and those which we might have expected under the null hypothesis of independence. Although we made this comparison only with reference to $r$ by $k$ tables, the chi-square criterion applies to many other situations in which we are interested in deciding whether differences between observed frequencies and expected frequencies may be attributed to chance.

For instance, the chi-square criterion may be used to decide whether it is reasonable to approximate an observed distribution by means of a normal curve. The reader will recall that in Section 8.8 we considered a distribution of the weights of 300 army recruits and calculated a set of frequencies which we referred to as "expected normal curve frequencies." These were the frequencies which we could have expected if we actually had a normal distribution with the same mean and standard deviation as the given data. The values which we obtained on page 187 were

| Weights (in pounds) | Observed Frequencies | Expected Normal Curve Frequencies |
|---|---|---|
| 150 – 158 | 9 | 9.0 |
| 159 – 167 | 24 | 25.4 |
| 168 – 176 | 51 | 51.5 |
| 177 – 185 | 66 | 71.2 |
| 186 – 194 | 72 | 67.8 |
| 195 – 203 | 48 | 44.6 |
| 204 – 212 | 21 | 20.2 |
| 213 – 221 | 6 ⎫ 9 | 6.3 ⎫ 7.7 |
| 222 – 230 | 3 ⎭ | 1.4 ⎭ |

In Section 8.8 we compared the two sets of frequencies *subjectively* by looking at the two histograms; now let us compare them by means of $\chi^2$ as calculated with the formula

$$\chi^2 = \sum \frac{(n_i - e_i)^2}{e_i} \tag{12.2.1} \blacktriangle$$

This formula differs from (12.1.2) only inasmuch as we are now comparing two sets of frequencies *arranged in single columns* instead of the rectangular arrays of $r$ by $k$ tables. We still square the difference between each pair of frequencies, divide by the expected frequency, and then add the quotients thus obtained.

Substituting the observed frequencies and the expected normal curve frequencies given above into (12.2.1), we get

$$\chi^2 = \frac{(9 - 9.0)^2}{9.0} + \frac{(24 - 25.4)^2}{25.4} + \frac{(51 - 51.5)^2}{51.5} + \frac{(66 - 71.2)^2}{71.2}$$

$$+ \frac{(72 - 67.8)^2}{67.8} + \frac{(48 - 44.6)^2}{44.6} + \frac{(21 - 20.2)^2}{20.2} + \frac{(9 - 7.7)^2}{7.7}$$

$$= 1.232$$

and it should be noted that we combined the last two classes in accordance with the rule that the expected frequencies must be at least 5 (see page 281).

Using the value calculated for $\chi^2$, we can now decide whether the normal curve provides a good fit to the original data. *If $\chi^2$ is very small the fit is good; if it is large the fit is bad.* Actually, we shall test the hypothesis that *the observed distribution constitutes a sample from a population having a normal distribution* with the following criterion:

*reject the hypothesis (and state that the fit is poor) if $\chi^2 > \chi^2_{.05}$; accept the hypothesis (and state that the fit is good) if $\chi^2 \leq \chi^2_{.05}$, where $\chi^2$ is to be calculated with (12.2.1) and the number of degrees of freedom is $k - 3$. Here $k$ is the number of terms added in (12.2.1).*

In our example $k - 3 = 8 - 3 = 5$ and, hence, $\chi^2_{.05} = 11.070$ according to Table III on 386 page. Since the calculated value, namely, $\chi^2 = 1.232$, is *less* than $\chi^2_{.05}$, we shall conclude that *the normal curve provides a good fit.*

In order to explain the formula for the number of degrees of freedom, let us point out that in Section 8.8 the expected frequencies which we calculated depended on 3 quantities obtained from the observed data: the total frequency, the mean, and the standard deviation. *Generally speaking, in a chi-square test of goodness of fit the number of degrees of freedom equals the number of terms added in (12.2.1), that is, the number of pairs of frequencies which we want to compare, minus the number of quantities, determined from the observed data, that are used to calculate the expected frequencies.*

To consider another example in which chi-square is used to test goodness of fit, let us suppose that in Exercise 1 on page 153, where we were asked to toss 4 coins 160 times, we obtained 0, 1, 2, 3, and 4 heads with frequencies of 16, 48, 55, 33, and 8, respectively. Using the formula for the binomial distribution with $n = 4$ and $p = 0.50$ (see page 157), we find that under the assumption that the coins are balanced the probabilities of getting 0, 1, 2, 3, and 4 heads are $\frac{1}{16}$, $\frac{4}{16}$, $\frac{6}{16}$, $\frac{4}{16}$, and $\frac{1}{16}$. Multiplying these probabilities by 160, we obtain the *expected* frequencies shown together with the *observed* frequencies in the following table:

| Number of Heads | Observed Frequencies | Expected Frequencies |
|:---:|:---:|:---:|
| 0 | 16 | 10 |
| 1 | 48 | 40 |
| 2 | 55 | 60 |
| 3 | 33 | 40 |
| 4 | 8 | 10 |

Substituting these frequencies into (12.2.1), we obtain

$$x^2 = \frac{(16 - 10)^2}{10} + \frac{(48 - 40)^2}{40} + \frac{(55 - 60)^2}{60} + \frac{(33 - 40)^2}{40}$$

$$+ \frac{(8 - 10)^2}{10}$$

$$= 7.24$$

and this is indicative of how well the binomial distribution fits to the observed data. Actually, we are testing the hypothesis that *the probability of getting heads is 0.50 for each coin* against the alternative that *at least one of the coins is not balanced.* It is tacitly assumed that the coins are properly tossed.

The criterion which we shall use to decide whether to accept or reject the hypothesis is the same as the one on page 284 except that the formula for the number of degrees of freedom is now $k - 1$. This agrees with the rule given above — the total frequency of 160 is the only quantity, obtained from the observed data, which was used in the calculation of the expected frequencies.

Since the value of 7.24 which we obtained for $x^2$ in our example is *less* than $x^2_{.05} = 9.488$, the value given in Table III for $x^2_{.05}$ with $k - 1 = 5 - 1 = 4$ degrees of freedom, *we cannot reject the hypothesis that the coins are balanced; we shall say that the binomial distribution provides a good fit.*

## EXERCISES

1. Test the goodness of the fit of the normal curve which was fitted to the speed-check distribution in Exercise 6 on page 189. Use a level of significance of 0.05.

2. Test the goodness of the fit of the normal distribution which was fitted in Exercise 7 on page 189. Use a level of significance of 0.01.

3. Test the goodness of the fit of the normal curve fitted to the distribution of time lapses between eruptions of Old Faithful in Exercise 8 on page 190. Use a level of significance of 0.01.

4. Assuming that the expected normal curve frequencies given below were calculated according to the method of Section 8.8, test for goodness of fit at a level of significance of 0.05

| Observed Frequencies | Expected Normal Curve Frequencies |
|---|---|
| 19 | 17 |
| 107 | 104 |
| 209 | 208 |
| 135 | 143 |
| 28 | 27 |
| 2 | 1 |

5. Use the $\chi^2$ criterion to compare the observed and expected frequencies of Exercise 3 on page 153. Test for goodness of fit at a level of significance of 0.05.

6. The following table contains a distribution obtained in 320 tosses of 6 coins and the corresponding expected frequencies calculated with the formula for the binomial distribution with $p = 0.50$ and $n = 6$

| Number of Heads | Observed Frequencies | Expected Frequencies |
|---|---|---|
| 0 | 9 | 5 |
| 1 | 31 | 30 |
| 2 | 66 | 75 |
| 3 | 108 | 100 |
| 4 | 83 | 75 |
| 5 | 19 | 30 |
| 6 | 4 | 5 |

Test at a level of significance of 0.05 whether the 6 coins are balanced.

7. In order to see whether a die is balanced it was rolled 120 times and the following results were obtained: 1 occurred 17 times, 2 occurred 19 times, 3 occurred 25 times, 4 occurred 23 times, 5 occurred 14 times, and 6 occurred 22 times. Using the fact that the expected frequencies are all 20, calculate $\chi^2$ and test the hypothesis that the die is balanced at a level of significance of 0.05.

## 12.3 / Tests Concerning $k$ Means

In the beginning of this chapter we considered the problem of deciding whether differences among *more than two proportions* can be attributed to chance; now let us generalize the work of Section 11.7 and consider the problem of deciding whether differences among *more than two means* can be attributed to chance. For example, we may want to decide whether there really is a difference among the performance of 3 kinds of tires if 5 tires made by Company A lasted on the average 22,000 miles, 5 tires made by Company B lasted on the average 21,500, while 5 tires made by Company C lasted on the average 20,800 miles. Similarly, we may wish to test whether there really is a difference in the performance of the students in 4 different schools on the basis of a test given to random samples of 10 students of each school. Suppose, for example, that the results obtained in the test are

| School 1 | School 2 | School 3 | School 4 |
|----------|----------|----------|----------|
| 69 | 82 | 71 | 69 |
| 53 | 93 | 82 | 62 |
| 91 | 94 | 75 | 86 |
| 74 | 60 | 64 | 90 |
| 82 | 78 | 52 | 39 |
| 57 | 85 | 73 | 56 |
| 76 | 98 | 86 | 74 |
| 94 | 72 | 68 | 83 |
| 60 | 83 | 54 | 47 |
| 74 | 75 | 75 | 64 |

The means of these four samples are 73, 82, 70, and 67, and *what we would like to know is whether the discrepancies among these means are significant or whether they may reasonably be attributed to chance.*

Letting $\mu_1$, $\mu_2$, $\mu_3$, and $\mu_4$ stand for the average scores we would obtain if we gave the test to *all* the students in the four schools, we shall want to test the hypothesis

$$\text{Null hypothesis:} \quad \mu_1 = \mu_2 = \mu_3 = \mu_4$$

against the alternative that the four $\mu$'s are *not* all the same.

It stands to reason that this null hypothesis should be rejected if the differences among the $\bar{x}$'s are *very large* and that it should be accepted if the differences among the $\bar{x}$'s are *very small*. What remains to be seen is how to decide whether the discrepancies are too large to be attributed to chance.

An obvious way to measure the differences among the $\bar{x}$'s is to find their standard deviation, or as we shall do here, the *square* of their standard deviation which we called their *variance*. In order to use formula (4.4.2), we first find that the mean of the four $\bar{x}$'s is

$$\frac{73 + 82 + 70 + 67}{4} = 73$$

and we then get for their *variance*

$$\frac{(73 - 73)^2 + (82 - 73)^2 + (70 - 73)^2 + (67 - 73)^2}{4 - 1} = 42$$

In order to decide whether the figure which we obtained for the variance of the four $\bar{x}$'s may be attributed to chance, that is, whether it may be looked upon as a measure of *chance variation*, we shall have to get an indication of the size of the chance fluctuations among the given data *from some other source*. Since this may be obtained by looking at the fluctuations *within* the four samples, let us calculate their variances, which we shall denote $s_1^2$, $s_2^2$, $s_3^2$, and $s_4^2$. Using again formula (4.4.2) we find that

$$s_1^2 = \frac{1}{10-1} \left\{ \begin{array}{l} (69 - 73)^2 + (53 - 73)^2 + (91 - 73)^2 + (74 - 73)^2 + (82 - 73)^2 \\ + (57 - 73)^2 + (76 - 73)^2 + (94 - 73)^2 + (60 - 73)^2 + (74 - 73)^2 \end{array} \right\}$$

$$= 188.67$$

and the reader can easily verify that

$$s_2^2 = 131.11 \qquad s_3^2 = 120.00 \qquad s_4^2 = 282.00$$

Before we go any further, let us state an assumption which is required to perform the test we are planning to describe. *We shall have to assume that all of our samples come from populations having normal distributions with the identical standard deviation $\sigma$.* Combining this assumption with the null hypothesis that the populations also have *equal means*, we can look upon our four samples as *samples from one and the same population*.

Consequently, the *variance* which we calculated for the four $\bar{x}$'s may be looked upon as an *estimate* of $\sigma_{\bar{x}}^2 = \sigma^2/n$, see formula (9.3.1). In other words, $n$ times the quantity which we obtained, namely $10 \cdot 42 = 420$, may be looked upon as an estimate of $\sigma^2$. (The size of each sample was $n = 10$.) On the other hand, the sample variances and their average

$$\frac{s_1^2 + s_2^2 + s_3^2 + s_4^2}{4} = \frac{188.67 + 131.11 + 120.00 + 282.00}{4}$$

$$= 180.44$$

are also estimates of $\sigma^2$. Whereas the first estimate, 420, is based on the *variation between the sample means*, the second, 180.44, is based on the *variation within the samples* and, hence, it may be looked upon as a measure of *chance variation*. The variation between the four $\bar{x}$'s is thus bigger than our estimate of chance variation; it remains to be seen, however, whether the variation between the $\bar{x}$'s is *significantly* bigger than chance variation.

The statistic which we shall employ to put this decision on a precise basis is called $F$ and it consists very simply of the *ratio* of the two estimates of $\sigma^2$ which we have calculated above. Thus, in our example

$$F = \frac{420}{180.44} = 2.33$$

and we shall have to see whether this value is *large enough* to reject the null hypothesis that the four samples came from populations with equal means.

This decision will be based on the sampling distribution of the $F$ statistic, appropriately called the $F$-distribution; an example of this theoretical distribution is shown in Figure 12.2. Depending on the level of significance, we shall be interested in $F_{.05}$ or $F_{.01}$, namely, in values which are such that 5 per cent or 1 per cent of the area under

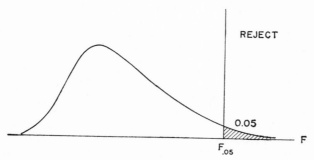

**Fig. 12.2.** An F-distribution.

the curve lies to their right. These values, which provide the dividing lines of our criterion, are given in Tables IVa and IVb on pages 387 and 388.

Tables IVa and IVb differ from the corresponding tables for $\chi^2$ and $t$ inasmuch as their entries depend on *two* quantities, *the number of degrees of freedom for the numerator of F* and *the number of degrees of freedom for the denominator of F*. The numerator of $F$ consists of the variance of four $\bar{x}$'s in our example and it, thus, has $4 - 1 = 3$ degrees of freedom (see discussion on page 97). The denominator of $F$ consists of the mean of the four sample variances, each of which is based on 10 observations. For each sample variance we thus have $10 - 1 = 9$ degrees of freedom, and for their sum or their mean we have $4 \cdot 9 = 36$ degrees of freedom.

Using a level of significance of 0.05, Table IVa shows that for 3 and 36 degrees of freedom $F_{.05}$ lies somewhere between 2.92 and 2.84. The exact value is not given in this table, but since $F = 2.33$, the quantity which we obtained in our example, is less than 2.84 anyhow, *we cannot reject the null hypothesis that the four samples came from populations with equal means.* Although the four sample means differed considerably, the differences among them are not statistically significant.

So far we have illustrated the method used to test whether differences among several means are significant with reference to a particular numerical example. To study the general case, let us suppose that we have $k$ random samples of size $n$ from $k$ different populations and that our observations (measurements) are arranged in the following kind of table:

|  | 1st Sample | 2nd Sample | ... | kth Sample |
|---|---|---|---|---|
|  | $x_{11}$ | $x_{12}$ | ... | $x_{1k}$ |
|  | $x_{21}$ | $x_{22}$ | ... | $x_{2k}$ |
|  | $x_{31}$ | $x_{32}$ | ... | $x_{3k}$ |
|  | ... | ... | ... | ... |
|  | $x_{n1}$ | $x_{n2}$ | ... | $x_{nk}$ |
| *Means:* | $\bar{x}_1$ | $\bar{x}_2$ |  | $\bar{x}_k$ |

In this notation the *first subscript* is 1, 2, 3, ..., or $n$, depending on whether we are referring to the first, second, third, ..., or $n$th observation of the respective sample, while the *second subscript* is 1, 2, 3, ..., or $k$ depending on whether we are referring to the first, second, third, ..., or $k$th sample. Thus, $x_{ij}$ stands for the $i$th observation of the $j$th sample. The means of the $k$ samples are written as $\bar{x}_1, \bar{x}_2, \bar{x}_3, \ldots, \bar{x}_k$ and the *over-all mean*, the mean of all the observations, is written as $\bar{x}$.

If we now write the means of the $k$ populations from which the samples were obtained as $\mu_1, \mu_2, \mu_3, \ldots,$ and $\mu_k$, the null hypothesis which we shall want to test is

*Null hypothesis:* $\mu_1 = \mu_2 = \mu_3 = \ldots = \mu_k$

and the alternative hypothesis is that *these μ's are not all the same.* As in our numerical example, we shall have to assume that *the k samples are random and that they come from populations having normal distributions with the same standard deviation σ.*

Writing $F$ as before as the *ratio* of $n$ times the variance of the $\bar{x}$'s to the mean of the $k$ sample variances, simplifications yield the following formula

$$F = \frac{kn(n-1) \cdot \sum_{j=1}^{k} (\bar{x}_j - \bar{x})^2}{(k-1) \cdot \sum_{i=1}^{n} \sum_{j=1}^{k} (x_{ij} - \bar{x}_j)^2} \qquad (12.3.1)\blacktriangle$$

The summation in the numerator of (12.3.1) is obtained by subtracting $\bar{x}$, the over-all mean, from each of the sample means, and then adding the squares of the deviations. The *double* summation in the denominator is obtained by subtracting from each observation the mean of the sample to which it belongs and then adding the squares of the deviations. Short-cut formulas for computing these sums of squares are referred to in the Bibliography on page 293.

Using the theoretical distribution discussed on page 289 (see also Figure 12.2), we can now test the null hypothesis that the samples came from populations with equal means with the following criterion

*reject the hypothesis if $F > F_{.05}$; accept the hypothesis (or reserve judgment) if $F \leq F_{.05}$, where $F$ is to be calculated with formula (12.3.1) and the number of degrees of freedom for the numerator and denominator of $F$ are $k-1$ and $k(n-1)$, respectively.*

To change the level of significance of this one-tail criterion to 0.01, we have only to substitute $F_{.01}$ for $F_{.05}$. *As a word of caution let us remind the reader that the above criterion can be used only if it is reasonable to assume that the samples come from populations having normal distributions and equal standard deviations.*

The method we have studied here belongs to a very important branch of statistics called the *analysis of variance.* We, so to speak, analyze what part of the fluctuations of our data can be attributed to various sources of variation; we then proceed, as in our example, to compare fluctuations attributed to a specific source with chance variation. Reference to fairly elementary introductions to the subject of analysis of variance are given below.

## EXERCISES

**1.** The following are 3 consecutive weeks' earnings (in dollars) of 3 salesmen employed by a given firm:

| Mr. Black | Mr. Green | Mr. White |
|-----------|-----------|-----------|
| 152 | 181 | 160 |
| 175 | 171 | 130 |
| 180 | 203 | 124 |

Calculate $F$ with formula (12.3.1) and, assuming that the necessary assumptions can be met, test at a level of significance of 0.05 whether the differences among the average weekly earnings of these three salesmen are significant.

**2.** Random samples of 4 brands of tires required the following braking distances while going at 30 miles per hour:

| Brand A | Brand B | Brand C | Brand D |
|---------|---------|---------|---------|
| 25 | 29 | 26 | 27 |
| 28 | 28 | 30 | 27 |
| 23 | 24 | 29 | 26 |
| 24 | 23 | 31 | 24 |

Calculate $F$ with formula (12.3.1) and, assuming that the necessary assumptions can be met, test at a level of significance of 0.05 whether the differences among the average braking distances are significant.

**3.** A study designed to test whether there is a difference in musical talent among the teenagers in 3 different parts of the country produced the following results (units are scores obtained in a standard test):

| Region A | Region B | Region C |
|----------|----------|----------|
| 81 | 94 | 81 |
| 69 | 52 | 75 |
| 53 | 77 | 80 |
| 94 | 84 | 62 |
| 63 | 83 | 32 |

Calculate $F$ with formula (12.3.1) and, assuming that the necessary assumptions can be met, test at a level of significance of 0.01 whether the differences among the means are significant.

**4.** (*Theoretical Exercise*) Show, symbolically, that when $k = 2$, the value of $F$ obtained according to the method of this section equals the *square* of the value given for $t$ by formula (11.7.5) on page 270 with $n_1 = n_2 = n$. This shows that when $k = 2$ and the two samples are of equal size, the small sample $t$-test of Exercise 5 on page 270 and the $F$ test of this section are *equivalent*.

## BIBLIOGRAPHY

An informal treatment of the chi-square criterion and its various applications may be found in

> Moroney, M. J., *Facts from Figures*. London: Penguin Books, 1951, Chap. 15.

Rigorous formulations of the hypotheses tested in the first two examples of Section 12.1 are given in

> Freund, J. E., and Williams, F. J., *Modern Business Statistics*. Englewood Cliffs, N. J.: Prentice-Hall, 1958, p. 246 and p. 254.

Elementary introductions to the analysis of variance and related topics of experimental design are given in the book by Moroney mentioned above (Chapter 19) and, among others, in

> Dixon, W. J., and Massey, F. J., *Introduction to Statistical Analysis*, 2nd ed. New York: McGraw-Hill, 1957, Chap. 10.

> Rosander, A. C., *Elementary Principles of Statistics*. New York: Van Nostrand, 1951, Chaps. 30 and 31.

Short-cut formulas for calculating the sums of squares appearing in the numerator and denominator of $F$ may be found in each of the texts listed above. For a more advanced treatment of the theory underlying the chi-square and $F$ distributions, see

> Hoel, P. G., *Introduction to Mathematical Statistics*, 2nd ed. New York: John Wiley, 1954, Chaps. 9, 11, and 12.

Chapter *13*

# Nonparametric Tests

### 13.1 / Introduction

Most of the methods treated in the last two chapters required assumptions about the populations from which our samples were obtained; essentially, these methods consisted of tests concerning the *parameters* of these populations, their means, their standard deviations, etc. Since there are problems in which, among other things, the assumption that the population can be approximated closely with a normal curve *cannot be met*, statisticians have developed alternate techniques which have become known as *nonparametric tests*. This name is meant to imply that we are not testing hypotheses concerning the parameters of populations *of a given kind*.

Some nonparametric tests have become fairly popular since they also fall under the headings of "quick and easy" and "short-cut" statistics. Not only are these methods simpler so far as arithmetical detail is concerned, but they are often easier to explain and easier to grasp than the standard techniques of Chapters 11 and 12. Since the subject of nonparametric statistics has become fairly extensive in recent years, we shall limit our discussion here to a few examples: the *sign test*, the *U-test*, and tests based on *runs*.

### 13.2 / The Sign Test

In Exercise 7 on page 270 we suggested a method of testing the significance of the difference between two means in situations where the two samples are *not independent*. The example we used dealt with the weights of certain individuals before and after a diet and we tested for the effectiveness of the diet by considering only the *differences*, that is, the increases and decreases in weight. Subsequently we used the *t*-distribution and the method of Section 11.6, making the necessary assumption that the differences may be looked upon as a sample from a *population* which can be approximated closely with a normal curve. If for some reason this assumption is untenable, it is possible to employ an alternate test, called the *sign test*. This test is based on the *signs* of the differences (whether they are positive or negative) ignoring their magnitudes.

In order to illustrate the sign test, let us consider the following data giving the weights (in pounds) of 20 persons before and after a certain two-week diet:

|  | Weight before | Weight after | Sign of Difference |
|---|---|---|---|
| Mr. Brown | 186 | 175 | − |
| Mr. Jones | 147 | 144 | − |
| Mr. Taylor | 128 | 125 | − |
| Mr. Green | 167 | 167 | 0 |
| Mr. Smith | 183 | 182 | − |
| Mr. Black | 176 | 177 | + |
| Mr. Moore | 159 | 154 | − |
| Mr. Good | 212 | 203 | − |
| Mr. White | 192 | 187 | − |
| Mr. Collins | 177 | 169 | − |
| Mr. Miller | 158 | 158 | 0 |
| Mr. Carpenter | 204 | 197 | − |
| Mr. Grey | 188 | 182 | − |
| Mr. Warner | 157 | 160 | + |
| Mr. Doe | 189 | 181 | − |
| Mr. Fergueson | 149 | 151 | + |
| Mr. Norris | 172 | 169 | − |
| Mr. Roberts | 185 | 184 | − |
| Mr. Winter | 191 | 187 | − |
| Mr. Porter | 200 | 195 | − |

The right-hand column of this table shows whether there was an increase or decrease in weight, or whether there was no change. We find that in our example there are 15 *minus signs*, 3 *plus signs*, and 2 cases where there was no change.

Now then, the null hypothesis that *the diet is not effective* is equivalent to the hypothesis that *we are as likely to get a minus sign as we are to get a plus* (ignoring those cases where there was no change) and we shall, thus, test the hypothesis that the probability of getting a minus sign is $p = 0.50$ against the one-sided alternative that $p > 0.50$. This can be done by the method of Section 11.4; in fact, we have "15 successes in 18 trials" in our example, and proceeding as on page 182 we find that for $n = 18$ and $p = 0.50$ the mean and standard deviation of the binomial distribution are

$$\mu = 18(0.50) = 9$$

$$\sigma = \sqrt{18(0.50)(0.50)} = 2.12$$

Using the normal curve approximation to the binomial distribution, we get

$$z = \frac{15 - 9}{2.12} = 2.83$$

and since this exceeds the critical value of 1.64 (for a one-sided test with a level of significance of 0.05) we can *reject the null hypothesis and accept the alternative.** This is equivalent to accepting the hypothesis that a decrease in weight is more likely than an increase in weight or, in other words, that *the diet is effective.* Statistically speaking, what we have done here is really the same as testing whether a coin is balanced if 18 tosses produced 15 heads and 3 tails. The only difference is that we would then use a two-sided rather than a one-sided alternative. We used the one-sided alternative $p > 0.50$ because we wanted the acceptance of the alternative to mean that the diet is effective.

The illustration we have given here is only one of many uses of the sign test. Another application is presented in Exercise 3 on page 301. In fact, even when so-called standard techniques are applicable, the sign test is sometimes used because of its extreme simplicity.

### 13.3 / The *U*-Test

When we tested the significance of the difference between two or more sample means, we pointed out (see Exercise 5 on page 269 and Section 12.3) that our techniques required rather restrictive assumptions. *In order to compare the means of small samples we have to assume that these samples were obtained from normal populations with equal standard deviations.* To handle situations in which these assumptions cannot be met, statisticians have developed alternate

---

*When the sample size is very small, it may be preferable to use a table of binomial probabilities instead of the normal curve approximation.

tests, among them the *U-test* which we shall take up in this section. This test is sometimes referred to also as the Mann-Whitney test, named after the statisticians by whom it was developed.

To illustrate how the *U*-test works, let us suppose that an agricultural experiment was performed to compare two varieties of corn and that 9 test plots of Variety A and 10 test plots of Variety B yielded the following results (in bushels per acre):

*Variety A:*   83.4, 91.5, 86.4, 86.9, 90.3, 88.6, 92.7, 84.8, 92.8

*Variety B:*   84.1, 97.3, 95.2, 88.9, 103.2, 89.0, 99.7, 101.4, 87.2, 91.0

The means of these samples are 88.6 and 93.7, and the problem is to decide whether the difference between the two is significant. The standard way of handling this kind of problem is the *t*-test described in Exercise 5 on page 269, but inspection of the data shows that it may be quite unreasonable to assume that the two samples come from populations with *equal* standard deviations; the second sample seems to display considerably more variability than the first.

To perform the *U*-test, which is essentially based on a *sum of ranks,* we first rank the 19 measurements *jointly,* that is, as if they were one sample. Arranging the data in an increasing order of magnitude, we thus get

| 83.4 | 84.1 | 84.8 | 86.4 | 86.9 | 87.2 | 88.6 | 88.9 | 89.0 | 90.3 |
|------|------|------|------|------|------|------|------|------|------|
| A    | B    | A    | A    | A    | B    | A    | B    | B    | A    |

| (cont.) | 91.0 | 91.5 | 92.7 | 92.8 | 95.2 | 97.3 | 99.7 | 101.4 | 103.2 |
|---------|------|------|------|------|------|------|------|-------|-------|
|         | B    | A    | A    | A    | B    | B    | B    | B     | B     |

Giving Rank 1 to 83.4, the smallest observation, we find that the measurements of the *first sample* occupy ranks 1, 3, 4, 5, 7, 10, 12, 13, and 14, while those of the *second sample* occupy ranks 2, 6, 8, 9, 11, 15, 16, 17, 18, and 19.

In this example there are no *ties* in rank; if there are, we assign to each of the tied observations the mean of the ranks which they jointly occupy. Thus, if two observations are tied for ranks 4 and 5 we assign each rank $4\frac{1}{2}$; if three observations are tied for ranks 10, 11, and 12, we assign each rank 11.

The hypothesis which we shall want to test is that both samples come from the *same* population, or from equal populations, and it stands to reason that in that case the average ranks for the two samples should be more or less the same. Referring to the above ranks, we find that the *mean* of the ranks of the first sample is

$$\frac{1 + 3 + 4 + 5 + 7 + 10 + 12 + 13 + 14}{9} = \frac{69}{9} = 7.67$$

while the mean of the ranks of the second sample is

$$\frac{2 + 6 + 8 + 9 + 11 + 15 + 16 + 17 + 18 + 19}{10} = \frac{121}{10} = 12.1$$

If the mean of one population is considerably higher than that of the other, the sample from that population is apt to occupy also the higher ranks. This happened in our example where the values of the second sample occupy most of the higher ranks, but it remains to be seen, of course, whether this is significant or whether it may be attributed to chance.

Using *rank sums* instead of average ranks, this decision may be based on the statistic

$$U = n_1 n_2 + \frac{n_1(n_1 + 1)}{2} - R_1 \qquad (13.3.1)▲$$

where $n_1$ and $n_2$ are the sizes of the two samples, which are $n_1 = 9$ and $n_2 = 10$ in our example, while $R_1$ is the sum of the ranks obtained for the first sample.* Since $R_1 = 69$ in our example, we get

$$U = 9 \cdot 10 + \frac{9 \cdot 10}{2} - 69 = 66$$

Under the assumption that the 19 observations, or in general the $n_1 + n_2$ observations, come from *one* population (or equal populations), the arrangement of A's and B's on page 297 may be looked upon as *random*. Assuming then that the arrangement of A's and B's on which $R_1$, the rank sum for the first sample, is based is random, it can be shown that the *sampling distribution of U* has the mean

$$\mu_U = \frac{n_1 n_2}{2} \qquad (13.3.3)▲$$

and the standard deviation

$$\sigma_U = \sqrt{\frac{n_1 n_2 (n_1 + n_2 + 1)}{12}} \qquad (13.3.4)▲$$

*Instead of (13.3.1) we can also use the formula

$$U = n_1 n_2 + \frac{n_2(n_2 + 1)}{2} - R_2 \qquad (13.3.2) \quad ▲$$

depending on which rank sum is easier to obtain. Here $R_2$ is the sum of the ranks occupied by the second sample.

Furthermore, if $n_1$ and $n_2$ are both greater than 8, the sampling distribution of $U$ can be approximated closely with a normal curve. Using a level of significance of 0.05, we can thus test the hypothesis that the two samples came from equal populations with the criterion illustrated in Figure 13.1, namely,

*reject the hypothesis if $z < -1.96$ or $z > 1.96$; accept the hypothesis (or reserve judgment) if $-1.96 \leq z \leq 1.96$, where*

$$z = \frac{U - \mu_U}{\sigma_U}$$

*and where $\mu_U$ and $\sigma_U$ are to be calculated according to (13.3.3) and (13.3.4).*

So far as the rejection of the hypothesis is concerned, let us point out that the *U*-test is particularly sensitive to differences between the *population means.*

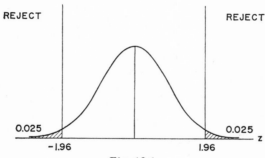

**Fig. 13.1**

Returning now to our numerical example where $n_1$ and $n_2$ equalled 9 and 10, respectively, we find that

$$\mu_U = \frac{9 \cdot 10}{2} = 45$$

$$\sigma_U = \sqrt{\frac{9 \cdot 10(9 + 10 + 1)}{12}} = 12.25$$

and therefore

$$z = \frac{66 - 45}{12.25} = 1.71$$

Since this value falls between $-1.96$ and 1.96, *we cannot reject the null hypothesis that the samples came from equal populations, particularly from populations with equal means.* Using this nonparametric test we were thus unable to obtain a significant difference in the yield of the two varieties of corn.

It is interesting to note that if we had used (13.3.2) in the calculation of $U$ we would have obtained

$$U = 9 \cdot 10 + \frac{10 \cdot 11}{2} - 121 = 24$$

and this is as much below the mean of $\mu_U = 45$ as $U = 66$ was above; so far as the test of significance is concerned, the outcome would have been exactly the same.

In the above we suggested that the sampling distribution of $U$ be approximated with a normal curve provided that $n_1$ and $n_2$ are both greater than 8. If either is too small, the test can be based on tables that are based on the exact sampling distribution of $U$ (see Bibliography on page 306).

The $U$-test has the decided advantage that it requires fewer assumptions than the $t$-test of Exercise 5 on page 269, and it furthermore has the desirable feature that the calculations are much easier to perform. (In fact, the only assumption needed is that the populations from which we are sampling are continuous.) *Like the sign test, the U-test is often used for reasons of simplicity even though "standard methods" could have been employed.*

### EXERCISES

*1;* A test rating a person's sense of humor on a scale from 0 to 100 was given to 15 married couples. Use the *sign test*, a two-sided alternative, and a level of significance of 0.05 to test the hypothesis that there is no difference in the average sense of humor of husbands and wives, if the following results were obtained:

| Husband | Wife |
|---------|------|
| 56 | 49 |
| 90 | 88 |
| 38 | 51 |
| 47 | 50 |
| 85 | 83 |
| 49 | 41 |
| 55 | 52 |
| 58 | 69 |
| 68 | 83 |
| 74 | 89 |
| 83 | 77 |
| 87 | 62 |
| 60 | 65 |
| 31 | 44 |
| 89 | 92 |

**2.** The following are the number of defective pieces produced by two machines during the month of June:

| | Number of Defectives | | | | Number of Defectives | |
| Day | Machine A | Machine B | | Day | Machine A | Machine B |
|---|---|---|---|---|---|---|
| June 1 | 8 | 9 | | June 16 | 10 | 8 |
| June 2 | 5 | 4 | | June 17 | 9 | 12 |
| June 3 | 10 | 12 | | June 18 | 13 | 13 |
| June 4 | 7 | 9 | | June 19 | 8 | 9 |
| June 5 | 9 | 10 | | June 20 | 4 | 6 |
| June 6 | 11 | 11 | | June 21 | 2 | 3 |
| June 7 | 3 | 6 | | June 22 | 8 | 9 |
| June 8 | 6 | 7 | | June 23 | 8 | 10 |
| June 9 | 6 | 8 | | June 24 | 6 | 9 |
| June 10 | 8 | 10 | | June 25 | 5 | 7 |
| June 11 | 5 | 6 | | June 26 | 10 | 11 |
| June 12 | 6 | 9 | | June 27 | 9 | 9 |
| June 13 | 9 | 11 | | June 28 | 4 | 6 |
| June 14 | 3 | 6 | | June 29 | 7 | 6 |
| June 15 | 7 | 7 | | June 30 | 3 | 5 |

Assuming that standard methods cannot be used owing to the fact that different raw materials were used on different days, use the *sign test*, a two-sided alternative, and a level of significance of 0.05 to test the hypothesis that there is no difference in the performance of the two machines.

3. Suppose that on the basis of the data given on page 212 we want to test whether the true average time it takes an adult to react to the given visual stimulus is $\mu = 0.11$ seconds. Replacing each measurement exceeding 0.11 with a plus sign, each measurement less than 0.11 with a minus sign, and omitting those equalling 0.11, use the *sign test* to test the above hypothesis ($\mu = 0.11$) at a level of significance of 0.05. Use a two-sided alternative hypothesis.

4. If 12 test runs with a gallon of one kind of gasoline yielded 18.2, 19.8, 17.4, 17.7, 20.3, 19.9, 18.4, 20.6, 19.6, 17.5, 20.2, and 20.5 miles while 12 test runs with a gallon of a second kind of gasoline yielded 19.3, 20.0, 21.7, 23.5, 20.9, 22.0, 23.1, 19.4, 21.0, 22.3, 19.0, and 21.3 miles, use the *U-test* and a level of significance of 0.05 to see whether it is reasonable to maintain that there is no difference in the true average mileage yielded by the two kinds of gasoline.

5. Random samples of third graders in two different schools obtained the following scores in a reading test.

School 1:   68, 77, 59, 93, 88, 70, 52, 41, 69, 84, 91, 75

School 2:   53, 61, 77, 90, 68, 55, 27, 38, 68, 44, 51, 20

Assuming that its application is reasonable in this example, use the *U-test* and a level of significance of 0.05 to test the hypothesis that the distributions of reading ability of third graders in these schools are the same.

### 13.4 / A Test Based on Runs

Randomness, as defined in Section 9.1, has served as a basic assumption for all of the tests and estimation procedures which we have discussed. Whether or not this assumption is reasonable raises difficult problems, particularly in situations where we have little or no control over the selection of our data. For example, if we wanted to predict a department store's volume of Christmas sales, we would have no choice but to use sales data from previous years and, perhaps, collateral information about economic conditions in general. None of this information constitutes a random sample in the sense that it was obtained with random numbers or other probability schemes. Similarly, we have no choice but to rely on whatever records happen to be available if we want to make long-range predictions of the weather, if we want to estimate the mortality rate of a disease, or if we want to study highway accidents.

There are several methods, developed in recent years, which make it possible to investigate the randomness of a sample on the basis of the *order* in which the individual observations were obtained. With these methods we can test whether patterns that look suspiciously non-random may be attributed to chance and, what is important, this can be done *after* the data have been collected. The method which we shall present in this section is based on the so-called *theory of runs;* alternate methods are referred to in the Bibliography on page 307.

*A run is defined as a succession of identical letters (or other kinds of symbols) which is followed and preceded by different letters or no letters at all.* To amplify this definition, let us consider the following arrangement of *defective*, *d*, and *non-defective*, *n*, pieces produced in the given order by a certain machine

$$n\ n\ n\ n\ n\ \underbrace{d\ d\ d\ d}\ \underbrace{n\ n\ n\ n\ n\ n\ n\ n\ n\ n}\ \underbrace{d\ d}\ \underbrace{n\ n}\ \underbrace{d\ d\ d\ d}$$

Using braces to combine the letters constituting the various runs, we find that there is first a run of *five n*'s, then a run of *four d*'s, then a run of *ten n*'s, then a run of *two d*'s, then a run of *two n*'s, and finally a run of *four d*'s. In all, there are *six* runs of varying lengths.

The total number of runs appearing in a sample of this kind is often a good indication of a possible lack of randomness. If there are *too few runs*, we might suspect a significant grouping or clustering, or perhaps a trend. If there are *too many runs*, we might suspect some sort of cyclic pattern. In our example there seems to be a definite clustering, that is, the defective pieces seem to come in groups. Whether this is significant, however, or whether it may be attributed to chance, will have to be seen.

To construct a criterion on the basis of which we can decide whether $u$, *the observed total number of runs*, is too large or too small, let us suppose that an arrangement consists of $n_1$ letters of one kind and $n_2$ letters of another. (It is immaterial which we refer to as $n_1$ and which as $n_2$.) We can then investigate the *sampling distribution of $u$*, namely, the distribution we could *expect* to obtain if we calculated $u$, the total number of runs, for repeatedly constructed random arrangements of $n_1$ letters of one kind and $n_2$ of another.

Although we shall not be able to prove it, since the mathematics is quite involved, let us use the fact that the *mean* of the sampling distribution of $u$ is

$$\mu_u = \frac{2n_1 n_2}{n_1 + n_2} + 1 \qquad (13.4.1)\blacktriangle$$

and that its *standard deviation* is

$$\sigma_u = \sqrt{\frac{2n_1 n_2 (2n_1 n_2 - n_1 - n_2)}{(n_1 + n_2)^2 (n_1 + n_2 - 1)}} \qquad (13.4.2)\blacktriangle$$

Derivations of these formulas are referred to in the Bibliography on page 307.

It can also be shown that unless $n_1$ and (or) $n_2$ are very small, the sampling distribution of $u$, the total number of runs, can be approximated closely with a normal curve. Hence, we can test the null hypothesis that an arrangement of two kinds of letters (or other symbols) is *random* with the following criterion:

*reject the hypothesis of randomness if $z < -1.96$ or $z > 1.96$;*
*accept the hypothesis (or reserve judgment) if $-1.96 \leq z \leq 1.96$,*
*where*

$$z = \frac{u - \mu_u}{\sigma_u}$$

*and where $\mu_u$ and $\sigma_u$ are to be calculated with formulas (13.4.1) and (13.4.2).*

This criterion provides a two-tail test at a level of significance of 0.05. To change the level of significance to, say, 0.01, we have only to substitute 2.58 for 1.96.

It is difficult to make an exact statement as to how large $n_1$ and $n_2$ must be so that the normal curve approximation and the above criterion may be used. Tables enabling us to make *exact* tests when $n_1$ and $n_2$ are both small are referred to in the Bibliography on page 307. We shall use the normal curve approximation so long as neither $n_1$ nor $n_2$ is less than 10.

Returning now to the numerical example on page 302, the one dealing with the defective and non-defective pieces turned out by the given machine, we find that $n_1 = 17$, $n_2 = 10$, and $u = 6$. Substituting these values of $n_1$ and $n_2$ into (13.4.1) and (13.4.2) we get

$$\mu_u = \frac{2 \cdot 17 \cdot 10}{17 + 10} + 1 = 13.59$$

$$\sigma_u = \sqrt{\frac{2 \cdot 17 \cdot 10 \left[2 \cdot 17 \cdot 10 - 17 - 10\right]}{(17 + 10)^2(17 + 10 - 1)}}$$

$$= 2.37$$

and we thus obtain

$$z = \frac{6 - 13.59}{2.37} = -3.20$$

Since this value is less than $-1.96$, *we can reject the null hypothesis of randomness.* The total number of runs is much smaller than expected and there is a strong indication that the defective pieces appear in clusters or groups.

### 13.5 / Runs Above and Below the Median

The usefulness of the method discussed in the preceding section is not limited to testing the randomness of series of attributes such as the $d$'s and $n$'s of our illustration. Any sample consisting of numerical measurements can be treated similarly by denoting each value falling *below the median* of the sample with the letter $b$ and each value falling *above the median* with the letter $a$. Numbers equalling the median are omitted. The resulting series of $a$'s and $b$'s can then be tested for randomness with the method of Section 13.4.

To illustrate this technique, let us consider the following data constituting a sample of the speeds (in miles per hour) with which passenger cars passed a certain check-point: 55, 57, 52, 46, 50, 48, 45, 44, 50, 52, 55, 41, 42, 58, 60, 45, 53, 54, 48, 46, 51, 49, 44, 43, and 56. The median of these numbers is 50 and, omitting the values which actually equal 50, we can write

$$a\ a\ a\ b\ b\ b\ b\ a\ a\ b\ b\ a\ a\ b\ a\ a\ b\ b\ a\ b\ b\ b\ a$$

Since $n_1 = 11$, $n_2 = 12$, and $u = 11$, substitution into (13.4.1) and (13.4.2) gives

$$\mu_u = \frac{2 \cdot 11 \cdot 12}{11 + 12} + 1 = 12.48$$

$$\sigma_u = \sqrt{\frac{2 \cdot 11 \cdot 12 \, [2 \cdot 11 \cdot 12 - 11 - 12]}{(11 + 12)^2(11 + 12 - 1)}} = 2.34$$

and

$$z = \frac{11 - 12.48}{2.34} = -0.63$$

Since this value falls between $-1.96$ and $1.96$, *we cannot reject the null hypothesis at a level of significance of 0.05, that is, there is no indication that the sample of speeds is not random.*

The method of runs above and below the median is particularly useful in detecting *trends* and *cyclic patterns*. If there is a *trend*, there will be first mostly $a$'s and later mostly $b$'s (or vice versa) and if there is a *cyclic pattern* there will be a systematic alternation of $a$'s and $b$'s and, probably, too many runs.

### EXERCISES

1. The following is the arrangement of a number of men and women lined up at the box office of a theater:

   $$m \; w \; m \; m \; m \; m \; m \; w \; m \; w \; m \; m \; w \; w \; w \; m \; m \; m \; w \; m$$

   (cont.) $w \; w \; w \; w \; m \; w \; w \; w \; m \; m \; m \; w \; w \; m \; m \; w \; w \; w \; m \; w$

   Test for randomness at a level of significance of 0.05.

2. At a professional meeting of mathematicians and statisticians the members of the two societies seated themselves in the following arrangement:

   $$M \; M \; M \; S \; S \; S \; S \; M \; M \; M \; M \; M \; M \; S \; M \; M \; M \; M \; M$$

   (cont.) $S \; S \; S \; S \; S \; S \; S \; M \; M \; M \; S \; M \; M \; M \; M \; M \; M \; M$

   Test for randomness at a level of significance of 0.05.

3. Flip a coin 80 times, recording an $H$ for each head and a $T$ for each tail. Then test at a level of significance of 0.01 whether the arrangement of $H$'s and $T$'s is random.

4. The theory of runs may also be used as an alternate to the $U$-test of Section 13.3. Given samples from two populations, we combine the two samples and rank all of the observations in an increasing or decreasing order. Writing an $A$ below each observation belonging to the first

sample and a *B* below each observation belonging to the second sample (as we did on page 297), we can then test the randomness of this arrangement of *A*'s and *B*'s. If there are *too few runs* this may be indicative of the fact that the samples came from populations with unequal means. Use this method on the data of Exercise 4 on page 301.

5. The following are the number of persons attending a movie theater on 25 successive Mondays:

|       |     |     |     |     |     |     |     |     |
|-------|-----|-----|-----|-----|-----|-----|-----|-----|
| 539   | 612 | 589 | 541 | 617 | 689 | 560 | 524 |     |
| (cont.) 674 | 631 | 590 | 472 | 481 | 495 | 514 | 587 |     |
| (cont.) 529 | 616 | 575 | 582 | 593 | 610 | 617 | 667 | 597 |

Use the method of runs above and below the median to test whether these figures may be looked upon as a random sample. Use a level of significance of 0.05.

6. Use the method of runs above and below the median to test whether the 60 measurements of Exercise 16 on page 27 may be looked upon as a random sample. Read successive rows across and use a level of significance of 0.05. The median was found in (a) of Exercise 12 on page 62.

7. Use the method of runs above and below the median to test whether it is reasonable to treat the successive time lapses between eruptions of Old Faithful in Exercise 17 on page 28 as a random sample. Read successive rows across and use a level of significance of 0.05.

8. The following figures represent the average bill (in dollars) for the residential use of 25 kilowatt hours of electricity from 1935 through 1955: 1.60, 1.53, 1.45, 1.43, 1.40, 1.36, 1.34, 1.34, 1.33, 1.33, 1.32, 1.28, 1.23, 1.24, 1.25, 1.24, 1.24, 1.24, 1.28, 1.29, 1.30. Test at a level of significance of 0.05 whether this arrangement may be looked upon as random or whether there is a significant trend.

## BIBLIOGRAPHY

A thorough treatment of the various nonparametric tests given in this chapter, their advantages and disadvantages, when they may or may not be used, etc., is to be found in

Siegel, S., *Nonparametric Statistics for the Behavioral Sciences*. New York: McGraw-Hill, 1956.

A much more theoretical presentation is given in

Fraser, D. A. S., *Nonparametric Methods of Statistics*. New York: John Wiley, 1957.

Tables needed to perform the $U$-test for very small samples are given in the book by Siegel mentioned above. Tables which make it possible to conduct exact tests of randomness using the theory of *runs* may be found in

> Swed, F. S., and Eisenhart, C., "Tables for testing randomness of grouping in a sequence of alternatives," *Annals of Mathematical Statistics*, vol. 14, p. 66.

A treatment of the theory underlying the distribution of runs is given in

> Wilks, S. S., *Mathematical Statistics*. Princeton, N. J.: Princeton University Press, 1944, Chap. 10.

Alternate tests of randomness are discussed in

> Hoel, P. G., *Introduction to Mathematical Statistics*, 2nd ed. New York: John Wiley, 1954, Chap. 13.

PART THREE

# Regression, Correlation, and Time Series

Chapter  *14*

# Linear Regression

## 14.1 / Introduction

The primary objective of many statistical investigations is to predict
such things as a student's performance in college, the merits of a
piece of machinery, the effectiveness of a drug, even over-all economic conditions. Although it would be nice if one could make
*infallible* predictions, predictions based on statistical data are seldom
of this type. Basing their predictions on samples and statistical
methods, scientists and business men can at best formulate their
predictions in terms of probabilities, being satisfied if they are right
a high percentage of the time or if their predictions are on the average
reasonably close.

Whenever possible, scientists strive to express relationships
between variables, that is, relationships between quantities that are
measured or observed and quantities that are to be predicted, in
terms of mathematical equations. This approach has been extremely
successful in the physical sciences, where it is known, for instance,
that at constant temperature the relationship between the volume, $v$,
and the pressure, $p$, of a gas is given by the formula

$$v \cdot p = k$$

where $k$ is a numerical constant. Similarly, in biological science it
has been discovered that the relationship between the size of a

culture of bacteria and the time that it has been exposed to certain favorable conditions may be written as

$$y = a \cdot b^x$$

where $y$ stands for the size of the culture, $x$ for time, and $a$ and $b$ are numerical constants.

Although the equations of the preceding paragraph were presented with reference to examples in physics and biology, they apply equally well to describe relationships in other fields. In economics, for instance, we could let $x$ stand for *price*, $y$ for *demand*, and write the equation of a so-called *demand curve* as $x \cdot y = k$.

The simplest and probably the most widely used equation for expressing relationships in various fields is the *linear equation* (in two unknowns) which is of the form

$$y = a + bx \tag{14.1.1}$$

Here $a$ and $b$ are numerical constants and once they are known (or at least estimated) we can calculate a predicted value of $y$ for any value of $x$ by direct substitution. *The importance of linear equations is not only due to the fact that there actually are many relationships which are of this form, but also because linear equations often provide good approximations to complicated relationships that would otherwise be difficult to describe in mathematical terms.*

Linear equations owe their name to the fact that, when plotted on ordinary graph paper, all pairs of values of $x$ and $y$ which satisfy (are solutions of) an equation of the form $y = a + bx$ will fall on a straight line. To illustrate, let us consider the equation

$$y = 21.9 + 3.3x$$

whose graph is shown in Figure 14.1. Here $x$ stands for the July rainfall in inches in a certain locality while $y$ stands for the corresponding yield of corn in bushels per acre. If in a given July there are 5 inches of rain in that locality, we find by substitution that the *predicted* yield of corn for that year is $y = 21.9 + 3.3(5) = 38.4$ bushels per acre. Similarly, if the July rainfall is 3 inches, the *predicted* yield of corn for that year is $21.9 + 3.3(3) = 31.8$ bushels per acre, and if the July rainfall is 2 inches, the predicted yield of corn for that year is $21.9 + 3.3(2) = 28.5$ bushels per acre. Taking many such values of $x$, calculating the corresponding values of $y$, and plotting the corresponding points, the reader can check for himself that these points will all fall on a straight line.

## 14.2 / The Method of Least Squares

To illustrate the general problem of *fitting* a straight line to data consisting of paired observations of two variables $x$ and $y$, let us

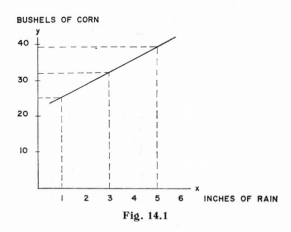

Fig. 14.1

consider the following example: let us suppose that a college official wants to be able to predict a student's college index at the end of his freshman year on the basis of his average high school grades. Let us suppose, furthermore, that a random sample of eight students showed the following results:

|  | High School Average | College Index |
|---|---|---|
| Student A | 85 | 2.3 |
| Student B | 65 | 1.2 |
| Student C | 73 | 1.5 |
| Student D | 90 | 1.9 |
| Student E | 82 | 1.8 |
| Student F | 80 | 2.0 |
| Student G | 68 | 1.3 |
| Student H | 88 | 2.1 |

(These college indexes are computed by letting each grade of A count as 3, each B as 2, each C as 1, each D as 0, and each F as $-1$. For the sake of simplicity we shall refer to these indexes *at the end of the freshman* year simply as the students' college indexes.)

Plotting the eight points corresponding to the high school

averages and college indexes as we have done in Figure 14.2, it is apparent that although the points do not actually fall on a straight line, they are reasonably close to the dotted line shown in that diagram. Deciding that a straight line will give a fairly good descrip-

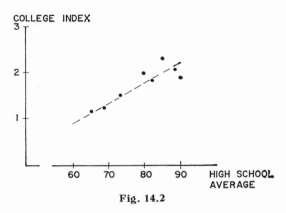

**Fig. 14.2**

tion of the relationship between high school averages and college indexes at the end of the freshman year, *whoever is making the study now faces the problem of finding the equation of the line which in some sense provides the best fit to the data and which, it is hoped, will later yield the best possible predictions.*

Anyone who has ever analyzed data which were plotted as points like those of Figure 14.2 has probably felt the urge to take a ruler, juggle it around, and draw in this way a line that presents a fairly good fit. Of course, this can be done, but it is highly questionable whether we should trust our eyesight and aesthetic judgment in choosing the line which supposedly will yield the "best possible" predictions. Another argument against *freehand curve fitting* is that it is largely subjective and that there is really no way in which we can assay the merits of subsequent predictions.

As there is no limit to the number of lines that can be drawn on a piece of paper, *we will have to have some criterion on the basis of which we will be able to single out one line as the line that provides the best possible fit.* There would be no problem if all the points actually fell on a straight line, but in most practical situations we will have to be satisfied with a straight line which, although it does not pass through all the points, has some less perfect though still desirable property.

The method which nowadays is used almost exclusively for fitting straight lines (and other kinds of curves) to numerical data was

suggested early in the 19th century by the French mathematician
Adrien Legendre; it is known as the *method of least squares*. The
method of least squares, as it is to be used in this chapter, requires
that *the sum of the squares of the vertical deviations (distances) from
the points to the line be as small as possible*. With reference to our
numerical example, the method of least squares demands that we

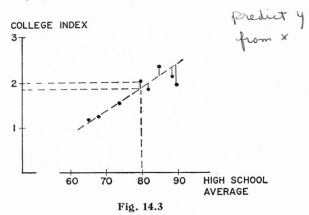

Fig. 14.3

choose the line for which the sum of the squares of the *solid* line
segments of Figure 14.3 be a minimum. The reason for this is the
following: the 6th student, for example, had a high school average
of 80 and a college index of 2.0. If we use the line of Figure 14.3
to predict his college index, we could do this by substituting $x = 80$
into the equation of the line or by reading his predicted index directly
off the diagram. *As can be seen from Figure 14.3, the vertical distance
from the point representing the 6th student to the dotted line is the
difference between his actual college index and his predicted college index
and it, thus, measures the error of this prediction.* Using the method
of least squares in this fashion, we are trying to minimize the errors
of our predictions.

Incidentally, we are minimizing the *sum of the squares* of the
vertical deviations (errors) and not just their *sum*, because we would
otherwise run into the same difficulties which we encountered in
discussing the standard deviation in Chapter 4.

As it does not matter which variable is called $x$ and which
variable is called $y$, *we shall agree to reserve y for the variable which is
to be predicted in terms of the other*. (If we wanted to predict $x$ in terms
of $y$, we would have to apply the method of least squares differently,

izing the sum of the squares of the *horizontal deviations* from one line. See Exercises 7 and 8 on page 320.)

To show how a *least squares line* is fitted to a set of data, let us consider $n$ pairs of numbers $x_1$ and $y_1$, $x_2$ and $y_2$, . . ., $x_n$ and $y_n$, which might represent the heights and weights of $n$ persons, I.Q.'s and test scores of $n$ students, measurements of the thrust and speed of $n$ experimental rockets, or the number of workers unemployed in two countries in $n$ different years. Let us suppose, furthermore, that the line which we fit to these data has the equation

$$y' = a + bx$$

using the symbol $y'$ to differentiate between *observed* values of $y$ and the corresponding values calculated by means of the equation of the line. For each given value of $x_i$ ($i = 1, 2, \ldots,$ or $n$) we thus have an *observed* value $y_i$ and a *calculated* value $y_i'$ obtained by substituting $x_i$ into $y_i' = a + bx_i$.

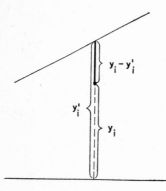

Fig. 14.4

In order to have the line satisfy the criterion of least squares, the constants $a$ and $b$ must be such that

$$\sum_{i=1}^{n} (y_i - y_i')^2 \qquad (14.2.1)$$

is as small as possible (see Figure 14.4). Since the derivation of the formulas which the method of least squares yields for $a$ and $b$ is fairly involved, requiring some knowledge of calculus or a great deal of algebra, let us merely state the result as

$$b = \frac{n(\sum x_i y_i) - (\sum x_i)(\sum y_i)}{n(\sum x_i^2) - (\sum x_i)^2} \qquad (14.2.2) \blacktriangle$$

$$a = \frac{\sum y_i - b(\sum x_i)}{n} \qquad (14.2.3) \blacktriangle$$

Here $n$ is the number of pairs of observations, $\sum x_i$ and $\sum y_i$ are, respectively, the sums of the given $x$'s and $y$'s, $\sum x_i^2$ is the sum of the squares of the $x$'s, and $\sum x_i y_i$ is the sum of the products of the corresponding $x$'s and $y$'s. (We simplified the appearance of the two formulas somewhat by not indicating that in each case the summation goes from 1 to $n$.)

It should be noted that by using (14.2.2) and (14.2.3) we first calculate $b$ and then use it to find $a$. Derivations of the two formulas are referred to in the Bibliography on page 324.

Returning now to our numerical example, let us use formulas (14.2.2) and (14.2.3) to fit a least squares line to the high school averages and college indexes. Copying the first two columns from page 313, we get

*predict*

| $x$ | $y$ | $x^2$ | $xy$ |
|-----|-----|-------|------|
| 85 | 2.3 | 7225 | 195.5 |
| 65 | 1.2 | 4225 | 78.0 |
| 73 | 1.5 | 5329 | 109.5 |
| 90 | 1.9 | 8100 | 171.0 |
| 82 | 1.8 | 6724 | 147.6 |
| 80 | 2.0 | 6400 | 160.0 |
| 68 | 1.3 | 4624 | 88.4 |
| 88 | 2.1 | 7744 | 184.8 |
| 631 | 14.1 | 50371 | 1134.8 |

and we thus have $n = 8$, $\sum x_i = 631$, $\sum y_i = 14.1$, $\sum x_i^2 = 50{,}371$, and $\sum x_i y_i = 1134.8$. Substituting these values into (14.2.2) we get

$$b = \frac{8(1134.8) - (631)(14.1)}{8(50371) - (631)^2} = 0.038$$

and subsequently (14.2.3) gives

$$a = \frac{14.1 - (0.038)(631)}{8} = -1.24$$

Finally, the equation of the least squares line can be written as

$$y' = -1.24 + 0.038x$$

and it can be used to predict a student's college index at the end of his freshman year on the basis of his high school average. For instance, if a student comes to college with a high school average of 86, we can predict that his index at the end of the freshman year will be

$$y' = -1.24 + 0.038(86) = 2.03$$

How such a prediction is to be interpreted and how its "goodness" can be evaluated will be touched upon later. Incidentally, the predicted value of $y$ can also be obtained by plotting the line and reading the predicted value directly off the diagram. To plot the line we have only to choose *two* arbitrary values of $x$, calculate the corresponding $y$'s, plot the two points, and through them draw the desired line.

Instead of calculating $a$ and $b$ with (14.2.2) and (14.2.3), these constants may also be obtained by solving the following two simultaneous equations, called the *normal equations:*

$$\sum y_i = a \cdot n + b \cdot \sum x_i \qquad (14.2.4)\blacktriangle$$

$$\sum x_i y_i = a \cdot \sum x_i + b \cdot \sum x_i^2 \qquad (14.2.5)\blacktriangle$$

Had we used these equations in our example, we would have had to solve the two simultaneous equations

$$14.1 = a(8) + b(631)$$

$$1134.8 = a(631) + b(50371)$$

Using the method of elimination or some other method discussed in algebra texts, we would again have obtained $a = -1.24$ and $b = 0.038$.

The calculation of $a$ and $b$ can be simplified by changing the scale of $x$ so that $\sum x_i$ is equal to zero. How this is done in the special problem of fitting a least squares trend line to a time series will be discussed in Section 17.2.

### EXERCISES

1. The following data were obtained in a study of road width (in feet) and the number of accidents occurring per hundred million vehicle miles:

| Road width: | $x$ | 73 | 50 | 62 | 30 | 25 |
|---|---|---|---|---|---|---|
| Number of accidents: | $y$ | 42 | 83 | 58 | 93 | 90 |

   (a) Use formulas (14.2.2) and (14.2.3) to find $a$ and $b$ for the equation of the least squares line which will make it possible to predict accident frequency in terms of road width.

   (b) Construct suitable scales for $x$ and $y$ and plot the original data as well as the line obtained in (a) in one diagram.

   (c) Predict the accident frequency for a road whose width is 55 feet.

2. Repeat (a) of Exercise 1 using the normal equations, (14.2.4) and (14.2.5) to find $a$ and $b$.

3. In the study of a portion of the stress-strain curve of a certain alloy an engineer obtained the following results (stress in hundred thousand pounds per square inch and strain in thousandths of inches):

| $x$ (stress) | $y$ (strain) |
|---|---|
| 0.5 | 6 |
| 1.2 | 9 |
| 0.8 | 8 |
| 0.3 | 4 |
| 0.1 | 1 |

$\Sigma y = an + b\Sigma x$

$\Sigma xy = a\Sigma x + b\Sigma x^2$

$28 = 5a + 2.9b \quad -(.58)$

$21.5 = 2.9a + 2.43b$

$-16.24 = -29a - 1.68b$

$21.5 = 2.9a + 2.43b$

$5.26 = .75b$

$b = 7.013$

$\Sigma x = 2.9$

$\Sigma y = 28$

$\Sigma x^2 = 2.43$

$\Sigma xy = 21.5$

(a) Use formulas (14.2.2) and (14.2.3) to fit a least squares line which will make it possible to predict strain in terms of stress.
(b) Plot the original data as well as the line found in (a) in one diagram.
(c) Using the equation obtained in (a), predict the strain that will be produced by a stress of 60,000 pounds per square inch.

4. The following are grades obtained by 10 students in final examinations in statistics and economics:    $21.5 = 2.9a + 2.43(7.01)$

| Statistics $x$ | Economics $y$ |
|---|---|
| 92 | 89 |
| 65 | 44 |
| 72 | 70 |
| 54 | 61 |
| 87 | 90 |
| 24 | 20 |
| 63 | 58 |
| 62 | 41 |
| 50 | 52 |
| 81 | 72 |

(a) Use formulas (14.2.2) and (14.2.3) to find the equation of the least squares line which will enable us to predict a student's final examination grade in economics in terms of his final examination grade in statistics.
(b) Plot the original data as well as the line obtained in (a) in one diagram.
(c) Predict a student's final examination grade in economics if he obtained a 68 in statistics.

5. Repeat (a) of Exercise 4 using the normal equations (14.2.4) and (14.2.5) to find $a$ and $b$.

*(Handwritten margin calculations)*

.25
1.44
.64
.09
.01
———
2.43

3.0
10.8
6.4
1.2
.1
———
21.5

.58
5)2.9

.58
28
4 )64
11 6
16.24

.58
2.9
522
1 1 6
1 6 8 2

21.50
−16.24
5.26

2.43
−1.68
.75
7.01

.75 )5.26
525
———
100
75
25

7.01
2.43
21 03
28 0 4
1 40 2
1 7.03 4 3

90
20
———
70

**6.** The following are the ages and second-hand prices charged for a certain make two-door sedan:

| Age (years) | Price (dollars) |
|:---:|:---:|
| 1 | 1685 |
| 3 | 1175 |
| 9 | 285 |
| 2 | 1395 |
| 5 | 795 |
| 5 | 685 |
| 8 | 495 |
| 1 | 1855 |

Use formulas (14.2.2) and (14.2.3) or the two normal equations to find the equation of the least squares line which will enable us to predict the second-hand price of this kind of two-door sedan on the basis of its age. What value would we obtain with this equation for a 4-year-old model of this kind of car?

**7.** Use formulas (14.2.2) and (14.2.3) to fit a least squares line of the form $y = a + bx$ to the following data:

| $x$ | 1 | 2 | 3 | 4 | 5 |
|:---:|:---:|:---:|:---:|:---:|:---:|
| $y$ | 8 | 9 | 13 | 18 | 27 |

Also, suppose that we wanted to predict $x$ in terms of $y$ for this kind of data with an equation of the form $x = c + dy$; applying the method of least squares so that the sum of the squares of the *horizontal deviations* from the line is minimized, find $c$ and $d$ by using formulas (14.2.2) and (14.2.3), respectively, with $x$ replaced by $y$ and $y$ replaced by $x$ wherever these letters occur. Show that the two equations obtained in this exercise are *not* the same.

**8.** Suppose that in Exercise 4 we had wanted to predict final examination grades in statistics in terms of final examination grades obtained in economics. Find the equation of the new least squares line and compare it with the one obtained in Exercise 4.

## 14.3 / Linear Regression

On page 317 we showed that the least squares line enables one to predict the college index of a student entering the given college with a high school average of 86 as 2.03. Now it stands to reason that we cannot expect *every* student entering this college with a high school average of 86 to have an index of 2.03 at the end of his freshman year; statistical predictions are never infallible, there are many factors involved, and we would certainly not be surprised if the indexes of some students entering the college with a high school average of 86 turned out to be 1.95, 2.10, 2.24, 1.72, . . . .

In view of the fact that predictions based on least squares equations fit to experimental data cannot be expected to be *perfect*, it would seem desirable, at least, to be able to say that students entering the given college with a high school average of 86 will *on the average* have an index of 2.03 at the end of their freshman year. We could then assert our prediction by saying that we *expect* such a student to attain an index of 2.03, using the word "expect" in the sense of a mathematical expectation.

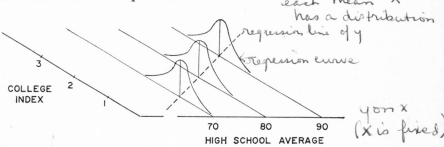

*each mean $\bar{X}$ has a distribution*

*regression line of y*

*regression curve*

*y on x (x is fixed)*

**Fig. 14.5**

To illustrate this situation graphically, let us consider Figure 14.5 in which we have shown several distributions, each representing the indexes of students who entered the college with the *same* high school average. The first is the distribution of the indexes obtained by all students entering the college with a high school average of 70, the second is the distribution of the indexes obtained by all students entering the college with a high school average of 80, and the third is the distribution of the indexes obtained by all students entering the college with a high school average of 90. To complete the picture, the reader should be able to visualize similar distribution curves for other values of $x$, that is, for the indexes of students entering the college with other high school averages.

The curve that is formed by the *means* of the distributions of Figure 14.5 is called a *regression curve*, although it might appropriately be called a *curve of means*. In particular, if this curve is a straight line, like the dotted line of Figure 14.5, it is called a *regression line*. To indicate that it contains the means of the $y$'s for fixed values of $x$, it is referred to more specifically as a *regression line of y* _on x._ (The term "regression" was first used in this connection by Francis Galton in his studies of heredity. For instance, a study of the heights of fathers and sons showed that tall fathers tend to have tall sons and short fathers, short sons; there is, thus, a _regression_, a turning back, from the heights of sons to the heights of their fathers.)

In this chapter we are considering only problems in which the true _regression curve_, the curve containing the true means of the _y_'s for fixed values of _x_, is a straight line, and we shall write its equation as

$$y = \alpha + \beta x \qquad y \text{ on } x$$

In the same sense in which we previously used $\sigma$ and $\mu$ for descriptions of populations, we are now using the Greek letters $\alpha$ _(alpha)_ and $\beta$ _(beta)_ when referring to the line containing the _true_ means of the _y_'s for fixed values of _x_. Also, in the same way in which we used $\bar{x}$ and $s$ as _estimates_ of $\mu$ and $\sigma$, we now use $a$ and $b$ in $y' = a + bx$ for the _estimated regression line_ obtained with the method of least squares.

It must be clear that if we repeated the study of the preceding section with different data, that is, with the high school averages and college indexes of a different sample of students, we could hardly expect to get identical values for $a$ and $b$. The constants $a$ and $b$ which we obtained are, thus, _estimated regression coefficients_, whereas $\alpha$ and $\beta$, the quantities they are supposed to estimate, are called the _(true) regression coefficients._ $\alpha, \beta$

Returning now to our numerical example, we will have to keep in mind that $y' = -1.24 + 0.038x$, the line which we obtained on page 317 with the method of least squares, is only an _estimate_ of the line whose equation would give us the _true_ average college index of students entering the college with given high school averages. Hence, it might be well to investigate any one or all of the following questions:

(1) Since $a$ and $b$ are only estimates of $\alpha$ and $\beta$, what can we say about the "goodness" of these estimates?

(2) If we used the calculated least squares equation to estimate, say, the average indexes of students entering the college with high school averages of, say, 86, what could we say about the "goodness" of this estimate?

(3) How can we obtain _limits_, two numbers, between which we can expect a student's index to fall, say, with a probability of 0.95, if his high school average is 86?

In reply to the first two questions we could construct *confidence intervals for $\alpha$ and $\beta$* and a *confidence interval for the true mean of the indexes of students entering the given college with a high school average of 86*. In principle this would not differ from our work in Chapter 10, but since the underlying mathematical theory is fairly advanced and the resulting formulas quite complicated, we shall not go into this subject. Suitable references to the construction of such confidence intervals are given in the Bibliography on page 325.

To answer the third question we would have to construct so-called *limits of prediction,* and since this is also quite involved we shall merely give references in the Bibliography on page 325. *What is important about all this is that none of the above questions could be answered if we fitted freehand lines; they can be answered (with some reservations) if we use the method of least squares.*

### 14.4 / Multiple Linear Regression

Although there are many problems in which one variable can be predicted quite accurately in terms of another, it stands to reason that our predictions might be improved if we consider additional relevant information. For instance, we should be able to make better predictions of the demand for pork chops if we considered not only their price but also the price of competing meats. Similarly, we should be able to make better predictions of a cow's yield of milk if we considered the amount of grain fed to it each day as well as its weight and age, and we should be able to make better predictions of the attendance at a theater if we considered the quality of the show in addition to the size of the community and, perhaps, its wealth.

There are many mathematical formulas with which relationships between more than two variables can be expressed, but the most widely used in statistics (partly for reasons of simplicity) are linear equations of the form

$$y = a + bx_1 + cx_2 + dx_3 + \ldots \qquad (14.4.1)$$

Here $y$ is the variable which is to be predicted, while $x_1, x_2, x_3, \ldots,$ are the known variables on which the prediction is to be based. As before, $a, b, c, d, \ldots,$ are numerical constants which have to be determined in some way on the basis of appropriate data.

To give an example of a *multiple linear regression equation,* as these equations are called, the following arose in a study of the demand for beef and veal:*

$$y = 3.4892 - 0.0899x_1 + 0.0637x_2 + 0.0187x_3$$

where $y$ stands for the total consumption of federally inspected beef and veal in millions of pounds, $x_1$ stands for the retail price of beef in cents per pound, $x_2$ stands for the retail price of pork in cents per pound, and $x_3$ stands for income as measured by a certain payroll index. Having obtained an equation like this it is possible to forecast the total consumption of federally inspected beef and veal on the basis of known or estimated values of $x_1$, $x_2$, and $x_3$.

The main problem of fitting a linear equation in more than two unknowns to a given set of data is that of finding numerical values for $a$, $b$, $c$, $\ldots$, so that the resulting equation will yield the best possible predictions. This problem is usually solved by using the *method of least squares* which provides the values of $a$, $b$, $c$, $\ldots$, that make $\sum (y_i - y_i')^2$ as small as possible. Here the $y_i$ are observed values of $y$ while the $y_i'$ are the corresponding values predicted by means of an equation like (14.4.1).

In principle, the problem of finding multiple regression equations is no different from that of fitting lines of the form $y = a + bx$. In practice, it is much more tedious because the method of least squares yields a set of normal equations consisting of as many equations as there are unknown constants $a, b, c, \ldots$. References to the calculation of such *multiple regression coefficients* are given below.

## BIBLIOGRAPHY

Derivations of equations (14.2.2) and (14.2.3) by means of calculus may be found in practically all textbooks of mathematical statistics, for example in

> Hoel, P. G., *Introduction to Mathematical Statistics*, 2nd ed. New York: John Wiley, 1954, Chap. 7.

A derivation which uses only algebra is given in

> Richardson, C. H., *An Introduction to Statistical Analysis*. New York: Harcourt, Brace, 1934, Chap. 7.

*H. Schultz, *The Theory and Measurement of Demand*. Chicago: University of Chicago Press, 1938, p. 582.

Confidence intervals for the regression coefficients $\alpha$ and $\beta$ are treated in the book by Hoel mentioned above, and confidence intervals for the true means of $y$ for fixed values of $x$ are given, among others, in

Neter, J., and Wasserman, W., *Fundamental Statistics for Business and Economics*. Boston: Allyn and Bacon, 1956, Chap. 11.

Formulas for finding limits of prediction may be found in

Freund, J. E., and Williams, F. J., *Modern Business Statistics*. Englewood Cliffs, N. J.: Prentice-Hall, 1958, Chap. 13.

For a brief discussion of multiple linear regression and the normal equations needed to calculate the coefficients, see

Croxton, F. E., and Cowden, D. J., *Practical Business Statistics*, 3rd ed. Englewood Cliffs, N. J.: Prentice-Hall, 1960.

# Chapter 15

# The Coefficient of Correlation

## 15.1 / Introduction

Having seen that there are formulas to describe almost any feature of a set of numerical data, it should not be surprising to find that there are also ways of measuring the *goodness of the fit* of a regression line. Since the method of least squares, as we used it in Section 14.2, defined "goodness of fit" in terms of the sum of the squares of the vertical deviations from the line (see Figure 14.3), it would seem appropriate to measure this goodness of fit by means of the quantity

$$\sum_{i=1}^{n} (y_i - y_i') \quad = \quad \overset{least}{number} \qquad (15.1.1)$$

If the differences between the observed values of $y$ and the corresponding calculated values are *small*, this sum of squares will be *small;* if the differences are *large*, the sum of squares will also be *large*.

Although (15.1.1) would seem suitable to measure goodness of fit, it has the disadvantage that it depends on the units of $y$. If in some problem the $y$'s happen to be wholesale prices of bananas at different times of the year, changing the units from dollars to cents would have the effect of multiplying the sum of squares in (15.1.1) by a factor of *ten thousand*. To eliminate this difficulty we shall measure the goodness of the fit of a regression line somewhat differently, namely, *by comparing* $\sum (y_i - y_i')^2$ *with* $\sum (y_i - \bar{y})^2$ *which is the sum of the squares of the deviations of the $y$'s from their mean.*

To illustrate, let us consider the two diagrams of Figure 15.1, whose points represent data on the number of customers who visited a certain restaurant on 12 consecutive days and the number of steaks

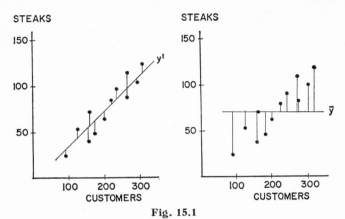

Fig. 15.1

served on the same days. The diagram on the left shows the vertical deviations of the $y$'s from the least squares line, the one on the right shows the deviations of the $y$'s from their mean. *It is apparent that in this example $\sum (y_i - y_i')^2$ is much smaller than $\sum (y_i - \bar{y})^2$.*

In contrast, let us now consider the diagrams of Figure 15.2, whose points represent data on the personal savings of individuals

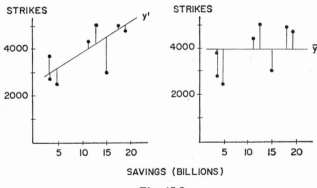

Fig. 15.2

in the United States from 1940 through 1947 and the number of work stoppages in the same years. Again the diagram on the left shows the vertical deviations of the $y$'s from the least squares line and the one on the right the deviations of the $y$'s from their mean, but *this time* $\sum (y_i - y_i')^2$ *is just about as large as* $\sum (y_i - \bar{y})^2$. It can thus be seen that *if the fit of the least squares line is good, as in Figure 15.1,* $\sum (y_i - y_i')^2$ *is much smaller than* $\sum (y_i - \bar{y})^2$, *and if the fit is poor, as in Figure 15.2, the two sums of squares are almost the same size.*

To put this comparison on a precise basis, it is customary to use the statistic

$$r = \pm\sqrt{1 - \frac{\sum (y_i - y_i')^2}{\sum (y_i - \bar{y})^2}} \qquad (15.1.2)$$

which is called the *coefficient of correlation.* If the fit is *poor*, the ratio of the two sums of squares is close to 1 and $r$, the coefficient of correlation, is close to 0. [The ratio can never actually exceed 1 since the line was fitted by the method of least squares, and the sum of the squares of the vertical deviations from any other line, even the horizontal line through $\bar{y}$, cannot be less than $\sum (y_i - y_i')^2$.] On the other hand, if the fit is *good*, the ratio of the two sums of squares is close to 0 and $r$, the coefficient of correlation, is close to $+1$ or $-1$. The significance of the *sign* of $r$ will be discussed on page 330.

The statistic we have just introduced is, probably, the most widely used measure of the *strength of the linear relationship between two variables.* It indicates the goodness of the fit of the line fitted by the method of least squares and this, in turn, tells us whether or not it is reasonable to say that there exists a linear relationship (correlation) between $x$ and $y$. If $r$ is close to 0, the fit is poor and *the relationship is very weak or nonexistent;* if $r$ is close to $+1$ or $-1$, the fit is good and *this is indicative of a strong relationship between $x$ and $y$.* The coefficient of correlation is sometimes referred to somewhat more elaborately as the *Pearson product-moment coefficient of correlation.*

Although formula (15.1.2) serves to *define* the coefficient of correlation, it is seldom, if ever, used in practice. In order to use it directly we would have to find the equation of the least squares line, calculate every $y_i'$ by substituting the given $x_i$, and then determine the sums of squares needed for substitution into (15.1.2). A good deal of this work can be avoided by using an alternate formula which is, mathematically speaking, equivalent to (15.1.2). This *short-cut computing formula for $r$* is

$$r = \frac{n \cdot \sum x_i y_i - (\sum x_i)(\sum y_i)}{\sqrt{n \cdot \sum x_i^2 - (\sum x_i)^2}\sqrt{n \cdot \sum y_i^2 - (\sum y_i)^2}} \qquad (15.1.3)\blacktriangle$$

and its derivation is referred to in the Bibliography on page 345. This formula may look even worse than (15.1.2), but it is actually much easier to use. To find $r$ we have only to calculate the five sums $\sum x_i, \sum y_i, \sum x_i^2, \sum y_i^2, \sum x_i y_i$, and substitute them together with $n$, the number of pairs of observations, into (15.1.3). We simplified the appearance of this formula somewhat by not indicating in each case that the summations go from 1 to $n$.

To illustrate the use of (15.1.3), let us calculate $r$ for the high school averages and college indexes given on page 313. Having already found that $\sum x_i = 631$, $\sum y_i = 14.1$, $\sum x_i^2 = 50{,}371$, and $\sum x_i y_i = 1134.8$, the only thing that remains to be done is find $\sum y_i^2$ and substitute these sums together with $n = 8$ into (15.1.3). Squaring the values given in the second column of the table on page 317, we get $\sum y_i^2 = 25.93$, and substitution into (15.1.3) yields

$$r = \frac{8(1134.8) - (631)(14.1)}{\sqrt{8(50371) - (631)^2}\,\sqrt{8(25.93) - (14.1)^2}} \qquad \frac{181.3}{(70.5)(2.94)}$$

$$= 0.89$$

To consider another example, let us calculate $r$ to measure the "degree of association" between $x$, *the annual per capita consumption*

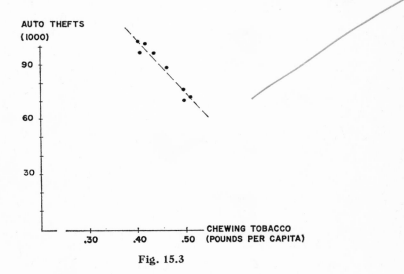

Fig. 15.3

*of chewing tobacco in the United States from 1948 through 1955*, and $y$, *the number of auto thefts reported in a sample of urban areas in the same years.* Writing the original data in the first two columns, the necessary sums, sums of squares, and sums of products may be obtained as in the following table.

| | $x$ (pounds) | $y$ (thousands) | $x^2$ | $y^2$ | $xy$ |
|---|---|---|---|---|---|
| 1948 | 0.52 | 73 | 0.2704 | 5,329 | 37.96 |
| 1949 | 0.49 | 71 | 0.2401 | 5,041 | 34.79 |
| 1950 | 0.49 | 77 | 0.2401 | 5,929 | 37.73 |
| 1951 | 0.45 | 89 | 0.2025 | 7,921 | 40.05 |
| 1952 | 0.43 | 97 | 0.1849 | 9,409 | 41.71 |
| 1953 | 0.42 | 102 | 0.1764 | 10,404 | 42.84 |
| 1954 | 0.41 | 97 | 0.1681 | 9,409 | 39.77 |
| 1955 | 0.40 | 104 | 0.1600 | 10,816 | 41.60 |
| | 3.61 | 710 | 1.6425 | 64,258 | 316.45 |

(If the calculations are done by machine, the totals of the various columns may be accumulated directly without having to write down the individual products and squares.) Substituting $n = 8$ and the various totals into (15.1.3), we get

$$r = \frac{8(316.45) - (3.61)(710)}{\sqrt{8(1.6425) - (3.61)^2} \sqrt{8(64258) - (710)^2}}$$

$$= -0.96$$

Having obtained a *positive* value of $r$ in the first example and a *negative* value in the second, let us investigate briefly what significance there is attached to the sign of $r$. Plotting the chewing tobacco and auto theft data as we have done in Figure 15.3, it can be seen that *small values of x go with large values of y while large values*

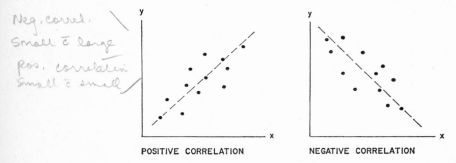

Neg. correl.
Small c large

Pos. correlation
Small c small

POSITIVE CORRELATION        NEGATIVE CORRELATION

**Fig. 15.4**

*of x go with small values of y.* This characterizes what is called a *negative correlation.* If *small values of x go with small values of y and large values of x with large values of y* (as in Figure 14.2 showing the high school average and college index data), $r$ will be *positive* and there is said to be a *positive correlation*. Geometrically speaking, a correlation is *positive* when, going from left to right, the regression line has an *upward slope* and it is *negative* when, going from left to right, the regression line has a *downward slope* (see Figure 15.4). As can be seen from our numerical examples, the sign of $r$ is automatically determined if we use formula (15.1.3).

Since we obtained a strong negative correlation for the chewing tobacco and auto theft data, $r$ was close to $-1$, we might be led to believe that there exists a "real" relationship between the consumption of chewing tobacco and the incidence of auto thefts. This does not make much sense and we shall have more to say about it in Section 15.2. For the moment let us be careful to interpret $r$ only as a quantity which measures how closely a regression line fits to a given set of data.

Before starting any of the exercises at the end of this section, the reader will benefit by considering some of the following tricks which are designed to simplify the calculation of $r$: since $r$ does not depend on the scale of $x$ or $y$, but is based on the (dimensionless) ratio of $\sum (y_i - y_i')^2$ to $\sum (y_i - \bar{y})^2$, the arithmetic needed to find $r$ can often be simplified by *adding an arbitrary positive or negative number to each $x$, each $y$, or both, or by multiplying each $x$, each $y$, or both by arbitrary positive constants*. In the chewing tobacco and auto theft example we might, thus, have multiplied each $x$ by 100 and then subtracted 45, substituting $7, 4, 4, 0, -2, -3, -4$, and $-5$ into the first column. The reader may wish to verify for himself, in Exercise 6 below, that $r$ would still be $-0.96$. To simplify things further, we could also have subtracted 90 (or some other number) from each $y$. What numbers to add or subtract and by what numbers to multiply will have to depend on the nature of the data. The important thing to keep in mind is that the purpose of these operations is to simplify the arithmetic as much as possible.

### EXERCISES

1. Calculate $r$ for the road widths and accident frequencies of Exercise 1 on page 318.

2. Calculate $r$ for the stresses and strains of Exercise 3 on page 319.

3. Calculate $r$ for the statistics and economics grades of Exercise 4 on page 319.

4. Calculate $r$ for the data of Exercise 7 on page 320.

5. If you were asked to calculate $r$ for *each* of the following two sets of data:

| $x$ | $y$ | | $x$ | $y$ |
|-----|-----|---|-----|-----|
| 105 | 3 | | 230 | 111 |
| 124 | 7 | | 196 | 162 |

would you be surprised to get $r = 1$ and $r = -1$, respectively? Explain.

6. Recalculate $r$ for the chewing tobacco and auto theft data given in the test after multiplying each $x$ by 100 and subtracting 45, and subtracting 90 from each $y$.

7. The following are the average hourly wages paid for unskilled labor employed in road building on federal-aid projects in New England, $x$, and the Pacific States, $y$, for the years 1946 through 1955:

| $x$ (dollars) | $y$ (dollars) |
|---------------|---------------|
| 0.83 | 1.21 |
| 0.91 | 1.32 |
| 1.02 | 1.51 |
| 1.13 | 1.66 |
| 1.19 | 1.73 |
| 1.27 | 1.78 |
| 1.41 | 1.97 |
| 1.49 | 2.10 |
| 1.53 | 2.15 |
| 1.71 | 2.26 |

Calculate $r$ after making suitable simplifications.

8. The following are the ages, $x$, and second-hand prices, $y$, charged for a certain kind of two-door sedan:

| $x$ (years) | $y$ (dollars) |
|-------------|---------------|
| 1 | 1995 |
| 3 | 875 |
| 6 | 695 |
| 10 | 345 |
| 5 | 595 |
| 2 | 1795 |

Fit a least squares line and also calculate $r$ for these data. What price would the least squares equation yield for a 4-year-old model of this kind of car?

9. Calculate $r$ for the weekly wages and weekly expenditures on entertainment given in the text on page 339.

**10.** State in each case whether you would expect to find a positive correlation, a negative correlation, or no correlation:

(a) The number of years of college attended by husbands and wives.

(b) Temperature and automobile accidents per vehicle mile in New York State.

(c) Shoe size and intelligence.

(d) Insurance companies' profits and the number of claims they have to pay.

(e) Hair color and income.

(f) Intelligence and standard of clothing of school children.

## 15.2 / Interpretation of *r*

We already know how to interpret *r* when it equals 0, $+1$, or $-1$; if it is 0, the points are so scattered, the fit of the regression line is so poor, that knowledge of *x* does not aid in the prediction of *y;* if it is $+1$ or $-1$, all points actually lie on a straight line and it stands to reason that we should be able to make excellent predictions of *y* with the equation of the line. Values of *r* falling *between 0 and +1* or *between 0 and −1* are more difficult to explain; a person who has no knowledge of statistics might easily be led to the erroneous idea that a correlation of $r = 0.80$ is "twice as good" as a correlation of $r = 0.40$, or that a correlation of $r = 0.75$ is "three times as good" or "three times as strong" as a correlation of $r = 0.25$.

To explain the meaning of intermediate values of *r*, let us again consider the high school average and college index data introduced on page 313. It is apparent from these data that there are considerable differences between the college indexes — they range from 1.2 to 2.3 — and it would seem appropriate to investigate *why* such differences exist. An obvious factor is the students' ability, but then there is also the students' health, their adjustment to college life, their choice of instructors, and probably quite a bit of luck in the choice of courses and in taking exams. To illustrate our point, let us group these factors determining the college indexes into

(1) *ability as measured by high school averages,*

(2) *all other factors including luck.*

This raises the question as to how much of the total variation of the college indexes may be attributed to ability and how much to all other factors.

Measuring the *total* variation among the college indexes by means of the quantity $\sum (y_i - \bar{y})^2$, *the sum of the squares of their deviations from the mean,* rather complicated algebraic manipulations will show that this sum of squares can be written as

$$\sum (y_i - \bar{y})^2 = \sum (y_i - y_i')^2 + \sum (y_i' - \bar{y})^2 \qquad (15.2.1)$$

The first term on the right-hand side of (15.2.1) consists of the sum of the squares of the vertical deviations from the regression line and *it measures the variation among the college indexes of students having identical high school averages.* (It is indicative of the spread or variation of the distributions shown in Figure 14.5 on page 321, assuming, as is necessary in this case, that all these distributions have the *same* standard deviation.) *Hence, this term gives us the portion of the total variation among the college indexes that is due to factors other than ability as measured by high school averages.*

Since the left-hand member of (15.2.1) measures the *total variation* among the college indexes, we find by subtraction that $\sum (y_i' - \bar{y})^2$, namely, the second term on the right-hand side, must measure *that portion of the total variation among the college indexes that can be attributed directly to differences in ability as measured by high school averages.* Numerically, we find that the *total variation* among the college indexes is given by the quantity

$$\sum (y_i - \bar{y})^2 = 1.08$$

and referring to the line $y' = -1.24 + 0.038x$ on page 317, it can be shown that

$$\sum (y_i - y_i')^2 = 0.22 \quad \text{and} \quad \sum (y_i' - \bar{y})^2 = 0.86$$

Thus, $0.86/1.08 = 0.796$ or *79.6 per cent of the total variation among the college indexes is due to differences in the students' ability.*

Duplicating this last argument symbolically, we find that *the percentage of the total variation among the y's which is due to differences in x* (due to the relationship with $x$) is

$$\frac{\sum (y_i' - \bar{y})^2}{\sum (y_i - \bar{y})^2} \cdot 100 \qquad (15.2.2)$$

and it can easily be shown (see Exercise 8 on page 339) that this quantity equals $100 \cdot r^2$. *In general, if the coefficient of correlation between two variables x and y equals r, then $100 \cdot r^2$ per cent of the variation of the y's is accounted for by differences in x, that is, by the relationship with x.* If in a given problem $r = 0.60$, then 36 per cent of the variation of the $y$'s is accounted for (perhaps caused) by differences in $x$; similarly, if $r = 0.40$, only 16 per cent of the variation of the $y$'s is accounted for by the relationship with $x$. In the sense of "percentage of variation accounted for," we can thus say that a correlation of $r = 0.80$ is *four times as strong* as a correlation of $r = 0.40$, and that a correlation of $r = 0.75$ is *nine times as strong* as a correlation or $r = 0.25$.

Trying to verify that (15.2.2) equals $100 \cdot r^2$ with reference to the high school average and college index example, we find that $r = 0.89$, the value we obtained on page 329, gives $100 \cdot r^2 = 100(0.89)^2 = 79.2$ per cent. The difference between this figure and the value of 79.6 obtained above is due entirely to rounding off.

In the preceding we did not mention the *sign* of $r$ since this has no bearing on the strength of the relationship. The only distinction between values such as $r = 0.60$ and $r = -0.60$ is that one regression line has an *upward* slope while the other's slope is *downward;* this has nothing to do with the goodness of the fit or the strength of the relationship between $x$ and $y$.

As a word of caution let us add that the coefficient of correlation is not only the most widely used but also the most widely *abused* of statistical formulas. It is abused in the sense that (1) it is often overlooked that $r$ measures only the strength of *linear* relationships and that (2) it does *not* necessarily imply a cause-effect relationship.

If $r$ is calculated indiscriminately, for instance, for the data of Figure 15.5, a small value of $r$ does not mean that the two variables are not related. The dotted curve of Figure 15.5 provides an *excellent fit* even though the straight line does not. Let us remember, therefore, that $r$ *measures only the strength of linear relationships.*

The fallacy of interpreting high values of $r$ as implying cause-effect relationships is best explained with a few examples. One such example, which is frequently used as an illustration, is the high positive correlation obtained for data pertaining to teachers' salaries and the consumption of liquor over the years. This is obviously not a cause-effect relationship; it re-

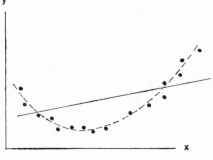

Fig. 15.5

sults from the fact that both variables are effects of a common cause, that is, the over-all standard of living. Another classical example is the strong positive correlation obtained for the number of storks seen nesting in English villages and the number of child births recorded in the same communities. We shall leave it to the reader's ingenuity to figure out why there is a strong positive correlation without there being a cause-effect relationship between babies and storks. A third example is the strong negative correlation which we obtained on page 330 for the chewing tobacco and auto theft data. In this case the high correlation is due to the dependence of both variables on social patterns changing with time.

The examples of the preceding paragraph certainly demonstrate that it is much safer to interpret correlation coefficients as measures of *association* rather than *causation*. For further information about such *spurious* correlations see the Bibliography on page 345.

### 15.3 / A Significance Test for *r*

Suppose we take a pair of dice, one red and one green, and that five rolls produce the following result:

| Red Die | Green Die |
|:---:|:---:|
| *x* | *y* |
| 4 | 5 |
| 2 | 2 |
| 4 | 6 |
| 2 | 1 |
| 6 | 4 |

Calculating *r* for these data, we get the surprisingly high value of $r = 0.67$, and this raises the question whether there is anything wrong with the natural assumption that there should be no relationship between the results produced by the two dice. *After all, one die does not know what the other one is doing.* In order to answer this question we shall have to see whether we might have obtained the high value of *r by chance* even though there is actually no relationship between the performances of the dice.

Whenever a correlation coefficient is calculated on the basis of a *sample*, as in the above example, the value which we obtain for *r* is only an estimate of $\rho$ *(rho)*, the *true* correlation coefficient which we would obtain for the entire population. (In our example, the populations, hypothetical as they are, consist of all possible rolls of the given dice.)

To test the null hypothesis that there is *no correlation*, that $\rho = 0$, we shall as before have to consider the sampling distribution of the statistic on which our decision is to be based, in this case the sampling distribution of *r*. Such a sampling distribution could be obtained *experimentally* for the above example by repeatedly rolling the pair of dice 5 times, calculating *r* in each case, and grouping the results into an appropriate distribution (see Exercise 7 on page 339).

Since the mathematical theory underlying sampling distributions of *r* in general is considerably beyond the scope of this text, let us merely state that *under the null hypothesis of no correlation, the sampling distribution of r can be approximated closely with a normal curve having the mean 0 and the standard deviation* $1/\sqrt{n-1}$, *provided that n is large and that the observations x and y can be looked upon as samples from normal populations.* Following the terminology of Section 10.5, the standard deviation of this sampling distribution is called the *standard error of r* and it is written as

$$\sigma_r = \frac{1}{\sqrt{n-1}} \qquad (15.3.1)\blacktriangle$$

It must be remembered, or course, that *this formula applies only when the null hypothesis of no correlation, the hypothesis that* $\rho = 0$, *is true.*

Considering the normal curve of Figure 15.6, representing (or

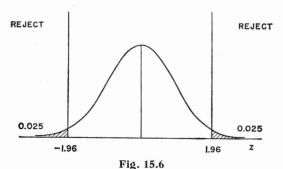

**Fig. 15.6**

approximating) the sampling distribution of *r* under the null hypothesis of no correlation, we can now test this hypothesis at a level of significance of 0.05 with the following criterion:

*reject the null hypothesis if* $z < -1.96$ *or* $z > 1.96$; *accept the hypothesis (or reserve judgment) if* $-1.96 \le z \le 1.96$, *where*

$$z = r\sqrt{n-1} \qquad (15.3.2)\blacktriangle$$

This formula for *z* was obtained by subtracting from *r* the mean of its sampling distribution, namely, 0, and then dividing by its standard deviation as given by (15.3.1). To change the level of significance to, say, 0.01, we have only to replace 1.96 with 2.58.

To illustrate the use of this criterion, let us suppose that a sample of 100 paired observations produced a correlation of $r = 0.32$. Since

$$z = r\sqrt{n - 1} = 0.32\sqrt{100 - 1} = 3.18 \quad \textit{significant relationship}$$

we can *reject* the null hypothesis of no correlation or, as is customary, *we can say that there is a significant relationship.* (This would be true at a level of significance of 0.05 as well as 0.01.) Returning now to the example of the two dice, we find that *No corvel.*

$$z = r\sqrt{n - 1} = 0.67\sqrt{5 - 1} = 1.34$$

and since this value lies between $-1.96$ and $1.96$ we conclude that there is *no significant correlation.* In other words, the value of $r = 0.67$ which we obtained may be attributed to chance.

Although the criterion which we have presented is based on a normal curve approximation to the sampling distribution of $r$, it is generally *safe* to use it even when $n$ is small. It is *conservative* in the sense that if our criterion allows us to say that a sample value of $r$ is significant at a certain level of significance, an exact test based on the actual sampling distribution of $r$ would do the same. A reference to an exact small sample test based on the Student-$t$ distribution is given in the Bibliography on page 345.

Let us also point out that if a correlation coefficient is *statistically* significant, this does not necessarily imply that it is also significant in the sense of being meaningful. The correlation which we obtained for the chewing tobacco and auto theft data was $-0.96$, and this is *significant* for $n = 8$ at a level of significance of 0.05. Nevertheless, this correlation is spurious; it is not indicative of a *direct* relationship.

### EXERCISES

1. Assuming that the assumptions underlying the criterion on page 337 can be met, test at a level of significance of 0.05 whether the following values of $r$ are significant:
   (a) $r = 0.65$ and $n = 37$    $z = .65\sqrt{36}$    3.90   yes
   (b) $r = -0.30$ and $n = 50$    $z = .30\sqrt{49} =$   2.10   yes
   (c) $r = 0.80$ and $n = 10$            2.4   yes
   (d) $r = -0.15$ and $n = 226$   $z = .15\sqrt{225}$   2.25   yes
   (e) $r = 0.08$ and $n = 65$    $z = .08\sqrt{64}$    .64   no

2. Repeat Exercise 1 using a level of significance of 0.01.

3. Test whether the value obtained for $r$ on page 329 for the high school averages and college indexes is significant at a level of significance of 0.05.    $Z = .89\sqrt{7} = .89(2.64) = 2.35$   yes   significant

4. Test whether the value of $r$ obtained in Exercise 1 on page 331 is significant at a level of significance of 0.05.

5. Test whether the value of $r$ obtained in Exercise 7 on page 332 is significant at a level of significance of 0.01.

6. Test whether the value of $r$ obtained in Exercise 8 on page 332 is significant at a level of significance of 0.05.

7. (*Group Exercise*) Using a pair of dice, one red and one green (or otherwise distinguishable), take a large number of samples, each consisting of 5 rolls of the dice. Calculate $r$ separately for each sample, group these $r$'s into a frequency distribution, and compare the standard deviation of this *experimental sampling distribution of r* with the value which we should expect according to (15.3.1).

8. (*Theoretical Exercise*) Using (15.2.1), show that (15.2.2) equals $100 \cdot r^2$.

## 15.4 / The Calculation of r from Grouped Data

In Chapters 3 and 4 we saw that the calculation of the mean and standard deviation of a large set of data can be simplified to quite an extent by first grouping the data into a frequency table and then determining $\bar{x}$ and $s$ directly from the distribution. Since the calculation of $r$ can be tedious when $n$ is large and the work has to be done without a machine, let us now show how $r$ can be obtained from grouped data.

In order to illustrate the steps needed to group paired observations and to calculate $r$ on the basis of the resulting *two-way frequency table*, let us refer to the following sample of size 40 in which $x$ stands for *weekly wages of workers in a certain industry* and $y$ stands for their *weekly expenditures for entertainment, movies, sports, etc., in dollars*:

| $x$ | $y$ | $x$ | $y$ | $x$ | $y$ | $x$ | $y$ |
|------|------|--------|------|--------|-------|-------|------|
| 57.30 | 2.47 | 87.27 | 7.40 | 84.30 | 3.75 | 89.40 | 6.85 |
| 93.50 | 7.12 | 79.25 | 7.48 | 91.20 | 4.90 | 56.90 | 2.49 |
| 71.15 | 5.62 | 60.87 | 0.75 | 103.20 | 7.50 | 86.00 | 7.50 |
| 68.75 | 4.76 | 83.75 | 7.82 | 83.25 | 7.50 | 93.00 | 7.46 |
| 85.60 | 3.81 | 110.90 | 9.65 | 49.15 | 1.85 | 79.80 | 3.72 |
| 105.25 | 8.75 | 72.10 | 6.55 | 112.50 | 11.67 | 98.00 | 9.00 |
| 78.40 | 6.67 | 79.82 | 5.63 | 71.05 | 4.63 | 80.00 | 5.50 |
| 75.00 | 3.69 | 94.50 | 6.75 | 93.70 | 5.33 | 61.60 | 4.83 |
| 87.25 | 4.75 | 98.00 | 5.62 | 98.10 | 7.85 | 84.90 | 7.90 |
| 90.00 | 8.92 | 67.20 | 5.00 | 95.20 | 9.36 | 90.30 | 5.60 |

The problems we must consider when grouping *paired observations* are almost identical with those which we met in the construction of ordinary frequency distributions. *We must decide how many classes to use for each of the two variables and from where to where each class is to go.* Selecting the *five* classes \$40–\$54.99, \$55–\$69.99, \$70–\$84.99, \$85–\$99.99, and \$100–\$114.99 for the *wages* and the *six* classes \$0–\$1.99, \$2–\$3.99, \$4–\$5.99, \$6–\$7.99, \$8–\$9.99, and \$10–\$11.99 for the *expenditures* on entertainment, we arrive at the following *two-way table.*

*Weekly Wages*

| | 40–54.99 | 55–69.99 | 70–84.99 | 85–99.99 | 100–114.99 |
|---|---|---|---|---|---|
| 0–1.99 | | | | | |
| 2–3.99 | | | | | |
| 4–5.99 | | | | | |
| 6–7.99 | | | | | |
| 8–9.99 | | | | | |
| 10–11.99 | | | | | |

*Expenditures on entertainment*

Having constructed this table, the next step is to *tally* the data by putting checks in the cells corresponding to the 40 pairs of observations. For instance, $x = 57.30$ and $y = 2.47$ goes into the cell belonging to the *second* row and *second* column, $x = 93.50$ and $y = 7.12$ goes into the cell belonging to the *fourth* row and *fourth* column, and $x = 71.15$ and $y = 5.62$ goes into the cell belonging to the *third* row and *third* column. After counting the number of cases falling into each cell, we obtain the following *two-way frequency distribution:*

*Weekly Wages*

| | 40–54.99 | 55–69.99 | 70–84.99 | 85–99.99 | 100–114.99 |
|---|---|---|---|---|---|
| 0–1.99 | 1 | 1 | | | |
| 2–3.99 | | 2 | 3 | 1 | |
| 4–5.99 | | 3 | 4 | 5 | |
| 6–7.99 | | | 6 | 7 | 1 |
| 8–9.99 | | | | 3 | 2 |
| 10–11.99 | | | | | 1 |

*Expenditures on entertainment*

Graphically, this two-way distribution is shown in the three-dimensional histogram of Figure 15.7. Here the *heights* of the blocks represent the frequencies of the cells on which they stand just as the heights of the rectangles in ordinary histograms represent the class frequencies.

This takes care of the first problem, namely, that of grouping paired data, and we are now ready to demonstrate how $r$ is calculated on the basis of a two-way frequency table. To do this we shall assume, as in the case of the mean and standard deviation, that all measurements contained in a class are located at the class marks, and having made this assumption we shall use the same change of scale as in Chapters 3 and 4. Since we now have two variables, $x$ and $y$, we shall

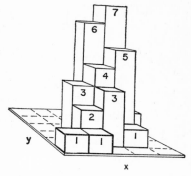

Fig. 15.7. A three-dimensional histogram.

replace the $x$-scale by a $u$-scale and the $y$-scale by a $v$-scale, doing this as before by numbering successive class marks ..., $-3$, $-2$, $-1$, $0$, $1$, $2$, $3$, .... In our example we thus get

| | $-2$ | $-1$ | $0$ | $1$ | $2$ | $u$-scale |
|---|---|---|---|---|---|---|
| $-2$ | 1 | 1 | | | | |
| $-1$ | | 2 | 3 | 1 | | |
| $0$ | | 3 | 4 | 5 | | |
| $1$ | | | 6 | 7 | 1 | |
| $2$ | | | | 3 | 2 | |
| $3$ | | | | | 1 | |

$v$-scale

where, as before, the choice of the zero of each scale is arbitrary. The new scales are chosen so as to make subsequent calculations as simple as possible.

As we pointed out on page 331, the coefficient of correlation will not be affected if we add a constant to all the $x$'s or all the $y$'s and if we multiply all the $x$'s or all the $y$'s by positive constants. *This implies that if we calculate r in terms of the u's and v's, we will get the same result as if we had used the class marks in the original scales.* Thus, substituting $u$'s and $v$'s for the $x$'s and $y$'s of (15.1.3) and allowing for the fact that we are now dealing with grouped data, *the formula for calculating r from grouped data* becomes

$$r = \frac{n \cdot \sum uvf - (\sum uf_u)(\sum vf_v)}{\sqrt{n \cdot \sum u^2f_u - (\sum uf_u)^2}\,\sqrt{n \cdot \sum v^2f_v - (\sum vf_v)^2}} \qquad (15.4.1)\blacktriangle$$

Like the short-cut formulas of Chapters 3 and 4, this formula for $r$ can be used only if the original class intervals for $x$ and $y$, respectively, have equal widths.

The sums that are needed for substitution into (15.1.4) are most conveniently obtained by arranging the necessary calculations as follows:

| | | | | | (1) | (2) *freq.* | (3) | (4) | (5) |
|---|---|---|---|---|---|---|---|---|---|
| | | | | | $v$ | $f_v$ | $vf_v$ | $v^2f_v$ | $uvf$ |
| 1 | 1 | | | | $-2$ | 2 | $-4$ | 8 | 6 |
| | 2 | 3 | 1 | | $-1$ | 6 | $-6$ | 6 | 1 |
| | 3 | 4 | 5 | | 0 | 12 | 0 | 0 | 0 |
| | | 6 | 7 | 1 | 1 | 14 | 14 | 14 | 9 |
| | | | 3 | 2 | 2 | 5 | 10 | 20 | 14 |
| | | | | 1 | 3 | 1 | 3 | 9 | 6 |
| | | | | | | 40 | 17 | 57 | 36 |
| (6) $u$ | $-2$ | $-1$ | 0 | 1 | 2 | | | | |
| (7) $f_u$ | 1 | 6 | 13 | 16 | 4 | 40 | | | |
| (8) $uf_u$ | $-2$ | $-6$ | 0 | 16 | 8 | 16 | | | |
| (9) $u^2f_u$ | 4 | 6 | 0 | 16 | 16 | 42 | | | |
| (10) $uvf$ | 4 | 4 | 0 | 12 | 16 | 36 | | | |

To simplify the over-all picture, we put the $u$- and $v$-scales at the bottom and at the right-hand side of this *correlation table*, labeling them row (6) and column (1), respectively. Column (2) contains the frequencies $f_v$, the number of times each $v$ occurs, and they are obtained by adding the frequencies in the respective rows. Column (3) contains the products $vf_v$, which are obtained by multiplying the corresponding entries of columns (1) and (2), and column (4) contains the products $v^2f_v$, which may be obtained by either squaring each entry of column (1) and multiplying by the corresponding entry of column (2) *or* by multiplying the corresponding entries of columns (1) and (3). The numbers shown in rows (7), (8), and (9) are obtained by performing the identical operations on the $u$'s and $f_u$'s.

The totals of columns (2), (3), and (4) provide $n$, $\sum vf_v$, and $\sum v^2f_v$, while the totals of rows (7), (8), and (9) provide $n$, $\sum uf_u$, and $\sum u^2f_u$. To calculate $r$ with (15.4.1) we still lack $\sum uvf$, which stands for the sum of all the quantities obtained by individually multiplying each cell frequency by the $u$ and $v$ of the row and column to which it belongs. To simplify this we shall work on each row separately, first multiplying each cell frequency by the corresponding $u$ and then multiplying the *sum* of these products by the corresponding $v$. For the *second* row we thus get

$$[2(-1) + 3(0) + 1(1)] (-1) = 1$$

for the *fourth* row we get

$$[6(0) + 7(1) + 1(2)] (1) = 9$$

and these are the corresponding entries shown in column (5).

Interchanging $u$ and $v$, we could also calculate $\sum uvf$ by working separately on each column, multiplying each cell frequency by the corresponding $v$, and then multiplying the *sum* of these products by the corresponding $u$. For the *fourth* column we would thus get

$$[1(-1) + 5(0) + 7(1) + 3(2)] (1) = 12$$

and this is the corresponding entry shown in row (10). The sum $\sum uvf$ is thus given by the totals of column (5) and row (10), and although it is unnecessary to find them both, it serves as a good check.

Substituting the totals of the appropriate rows and columns of our correlation table into (15.4.1), we finally get

$$r = \frac{40(36) - (16)(17)}{\sqrt{40(42) - (16)^2}\sqrt{40(57) - (17)^2}}$$

$$= 0.69$$

as a measure of the strength of the (linear) relationship between weekly wages and weekly expenditures on entertainment for workers in the given industry.

Having seen only this one example, the reader may feel that the calculation of $r$ for grouped data is quite involved; however, after having worked a few problems it should become apparent that the use of (15.4.1) can save a considerable amount of work, at least, so long as the calculations have to be done without a machine. Incidentally, had we calculated $r$ in this example *without* grouping the data (see Exercise 9 on page 332), we would have obtained a value somewhat greater than 0.69. It must be remembered that whenever we group data we are apt to lose some information.

### EXERCISES

**1.** The following are final examination grades in psychology, $x$, and economics, $y$, obtained by 36 students:

| $x$ | $y$ | $x$ | $y$ | $x$ | $y$ |
|-----|-----|-----|-----|-----|-----|
| 53 | 70 | 31 | 72 | 35 | 57 |
| 24 | 38 | 80 | 86 | 56 | 72 |
| 62 | 55 | 45 | 46 | 65 | 63 |
| 90 | 78 | 78 | 57 | 78 | 76 |
| 18 | 35 | 71 | 71 | 49 | 53 |
| 94 | 91 | 84 | 72 | 82 | 90 |
| 73 | 69 | 58 | 59 | 22 | 38 |
| 85 | 83 | 9 | 14 | 90 | 82 |
| 25 | 51 | 16 | 42 | 77 | 82 |
| 71 | 53 | 97 | 93 | 35 | 19 |
| 81 | 60 | 65 | 61 | 52 | 43 |
| 52 | 58 | 42 | 58 | 93 | 79 |

Group these data into a two-way table having classes going from 1 to 20, 21 to 40, 41 to 60, 61 to 80, and 81 to 100 for both $x$ and $y$. Then calculate $r$ using formula (15.4.1).

**2.** In the following table $x$ stands for the 1950 population of selected cities in the United States having populations between 50,000 and 75,000 and $y$ stands for the number of new dwelling units constructed in these cities in 1950:

| $x$ | $y$ | $x$ | $y$ | $x$ | $y$ | $x$ | $y$ |
|-----|-----|-----|-----|-----|-----|-----|-----|
| 64,430 | 103 | 55,725 | 977 | 70,252 | 341 | 63,685 | 919 |
| 61,657 | 981 | 66,568 | 322 | 51,502 | 155 | 65,679 | 683 |
| 71,508 | 243 | 57,951 | 475 | 66,113 | 157 | 52,696 | 858 |
| 50,576 | 406 | 50,676 | 696 | 71,899 | 999 | 66,731 | 763 |
| 52,523 | 289 | 54,661 | 321 | 58,479 | 307 | 65,198 | 636 |
| 62,860 | 170 | 63,232 | 282 | 73,726 | 645 | 58,891 | 130 |
| 70,174 | 135 | 57,704 | 139 | 63,529 | 93 | 50,211 | 122 |
| 74,549 | 547 | 68,071 | 383 | 57,112 | 802 | 59,953 | 77 |
| 66,269 | 389 | 63,774 | 192 | 57,702 | 103 | | |
| 54,263 | 132 | 51,910 | 287 | 73,681 | 584 | | |

Group these data into a suitable two-way table and then use formula (15.4.1) to find $r$.

**3.** Calculate $r$ for the following correlation table with $x$ standing for heights in inches and $y$ standing for weights in pounds:

|  |  | \| | \| | \| | \| | \| | \| |
|---|---|---|---|---|---|---|---|

$x$
(Heights)

| | | 60–62 | 63–65 | 66–68 | 69–71 | 72–74 | 75–77 |
|---|---|---|---|---|---|---|---|
| | 110–129 | 2 | 3 | 2 | 1 | | |
| | 130–149 | | 1 | 4 | 2 | 1 | |
| $y$ | 150–169 | | 1 | 3 | 6 | 4 | 2 |
| (Weights) | 170–189 | | | 2 | 10 | 8 | 2 |
| | 190–209 | | | 1 | 5 | 4 | 1 |
| | 210–229 | | | | 1 | 3 | |
| | 230–249 | | | | | 2 | 1 |

**4.** Calculate $r$ from the following table, with $x$ representing scores obtained by 115 cadets while firing from a kneeling position and $y$ standing for the scores they obtained firing from a standing position:

$x$
(Kneeling position)

| | | 75–79 | 80–84 | 85–89 | 90–94 | 95–99 |
|---|---|---|---|---|---|---|
| | 75–79 | 5 | 8 | 7 | 3 | |
| $y$ | 80–84 | 1 | 4 | 10 | 12 | 5 |
| (Standing position) | 85–89 | | 2 | 9 | 10 | 12 |
| | 90–94 | | | 5 | 8 | 10 |
| | 95–99 | | | | 1 | 3 |

### BIBLIOGRAPHY

A derivation of formula (15.1.3) may be found in

Richardson, C. H., *An Introduction to Statistical Analysis*. New York: Harcourt, Brace, 1944, Chap. 8.

Various types of spurious correlations are discussed in

Johnson, P. O., and Jackson, R. W., *Introduction to Statistical Methods*. Englewood Cliffs, N. J.: Prentice-Hall, 1953, Chap. 11.

and a more theoretical treatment is given in

Simon, H. A., "Spurious Correlation: A Causal Interpretation," *Journal of the American Statistical Association*, vol. 49, 1954, No. 267.

An exact small-sample test of the significance of $r$ based on the $t$-distribution may be found in

Neiswanger, W. A., *Elementary Statistical Methods as Applied to Business and Economic Data*, rev. ed. New York: Macmillan, 1956, Chap. 19.

# Chapter 16

# Further Problems of Correlation

## 16.1 / Rank Correlation

As we saw in connection with the *U*-test of Section 13.2, it is convenient at times to work with the *ranks* of observations instead of their actual numerical values. Although we may be losing some information, using ranks has the advantages that fewer assumptions are needed for tests of hypotheses and arithmetical details are usually simplified.

To illustrate the so-called *rank correlation coefficient*, let us consider data obtained in a study whose purpose was to determine the strength of whatever relationship there may exist between $x$, the number of motor vehicles registered in 1954 in the Mountain and Pacific States, and $y$, these states' mileage of rural and municipal roads. The first two columns of the table that follows contain the motor vehicle registrations in thousands and the mileages in 1000 miles:

| $x$ | $y$ | Rank of $x$ | Rank of $y$ |
|------|-------|------|------|
| 380  | 30.4  | 5  | 11 |
| 5698 | 136.8 | 1  | 1  |
| 682  | 75.4  | 4  | 2  |
| 315  | 41.8  | 6  | 7  |
| 314  | 72.4  | 7  | 3  |
| 115  | 31.5  | 11 | 8  |
| 310  | 62.6  | 8  | 4  |
| 765  | 61.2  | 3  | 5  |
| 307  | 31.3  | 9  | 9  |
| 1085 | 59.1  | 2  | 6  |
| 168  | 30.9  | 10 | 10 |

In the third column we ranked the $x$'s, giving Rank 1 to the highest value of 5698, Rank 2 to 1085, Rank 3 to 765, ...; in the fourth column we ranked the $y$'s, giving Rank 1 to 136.8, Rank 2 to 75.4, Rank 3 to 72.4, ..., and Rank 11 to the smallest value, which is 30.4.

Proceeding from here, we could calculate $r$ for the two sets of ranks using formula (15.1.3), but the *identical* result can be obtained faster and much less laboriously using the formula

$$r' = 1 - \frac{6(\sum d_i^2)}{n(n^2 - 1)} \qquad (16.1.1)$$

*which defines the coefficient of rank correlation.* (We are using the symbol $r'$, but there is little consistency in this respect. Other symbols that have been used are $r_r$, $r_s$, $S$, and $\rho$.)

In (16.1.1) which, incidentally, can be derived from (15.1.3) when the $x$'s and $y$'s are ranks and there are no ties, $d_i$ stands for the difference between the ranks of the $i$th $x$ and $y$ and $n$ stands for the number of pairs of observations. When using (16.1.1) it does not matter whether we give Rank 1 to the highest value or to the lowest, so long as we are consistent and use the same kind of ranking for both the $x$'s and the $y$'s.

The sum of squares of the $d_i$, needed for substitution into the formula f or $r'$, is easily found, for example, as in the following table:

| Rank of x | Rank of y | d | d² |
|:---:|:---:|:---:|:---:|
| 5 | 11 | −6 | 36 |
| 1 | 1 | 0 | 0 |
| 4 | 2 | 2 | 4 |
| 6 | 7 | −1 | 1 |
| 7 | 3 | 4 | 16 |
| 11 | 8 | 3 | 9 |
| 8 | 4 | 4 | 16 |
| 3 | 5 | −2 | 4 |
| 9 | 9 | 0 | 0 |
| 2 | 6 | −4 | 16 |
| 10 | 10 | 0 | 0 |
| | | | 102 |

Since $n = 11$ and $\sum d_i^2 = 102$, we thus get

$$r' = 1 - \frac{6(102)}{11(11^2 - 1)} = 0.54$$

If we tried to calculate $r'$ for the chewing tobacco and auto theft data on page 330, we would run into the problem of *ties in rank*. Giving the smallest value Rank 1, we find that among the $x$'s the value 0.49 occurs twice, occupying Ranks 6 and 7. As we already explained in connection with the $U$-test on page 297, *in the presence of ties it is customary to assign each value the mean of the ranks which they jointly occupy*. Thus, each of the two $x$'s gets a ranking of $(6 + 7)/2 = 6.5$. Had three of them tied, say, for Ranks 2, 3, and 4, we would give each a ranking of $(2 + 3 + 4)/3 = 3$. When there are ties in rank, $r'$ will generally not equal $r$, calculated for the ranks with (15.1.3), but if the number of ties is small the difference will not be very large.

Rank correlation methods can also be used to test the null hypothesis of no correlation. As a matter of fact, we can use the same criterion as for $r$, the one given on page 337, since the *standard error of $r'$* is

$$\sigma_{r'} = \frac{1}{\sqrt{n - 1}} \qquad (16.1.2)\blacktriangle$$

A definite advantage of using $r'$ instead of $r$ in this test of significance is that for $r'$ it is *nonparametric:* we no longer have to assume that our samples come from normal populations.

### EXERCISES

1. Calculate $r'$ for the high school averages and college indexes given in the text on page 313.

2. Calculate $r'$ for the accident frequencies and road widths of Exercise 1 on page 318.

3. Calculate $r'$ for the stress and strain data of Exercise 3 on page 319.

4. Calculate $r'$ for the statistics and economics grades of Exercise 4 on page 319 and test the null hypothesis of no correlation at a level of significance of 0.05.

5. Calculate $r'$ for the hourly wages paid in New England and the Pacific Coast States on the basis of the data of Exercise 7 on page 332 and test the null hypothesis of no correlation at a level of significance of 0.01.

6. Two students, asked to rank their preferences for 10 different subjects, gave the following replies:

|              | Mr. Taylor | Mr. Jones |
|--------------|:----------:|:---------:|
| English      | 2          | 7         |
| History      | 4          | 8         |
| Mathematics  | 9          | 1         |
| Physics      | 10         | 3         |
| Chemistry    | 8          | 2         |
| Psychology   | 6          | 6         |
| Economics    | 3          | 9         |
| Sociology    | 5          | 10        |
| Music        | 7          | 4         |
| Philosophy   | 1          | 1         |

Calculate $r'$ as a measure of the *consistency or inconsistency* of the two sets of ratings.

**7.** Two judges, asked to rank the 12 finalists in a beauty contest, did so as follows:

|                    | Judge A | Judge B |
|--------------------|:-------:|:-------:|
| Miss Alabama       | 4       | 6       |
| Miss California    | 10      | 7       |
| Miss Delaware      | 11      | 10      |
| Miss Colorado      | 1       | 5       |
| Miss Massachusetts | 6       | 9       |
| Miss New York      | 7       | 4       |
| Miss Vermont       | 2       | 1       |
| Miss Florida       | 9       | 8       |
| Miss Nevada        | 8       | 12      |
| Miss Iowa          | 3       | 2       |
| Miss Wisconsin     | 12      | 11      |
| Miss Texas         | 5       | 3       |

Calculate $r'$ as an indication of the *consistency or inconsistency* of the two judges.

## 16.2 / The Contingency Coefficient

Although we did not say so explicitly, it must be apparent from its formula that the coefficient of correlation applies only to *quantitative* data. It cannot be used if one or both of the variables are *qualitative*, for example, if one variable is geographical location, political affiliation, hair color, occupation, and so forth. Since problems involving qualitative, or categorical, variables arise in many fields of research, let us indicate briefly how one can measure the strength of whatever relationship there may exist between qualitative variables and how to test, in that case, the null hypothesis of no correlation.

This may, perhaps, come as a surprise, but the problem of testing the null hypothesis of no correlation between qualitative variables was already discussed in Section 12.1. Using the $\chi^2$ criterion on page 279 we showed that there is a *relationship* between the adequacy of families' milk consumption and the education of their homemakers by rejecting the hypothesis of independence. Similarly, in Exercises 4 and 5 on page 282 we asked the reader to check whether there is a correlation between students' ability in mathematics and physics and whether there is a correlation between salesmanship and sense of humor.

In Section 12.1 we performed these tests by calculating the expected cell frequencies under the assumption of independence (or no correlation), finding $\chi^2$ by means of formula (12.1.2), and then using the criterion on page 279. We also pointed out that *small values of $\chi^2$ support the null hypothesis that there is no relationship, while large values of $\chi^2$ are apt to lead to its rejection. As a matter of fact, the larger the calculated value of $\chi^2$, the stronger is the relationship between the variables.*

Utilizing this last observation, let us now define the following measure of the strength of the correlation between qualitative variables, called the *contingency coefficient:*

$$C = \sqrt{\frac{\chi^2}{\chi^2 + n}} \qquad (16.2.1)\blacktriangle$$

Here $n$ is the grand total of the frequencies of the *contingency table,* as we called $r$ by $k$ tables in connection with this kind of situation, and $\chi^2$ is the value obtained for the observed and expected cell frequencies with formula (12.1.2).

Contingency coefficients are in many respects similar to ordinary correlation coefficients, being close to 0 when there is no correlation and close to 1 when the relationship is strong. To interpret $C$ correctly, let us point out that for tables having very few rows and columns the maximum value of $C$ is actually less than 1. For a 2 by 2 table a "perfect" correlation yields $C = 0.707$ and for a 3 by 3 table $C = 0.816$.

Returning now to the example of Section 12.1, where we studied the relationship between the adequacy of a family's milk consumption and the education of its homemaker, we find that $n = 500$, $\chi^2 = 58.63$ (see page 279). Hence,

$$C = \sqrt{\frac{58.63}{58.63 + 500}} = 0.32$$

and we have a significant though not particularly strong relationship. The fact that it is significant was shown earlier (on page 280) by means of the $\chi^2$ criterion.

## EXERCISES

1. Calculate $C$ for the data of Exercise 4 on page 282 to measure the strength of the relationship between students' ability in mathematics and interest in statistics.
2. Calculate $C$ for the data of Exercise 5 on page 282 to measure the strength of the relationship between sense of humor and salesmanship.
3. The following table was obtained in a study of the relationship between temperament and the speed of promotions of the employees of a certain company:

*Speed of Promotions*

|  | Slow | Average | Fast |
|---|---|---|---|
| *Very self-controlled* | 112 | 63 | 72 |
| *Average temperament* | 48 | 119 | 81 |
| *Very impulsive* | 25 | 45 | 92 |

(a) Calculate $\chi^2$ by means of formula (12.1.2) and test the null hypothesis of no relationship at a level of significance of 0.05. (Use the criterion on page 279.)
(b) Calculate $C$ as an indication of the strength of the relationship.

## 16.3 / Multiple and Partial Correlation

The subjects of multiple and partial correlation are generally omitted in first courses in statistics because there is already enough material to be covered without going into these more advanced topics. Nevertheless, the concepts underlying multiple and partial correlation are fairly easy to grasp and we shall discuss them briefly so that the reader will at least know what they mean.

In Section 15.1 we defined the coefficient of correlation as a measure of the goodness of the fit of a least squares line of the form $y' = a + bx$. Without going into any detail, let us now extend this measure of goodness of fit to apply to problems in which $y$ is predicted by means of a *multiple regression equation* of the form

$$y' = a + bx_1 + cx_2 + dx_3 + \ldots \qquad (16.3.1)$$

On page 324 we illustrated such an equation with reference to a study of the relationship between the consumption of beef and veal and the price of beef, the price of pork, and personal income.

To measure how closely a set of *observed* values of $y$ agrees with the corresponding *calculated* values obtained with an equation of the form (16.3.1), we again use the formula

$$\sqrt{1 - \frac{\sum (y_i - y_i')^2}{\sum (y_i - \bar{y})^2}} \qquad (16.2.3)$$

which on page 328 served to define $r$. Now this formula defines the *multiple correlation coefficient*, provided, of course, that the $y_i'$ are calculated with a multiple regression equation like (16.3.1) and not just an ordinary regression equation of the form $y' = a + bx$.

In contrast to $r$, we can no longer say that a multiple correlation coefficient measures the goodness of the fit of a regression *line;* things are more complicated now because $y' = a + bx_1 + cx_2$ is the equation of a *plane* and if there is an $x_3$, an $x_4$, and so forth, we run into geometrical configurations that can no longer be visualized.

To illustrate the simplest case, let us suppose that we are given data on the age, $x_1$, height $x_2$, and weight, $y$, of a number of persons, and that we are interested in obtaining an equation which will

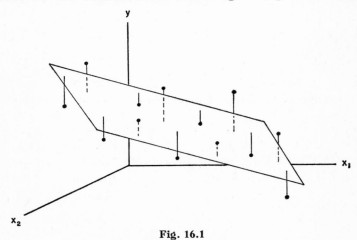

Fig. 16.1

enable us to predict weight in terms of age and height by means of an equation of the form $y' = a + bx_1 + cx_2$. Geometrically speaking, this equation is represented by the plane of Figure 16.1, $a$, $b$, and $c$

are found by the method of least squares, and the goodness of the fit is measured, essentially, by the sum of the squares of the vertical deviations shown in that diagram. *A multiple correlation coefficient thus measures how closely a plane (fit by the method of least squares) fits to the points representing a given set of data.* In our example it measures how closely weight is related to *both* age and height.

When we touched upon the problem of *correlation and causation*, we showed that a high correlation between two variables can sometimes be due to their individual dependence on a third variable. We illustrated this with the examples of birth registrations and storks as well as the examples of teachers' salaries and the consumption of liquor. Now, to give another example, let us consider $x_1$, *the weekly amount of hot chocolate sold by a refreshment stand in a summer resort,* and $x_2$, *the weekly number of tourists visiting the resort.* Furthermore, let us suppose that on the basis of large sets of weekly data we found that the correlation coefficient for the two variables is $r = -0.30$. This result is startling, saying the least, since we would expect higher sales of hot chocolate when there are more tourists and, hence, a *positive* correlation.

Investigating this more closely, we surmise that the negative correlation of $-0.30$ might be accounted for by the fact that sales of hot chocolate as well as the number of tourists visiting the resort are related to a third variable, $x_3$, *the average weekly temperature at the resort.* If the temperature is high, there will be many visitors, but they will prefer cold drinks to hot chocolate; if the temperature is low, there will be fewer visitors, and they will prefer hot chocolate to cold drinks. Getting data on the resort's average weekly temperatures for the same weeks for which we previously calculated $r$ for $x_1$ and $x_2$, let us suppose that the correlation coefficient for $x_1$ and $x_3$ is $-0.70$, while that for $x_2$ and $x_3$ is $0.80$. These values seem reasonable since low sales of hot chocolate should go with high temperatures, high sales with low temperatures, and since high temperatures should go with great numbers of tourists, low temperatures with fewer.

To study the actual effect of the number of tourists on the sale of hot chocolate, we will have to investigate the relationship between $x_1$ and $x_2$ *with all other factors, primarily temperature, held fixed.* As it is seldom possible to control things to such an extent, it has been found that a statistic called the *partial correlation coefficient* does a fair job of eliminating the effect of other variables. Writing the ordinary correlation coefficient for $x_1$ and $x_2$ as $r_{12}$, that for $x_1$ and $x_3$ as $r_{13}$, and that for $x_2$ and $x_3$ as $r_{23}$, *the partial correlation coefficient for $x_1$ and $x_2$ with $x_3$ fixed is defined as*

$$r_{12.3} = \frac{r_{12} - (r_{13})(r_{23})}{\sqrt{1 - r_{13}^2} \sqrt{1 - r_{23}^2}} \qquad (16.3.3)\blacktriangle$$

Substituting the numerical values given in our example, we get

$$r_{12.3} = \frac{(-0.30) - (-0.70)(0.80)}{\sqrt{1 - (-0.70)^2} \sqrt{1 - (0.80)^2}} = 0.62$$

and this shows that, as we should have expected, there is a *positive* correlation between sales of hot chocolate and the number of tourists visiting the resort *when the temperature is fixed.*

We have given this example primarily to illustrate what is meant by *partial correlation;* at the same time the example has also served to emphasize again that ordinary correlation coefficients can lead to very misleading conclusions unless they are interpreted with great care.

Formula (16.3.3) provides a measure of the strength of the correlation between $x_1$ and $x_2$ when $x_3$ is held fixed; it can easily be generalized to situations where more than one variable is held fixed. Detailed treatments of multiple and partial correlation, the necessary formulas and computing techniques, are referred to below.

### BIBLIOGRAPHY

A discussion of the significance test for $r'$ and other rank correlation methods may be found in

> Kendall, M. G., *Rank Correlation Methods*. London: Charles Griffin, 1948.

Detailed treatments of multiple and partial correlation are given in

> Ezekiel, M., *Methods of Correlation Analysis*, 2nd ed. New York: John Wiley, 1941.

Chapter *17*

# Time Series Analysis

## 17.1 / Introduction

Statistical data which are collected, observed, or recorded at successive intervals of time form what is generally called a *time series*. Although the term "time series" is most frequently used in connection with economic data, it applies equally well if a patient's temperature is taken at regular intervals of time, if a county clerk records the number of marriage licenses issued each day, or if a police department records the number of robberies committed each month. In the discussion of this chapter we shall limit ourselves mostly to economic data, but it should be understood that all of the methods apply equally well to time series belonging to other kinds of activity. Incidentally, the term "time series" is often abbreviated by dropping the word "time" and we thus refer to *series* of monthly farm prices, *series* of population data, or *series* of weekly freight car loadings.

It is virtually impossible nowadays to open a newspaper, enter an office, or even go to school without running into graphs of time series showing the behavior of stocks and bonds, reports of weekly or monthly sales, charts of daily attendance, etc. Some of these graphs look like straight lines, others like smooth curves, but most give the impression of the haphazard scrawlings of a three-year-old child. It is for this reason that special methods have been developed to bring some order into the irregular patterns and the seemingly erratic appearance of time series.

Since we shall devote only a relatively short chapter to this task, it must be understood that we will at best be able to introduce some of the basic problems and indicate a few of the most general methods used in time series analysis. If the reader's main interests lie in fields other than business or economics, a casual study of this chapter should help him to understand and, perhaps, interpret more critically the time series he cannot help but meet in everyday life. If business and economics are his main fields of interest, the material covered should suffice to clarify some of the basic ideas and the methods presented should provide a sufficient background for more advanced courses on this subject. References to more detailed and more advanced treatments of the subject of time series analysis are given in the Bibliography on page 374.

## 17.2 / The Behavior of Time Series

It has been the custom to classify the fluctuations of a time series into *four* basic types of variation which, superimposed and acting in concert, account for the changes in the series over a period of time and give the series its irregular appearance. These four *components* of a time series are

1. *Secular trend*
2. *Seasonal variation*
3. *Cyclical variation*
4. *Irregular variation*

and in the classical methods of time series analysis it is assumed that there is a *multiplicative* relationship between the four, that is, it is assumed that any particular value in a series is *the product of factors which can be attributed to the various components*. Whether this assumption is reasonable is debatable and we shall have more to say about this after we shall have explained what is actually meant by the four components listed above.

*By the secular (or long-term) trend of a time series we mean the smooth or regular movement of a series over a fairly long period of time.* Intuitively speaking, the trend of a time series displays the general sweep of its development, or better, it characterizes the gradual and persistent pattern of its changes. In most elementary problems trends are taken to be straight lines, which are fitted to the data and which are thus indicative of the gradual growth or decline of the series. For example, Figure 17.1 shows an over-all *upward trend* in the ownership of industrial life insurance in the United States, while Figure 17.2 shows a persistent *downward trend* in farm employment in the United States.

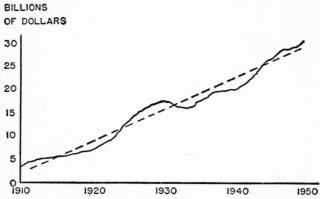

**Fig. 17.1.** Ownership of industrial life insurance in the United States.

Although it is common and convenient to picture trends as straight lines, there are many problems where they have to be expressed by means of more complicated kinds of mathematical curves. This is true particularly in series dealing with economic

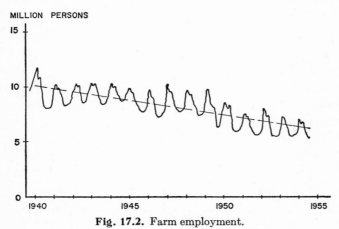

**Fig. 17.2.** Farm employment.

growth; for example, in the series of Figure 17.3, where the dotted curve has the shape of an elongated letter S. In view of the mathematical background assumed for this book, we shall limit the discussion of trends in Section 17.3 to *linear trends*. It must be understood, of course, that as in Chapter 14, straight lines should be used only if we can be sure that they will provide a reasonably good fit. References to methods of fitting *nonlinear* trends are given in the Bibliography on page 374.

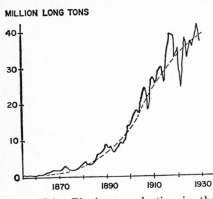

MILLION LONG TONS

**Fig. 17.3.** Pig iron production in the United States.

The kind of variation which is, perhaps, easiest to understand is the *seasonal variation,* *which consists of regularly repeating patterns* like those of Figure 17.4. Although the name seasonal variation implies a connection with the seasons of the year, like the variation we might find, for example, in monthly data on the production of eggs or the weekly sales of a department store, it is used to indicate any kind of variation which is of a *periodic* nature, provided that the length of its repeating cycles is at most one year.

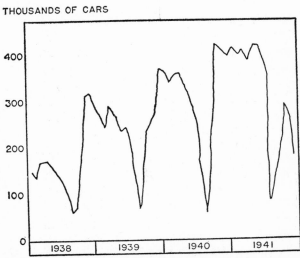

THOUSANDS OF CARS

**Fig. 17.4.** Monthly passenger car production in the United States.

Simple illustrations of seasonal patterns may be found, for example, in the hourly statistics on the number of passengers traveling (on weekdays) on the subways of New York City, or in monthly figures on the price of raspberries. It is easy to see that the rush hours during which people travel to and from work present a repeating pattern and that the price of raspberries is always low in the months during which they are in abundance and high when the supply is scarce.

Most economic time series show seasonal patterns depending on crops, weather conditions, paydays, vacation seasons, . . . , and the study of these patterns is, therefore, of major importance in the analysis of time series. In some cases the seasonal patterns, themselves, are of primary concern since little, if any, intelligent planning (of production, inventory, personnel, advertising, and the like) can be done without some statistical measures of seasonal variations. In other problems seasonal variations may be of secondary concern, but they must be measured to facilitate the investigation of *other* types of variation.

*Business cycles are sometimes defined as the variation which remains in a time series after the trend, seasonal variations, and irregular fluctuations have been eliminated.* (Actually, there is more to it than that, but the classical way of measuring business cycles is through such a process of elimination.) Generally speaking, a business cycle consists of a cyclical variation, an up and down movement of a time series, which differs from a seasonal variation inasmuch as it extends over a longer period of time *and*, supposedly, originates from general economic conditions. The periods of prosperity, recession, depression, and recovery, which are sometimes viewed as the *phases* of a complete cycle, are due to factors other than the weather, social customs, and such, which cause seasonal patterns. Theoretical explanations of business cycles vary from such scientific theories as the *change-in-income theory*, the *underconsumption theory*, the *fluctuations-in-discount theory*, . . . , to theories which attribute business cycles to sun spots and similar phenomena.

*Irregular variations of time series are those kinds of fluctuations which are either random or caused by such isolated special events as elections, bank failures, earthquakes, strikes, floods, wars,* . . . Considering the monthly sales of refrigerators, for example, there are certain chance factors which (like those determining individual flips of a coin) are unpredictable, but which in the long run more or less average out. Whether Mrs. Jones decides to buy a new refrigerator today or whether she decides to wait a few months might be determined by economic factors, by psychological factors, or purely by chance. If it is chance, there is little to be said about this kind of variation, except to note that in the long run it will tend to average out.

Irregular variations which are due to the occurrence of special events can be handled more readily; most of the time they can be recognized and correlated with the political changes, weather conditions, or sociological upheavals by which they are caused. They can then be eliminated from the data before we try to measure the trend, seasonal variation, or cyclical patterns.

In the beginning of this chapter we mentioned that, traditionally, any particular value of a time series is looked upon as the *product* of factors attributed to trend, seasonal, cyclical, and irregular variations. If this were actually the case and if we knew how to measure these four factors, time series analysis could take its place among the more exact sciences. Unfortunately, we really cannot be sure of any of these things and, to complicate matters, we find that there is little agreement even among the experts. Some economists feel that the classification is *too crude*, that there are more than four kinds of components; others feel that the components might be additive or combined in any one of a large number of different ways. In spite of all this, the traditional approach is the place to *begin* one's study of time series analysis. It has been and continues to be widely used in practice and it has, in many instances, provided very useful results.

### 17.3 / Secular Trends

The most widely used method for fitting trends, linear and otherwise, is the method of least squares which we already studied in Chapter 14. As we saw in that chapter, the problem of fitting a least squares line $y' = a + bx$ is essentially that of determining values of $a$ and $b$ which, for a given set of data, minimize $\sum (y_i - y_i')^2$. We found these two quantities with formulas (14.2.2) and (14.2.3) or the two normal equations.

Working with time series, the $x$'s practically always refer to successive years (days, weeks, or months) and the problem of fitting a trend line by the method of least squares can be simplified considerably by performing a *change of scale*. Taking the origin of the new scale at the *middle* of the series, that is, at the middle of the $x$'s, and numbering the years (or other time periods) so that in the new scale $\sum x_i = 0$, formulas (14.2.2) and (14.2.3) become

$$b = \frac{\sum x_i y_i}{\sum x_i^2} \quad \text{and} \quad a = \frac{\sum y_i}{n} \qquad (17.3.1)\blacktriangle$$

To illustrate how this simplification works, let us consider the following data on the purchases of ordinary life insurance in the United States:

| | Purchases of Ordinary Life Insurance (in millions of dollars) |
|---|---|
| 1951 | 17,975 |
| 1952 | 20,299 |
| 1953 | 23,489 |
| 1954 | 25,276 |
| 1955 | 30,827 |
| 1956 | 36,375 |
| 1957 | 45,635 |

Having an *odd* number of years, we label the years $-3$, $-2$, $-1$, 0, 1, 2, 3, that is, we perform the change of scale indicated in Figure 17.5. More generally, when dealing with an *odd* number of years we assign $x = 0$ to the middle year and number the others $\ldots$, $-5$, $-4$, $-3$, $-2$, $-1$, 0, 1, 2, 3, 4, 5, $\ldots$, so that the sum of the $x$'s is always equal to 0. (What to do in case there is an *even* number of years will be explained below.)

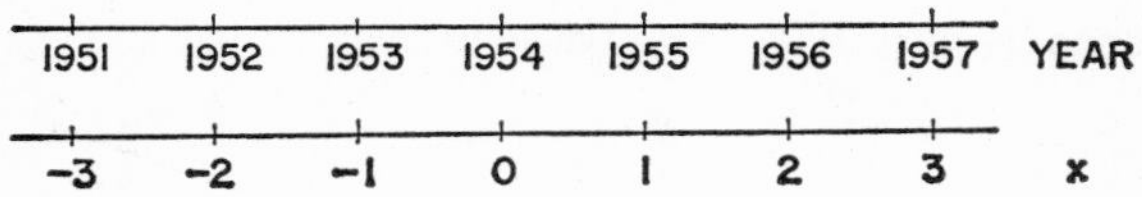

| 1951 | 1952 | 1953 | 1954 | 1955 | 1956 | 1957 | YEAR |
|---|---|---|---|---|---|---|---|
| −3 | −2 | −1 | 0 | 1 | 2 | 3 | x |

Fig. 17.5

The sums that are needed to find $a$ and $b$ with (17.3.1) are given by the totals of the $y$, $xy$, and $x^2$ columns in the following table, where $y$ stands for the purchases of ordinary in life insurance in the United States in millions of dollars:

| | $x$ | $y$ | $xy$ | $x^2$ |
|---|---|---|---|---|
| 1951 | −3 | 17,975 | −53,925 | 9 |
| 1952 | −2 | 20,299 | −40,598 | 4 |
| 1953 | −1 | 23,489 | −23,489 | 1 |
| 1954 | 0 | 25,276 | 0 | 0 |
| 1955 | 1 | 30,827 | 30,827 | 1 |
| 1956 | 2 | 36,375 | 72,750 | 4 |
| 1957 | 3 | 45,635 | 136,905 | 9 |
| | | 199,876 | 122,470 | 28 |

Substituting $n = 7$, $\sum y_i = 199{,}876$, $\sum x_i y_i = 122{,}470$, and $\sum x_i^2 = 28$ into the two formulas of (17.3.1), we get

$$b = \frac{122{,}470}{28} = 4374$$

$$a = \frac{199{,}876}{7} = 28{,}554$$

and the equation of the trend line may be written as

$$y' = 28{,}554 + 4374x$$

Having found this equation, we must be careful to indicate what the $x$'s and $y$'s mean, that is, the units and scales in which they are given. Specifying the origin of $x$, the units of $x$, and the units of $y$, it is advisable to add the following legend to the equation:

$$y' = 28{,}554 + 4374x$$

*(origin, 1954; x units, 1 year; y, annual purchases in millions of dollars)*

Using the least squares equation we can now find the trend values for any year by substituting the corresponding value of $x$. For instance, for 1951 we get a trend value of $y' = 28{,}554 + 4374(-3)$ $= 15{,}432$ and for 1957 we get $y' = 28{,}554 + 4374(3) = 41{,}676$.

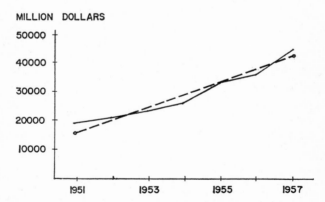

**Fig. 17.6.** Ordinary life insurance purchased in the United States.

Plotting these two trend values, we obtain the trend line shown in Figure 17.6.

When a time series is given for an *even* number of years, there will be no middle year and we shall have to perform a slightly different change of scale. For example, if there are 6 years we shall number them $-5$, $-3$, $-1$, $1$, $3$, $5$, if there are 8 years we shall number them $-7$, $-5$, $-3$, $-1$, 1, 3, 5, 7, and the sum of the $x$'s will in each case equal 0.

It is sometimes desirable to modify trend equations by *changing the origin of x*, by *changing the units of x*, or by *changing the units of y*. To show how this is done, let us first change the $y$ units from *annual* to *average monthly* purchases. Since each $y$ is, thus, divided by 12, this has the effect that $a$ as well as $b$ must be divided by 12, and we get

$$y' = 2379.5 + 364.5x$$

*(origin, 1954; x units, 1 year; y, average monthly purchases in millions of dollars)*

Having changed the $y$'s to average monthly purchases, let us modify the trend equation further by changing the $x$'s so that they refer to successive months. Since $b$ measures the *trend increment*, that is, the increase or decrease of the trend line, corresponding to one unit of $x$, it will have to be changed from an *annual trend increment* to a *monthly trend increment* and this is accomplished by dividing $b$ by 12. Leaving $a$ unchanged and dividing $b$ by 12, we thus get

$$y' = 2379.5 + 30.4x$$

*(origin, 1954; x units, 1 month; y, monthly purchases in millions of dollars)*

Finally, let us *change the origin of x* from the middle of 1954, where it is now, to, say, the middle of January 1954. (This will be helpful for the work of Section 17.5, where we shall want to calculate trend values corresponding to various months.) Since the middle of January 1954 is $5\frac{1}{2}$ months earlier than the origin of the above equation, that is, the middle of 1954, we can perform the desired change of origin by subtracting 5.5 monthly trend increments from 2379.5. The new $a$ is, thus, $2379.5 - 30.4(5.5) = 2212.3$, and we finally get

$$y' = 2212.3 + 30.4x$$

*(origin, January 1954; x units, 1 month; y, monthly purchases in millions of dollars)*

Having demonstrated how to fit trend lines by the method of least squares and simplify the work by performing suitable changes in the scale of $x$, let us point out that the method of least squares can also be used to fit *parabolic trend curves, exponential trend curves*, and curves given by even more complicated mathematical equations. References to these methods are given in the Bibliography on page 374.

## EXERCISES

1. The following are the 1948 through 1954 values of the purchasing power of the dollar (base year 1949) as measured by retail food prices: 96.1, 100.0, 98.8, 88.8, 87.3, 88.7, 88.8. Use the method of this section to fit a trend line to these data.

2. Modify the equation of Exercise 1 by changing the $x$ units to 1 month and moving the origin of $x$ to January 1951.

3. The following are the 1946 through 1954 values of the index of the volume of milk production in Virginia (base period 1935–1939): 125, 128, 135, 139, 142, 138, 136, 145, 147. Fit a least squares trend line to these data, calculate the 1946 and 1954 trend values, and draw a graph showing the trend line together with the original data.

4. The following are the 1946 through 1954 imports of crude gypsum in thousands of short tons: 1456, 2156 2860, 2592, 3192, 3448, 3068, 3184, 3360. Fit a least squares trend line to these data, calculate the 1946 and 1954 trend values, and draw a graph showing the trend line as well as the original data.

5. Modify the trend equation obtained in Exercise 4 by changing $y$ to average monthly imports of crude gypsum, the $x$ units to 1 month, and the origin of $x$ to January 1946.

6. The following are the 1945 through 1954 totals of factory production of cheese in the United States in millions of pounds: 1116.0, 1106.4, 1183.2, 1098.0, 1200.0, 1191.6, 1161.6, 1170.0, 1345.2, 1353.6. Fit a least squares trend line by the method of this section. (Note that using the change of scale indicated on page 362, the $x$ units are 6 months.)

7. Modify the trend equation obtained in Exercise 6 by changing $y$ to average monthly production, the $x$ units to 1 month, and the origin of $x$ to January 1952.

### 17.4 / Moving Averages

In problems in which we are interested mainly in the general "behavior" of a series, be it a trend, a business cycle, or possibly both, the general pattern of its growth may be described quite adequately by what is called a *moving average*. *A moving average is an artificially constructed time series in which each annual (monthly, daily, or hourly) figure is replaced by the mean of itself and values corresponding to a number of preceding and succeeding periods.* For instance, in a *three-year moving average* each annual figure is replaced by the mean of itself and those of the immediately preceding and succeeding years; in a *five-year moving average* each annual figure is replaced by the mean of itself, those of the two preceding years, and those of the two succeeding years. (If we average over an *even* number of periods, say, 6 years or 12 months, we run into the difficulty that the moving average will be "centered" between successive years or months. It is customary in that case to bring the values back in line by constructing a subsequent two-year (or two-month) moving average. Since this method belongs to the more advanced subject of *weighted moving averages*, we shall limit our discussion here to the case where the number of periods over which we average is *odd*.)

To illustrate the work needed in the construction of a moving average, let us calculate a five-year moving average to *smooth* the time series of factory sales of automobiles and trucks in the United States from 1930 through 1954. In the table shown below, the first column contains the actual annual factory sales in millions of vehicles. The second column contains the *five-year moving totals*, which for any given year consists of the *sum* of that year's sales plus those of the two preceding and the two succeeding years. The last column contains the desired five-year moving average and it is obtained by dividing each corresponding entry of the preceding column by 5.

|  | Annual Sales | Five-year Moving Totals | Five-year Moving Averages |
|---|---|---|---|
| 1930 | 3.4 | | |
| 1931 | 2.4 | | |
| 1932 | 1.4 | 11.9 | 2.4 |
| 1933 | 1.9 | 12.4 | 2.5 |
| 1934 | 2.8 | 14.5 | 2.9 |
| 1935 | 3.9 | 17.9 | 3.6 |
| 1936 | 4.5 | 18.3 | 3.7 |
| 1937 | 4.8 | 19.1 | 3.8 |
| 1938 | 2.3 | 19.7 | 3.9 |
| 1939 | 3.6 | 20.0 | 4.0 |
| 1940 | 4.5 | 16.2 | 3.2 |
| 1941 | 4.8 | 14.6 | 2.9 |
| 1942 | 1.0 | 11.7 | 2.3 |
| 1943 | 0.7 | 7.9 | 1.6 |
| 1944 | 0.7 | 6.2 | 1.2 |
| 1945 | 0.7 | 10.0 | 2.0 |
| 1946 | 3.1 | 14.6 | 2.9 |
| 1947 | 4.8 | 20.2 | 4.0 |
| 1948 | 5.3 | 27.5 | 5.5 |
| 1949 | 6.3 | 31.2 | 6.2 |
| 1950 | 8.0 | 31.9 | 6.4 |
| 1951 | 6.8 | 33.9 | 6.8 |
| 1952 | 5.5 | 34.2 | 6.8 |
| 1953 | 7.3 | | |
| 1954 | 6.6 | | |

A minor disadvantage of this method of smoothing a time series is that a few years are lost at each end of the table. In our example we lost two years at each end, and had we calculated a seven-year moving average we would have lost three. Generally, this is not very serious unless a time series is very short or all values are needed for further calculations.

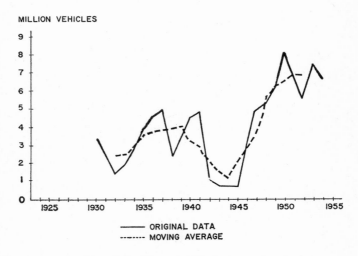

MILLION VEHICLES

ORIGINAL DATA
MOVING AVERAGE

**Fig. 17.7.** Motor vehicle factory sales.

The practical effect of a moving average can readily be seen from Figure 17.7, in which we have plotted the five-year moving average of the factory sales of cars together with the original data. The moving average has eliminated the lesser fluctuations to some extent and it has, thus, *smoothed* the over-all appearance of the series.

## EXERCISES

1. Calculate a three-year moving average for the factory sales data of automobiles and trucks given in the first column of the table on page 365.

2. Calculate a five-year moving average for the following data on the average monthly import of coffee to the United States from 1929 through 1954 (in millions of dollars):

|      | *Import* |      | *Import* |
|------|---------|------|---------|
| 1929 | 25.2    | 1942 | 17.1    |
| 1930 | 17.5    | 1943 | 22.8    |
| 1931 | 14.6    | 1944 | 27.2    |
| 1932 | 11.4    | 1945 | 28.8    |
| 1933 | 10.3    | 1946 | 39.4    |
| 1934 | 11.1    | 1947 | 50.1    |
| 1935 | 11.4    | 1948 | 58.1    |
| 1936 | 11.2    | 1949 | 66.3    |
| 1937 | 12.5    | 1950 | 91.0    |
| 1938 | 11.5    | 1951 | 113.5   |
| 1939 | 11.6    | 1952 | 114.7   |
| 1940 | 10.6    | 1953 | 122.4   |
| 1941 | 14.8    | 1954 | 123.8   |

Also plot a graph showing the moving average as well as the original data.

**3.** Fit a three-year moving average to the data of Exercise 2 and draw a graph showing the moving average as well as the original data.

**4.** Fit a seven-year moving average to the data of Exercise 2 and draw a graph showing the moving average as well as the original data.

## 17.5 / Seasonal Variation

Having discussed the measurement of trend in Section 17.3, let us now consider briefly the problem of measuring seasonal variation, that is, the problem of constructing an *index of seasonal variation*. For monthly data, such a *seasonal index*, as it is also called, consists of 12 numbers, one for each month. For instance, if the seasonal index for a store's January sales is 112, this means that its January sales are 112 per cent of those of the average month. Similarly, if the seasonal index of an area's cash receipts from farm marketings in July is 71, this means that these July cash receipts are 71 per cent of those of the average month. *In a seasonal index each month is, thus, represented by a figure expressing it as a percentage of the average month.*

An understanding of seasonal patterns is as essential for the business man in the daily operation of his business as it is for the layman in understanding changes taking place in various phases of our economy. Otherwise, there might be dire consequences if he misinterpreted, say, a 15 per cent drop in orders from April to May or a 25 per cent increase in sales from October to November. If these are regularly occurring seasonal patterns, they can be adjusted to intelligently and without panic. If they are misunderstood, the 15 per cent drop might lead to unnecessary advertising, or replacing of equipment with the hope of reducing cost, and the 25 per cent increase might lead to complacency and all sorts of uncalled-for actions.

As might be expected, there is not one but many ways in which a seasonal index can be constructed. They differ in refinement, in the complexity of the mathematical calculations, and they all have their advantages and disadvantages. We shall discuss only one of these methods, called the *ratio-to-trend* or *percentage-of-trend* method; others go by the names of the *method of simple averages*, the *ratio-to-moving average* method, and the method of *link relatives*.

To illustrate the *ratio-to-trend* method, let us again refer to the purchases of ordinary life insurance in the United States: the following are the total monthly purchases for the years 1954, 1955, 1956, and 1957 in millions of dollars:

|           | *1954* | *1955* | *1956* | *1957* |
|-----------|------|------|------|------|
| January   | 1737 | 2206 | 2496 | 3228 |
| February  | 1838 | 2196 | 2653 | 3285 |
| March     | 2365 | 2781 | 3076 | 4017 |
| April     | 2177 | 2507 | 2913 | 3923 |
| May       | 2108 | 2585 | 3063 | 4073 |
| June      | 2182 | 2749 | 2966 | 3767 |
| July      | 2023 | 2416 | 2891 | 3796 |
| August    | 2038 | 2568 | 2923 | 3767 |
| September | 1965 | 2354 | 2698 | 3488 |
| October   | 2107 | 2575 | 3350 | 4067 |
| November  | 2253 | 2751 | 3451 | 3926 |
| December  | 2483 | 3139 | 3895 | 4298 |

In the ratio-to-trend method we begin by eliminating the trend by *division* and we then average out (at least to some extent) irregular and cyclical variations.

To eliminate the trend, we first calculate the trend value for each month of the years 1954 through 1957, using the trend equation already found on page 363, namely,

$$y' = 2212.3 + 30.4x$$

*(origin, January 1954; x units, 1 month; y average monthly purchases in millions of dollars)*

Substituting $x = 0$, $x = 1$, $x = 2$, ..., and $x = 47$ into this equation, we obtain the trend values shown in the following table, namely, those for January 1954, February 1954, March 1954, . . . , and December 1957. The figures are rounded to the nearest million.

|           | *1954* | *1955* | *1956* | *1957* |
|-----------|--------|--------|--------|--------|
| January   | 2212   | 2577   | 2942   | 3307   |
| February  | 2243   | 2608   | 2972   | 3337   |
| March     | 2273   | 2638   | 3003   | 3368   |
| April     | 2304   | 2668   | 3033   | 3398   |
| May       | 2334   | 2699   | 3064   | 3428   |
| June      | 2364   | 2729   | 3094   | 3459   |
| July      | 2395   | 2760   | 3124   | 3489   |
| August    | 2425   | 2790   | 3155   | 3520   |
| September | 2456   | 2820   | 3185   | 3550   |
| October   | 2486   | 2851   | 3216   | 3580   |
| November  | 2516   | 2881   | 3246   | 3611   |
| December  | 2547   | 2912   | 3276   | 3641   |

Next we *divide* the original data month by month by the corresponding trend values and multiply by 100. The resulting *percentages of trend* are shown in the first four columns of the following table:

|           | *1954* | *1955* | *1956* | *1957* | *Mean* | *Index* |
|-----------|--------|--------|--------|--------|--------|---------|
| January   | 78.5   | 85.6   | 84.8   | 97.6   | 86.6   | 89.1    |
| February  | 81.9   | 84.2   | 89.3   | 98.4   | 88.4   | 91.0    |
| March     | 104.0  | 105.4  | 102.4  | 119.3  | 107.8  | 110.9   |
| April     | 94.5   | 94.0   | 96.0   | 115.4  | 100.0  | 102.9   |
| May       | 90.3   | 95.8   | 100.0  | 118.8  | 101.2  | 104.1   |
| June      | 92.3   | 100.7  | 95.9   | 108.9  | 99.4   | 102.3   |
| July      | 84.4   | 87.5   | 92.5   | 108.8  | 93.3   | 96.0    |
| August    | 84.0   | 92.0   | 92.6   | 107.0  | 93.9   | 96.6    |
| September | 80.0   | 83.5   | 84.7   | 98.2   | 86.6   | 89.1    |
| October   | 84.8   | 90.3   | 104.2  | 113.6  | 98.2   | 101.0   |
| November  | 89.5   | 95.5   | 106.6  | 108.7  | 100.1  | 103.0   |
| December  | 97.4   | 107.8  | 118.9  | 118.0  | 110.5  | 113.7   |
|           |        |        |        |        | 1166.0 |         |

These values are now *free of trend* and what remains to be done is to eliminate also irregular and cyclical variations. (Let us point out that since we are using data for very few years, 7 years for the trend and 4 years for the seasonal index, it is actually impossible to differentiate between a trend and part of a long-range cycle. However, if the method of Section 17.3 were applied to a longer period of time it would be appropriate to refer to the line as a trend, and we shall do so in our example.)

To eliminate irregular and cyclical variations, we now *average* the four percentages of trend given for each month, and we can do this by using the mean, the median, or any other measure of central location. Using the *mean*, we get the values shown in the fifth column above and only one more step remains to complete the seasonal index. As we pointed out earlier, the seasonal index for each month should be a percentage of the average month and, hence, the sum of the 12 values must equal 1200. Since the total of the fifth column is 1166.0, we adjust for this by multiplying each of the means by $1200/1166 = 1.029$ and we finally obtain the seasonal index shown in the right-hand column.

This index tells us, for example, that typical January purchases of ordinary life insurance in the United States are 89.1 per cent of those of the average month, that typical December purchases are 113.7 per cent of those of the average month, etc.

Once a seasonal index has been computed, it finds various kinds of applications, for instance, in *forecasting* and in what is called *deseasonalizing* data. To illustrate its use in forecasting, let us predict the December 1961 purchases of ordinary life insurance in the United States, assuming that no information other than that given here and in Section 17.3 is available. Finding first the trend value for December 1961, we substitute $x = 95$ into the equation on page 363, getting

$$y' = 2212.3 + 30.4(95) = 5100.3$$

and this would be our prediction if we did not account for seasonal variation. To take care of the fact that typical December purchases are 13.7 per cent above average according to our index, we now multiply 5100.3 by 113.7, getting 5799.0. *Thus, our forecast for December 1961 is that purchases of ordinary life insurance in the United States will amount to 5799 million dollars.*

There are many problems in business and economics in which it is desirable to *remove* seasonal patterns in order to study whatever other sources of variation might be at play. As we pointed out above, it can be very important to know whether an increase or a decrease is "real" or whether it is due only to seasonal influences. To illustrate how a time series can be *deseasonalized*, let us perform this operation on the 1957 purchases of ordinary life insurance in the United States given on page 368. In the table that follows all figures in the first and third columns are again in millions of dollars:

|  | Actual 1957 Purchases | Seasonal Index | Deseasonalized 1957 Purchases |
|---|---|---|---|
| January | 3228 | 89.1 | 3623 |
| February | 3285 | 91.0 | 3610 |
| March | 4017 | 110.9 | 3622 |
| April | 3923 | 102.9 | 3812 |
| May | 4073 | 104.1 | 3913 |
| June | 3767 | 102.3 | 3682 |
| July | 3796 | 96.0 | 3954 |
| August | 3767 | 96.6 | 3900 |
| September | 3488 | 89.1 | 3915 |
| October | 4067 | 101.0 | 4027 |
| November | 3926 | 103.0 | 3812 |
| December | 4298 | 113.7 | 3780 |

In the first column of this table we copied the actual monthly purchases in 1957, in the second column we copied the seasonal index from page 369, and in the third column are the deseasonalized data, obtained by dividing the actual figure given for each month by the corresponding value of the seasonal index.

It can be seen from these deseasonalized data that, for instance, the *increase* in purchases from January to February should be viewed with concern; it is *less* than it should have been according to typical seasonal patterns. Similarly, the *decrease* in purchases from March to April is nothing to worry about; it is actually *less* than we could have expected according to typical seasonal patterns.

## EXERCISES

1. The following are the 1952 through 1954 totals on construction activity in the United States in millions of dollars:

|  | 1952 | 1953 | 1954 |
|---|---|---|---|
| January | 2196 | 2396 | 2454 |
| February | 2118 | 2323 | 2358 |
| March | 2362 | 2563 | 2579 |
| April | 2566 | 2789 | 2814 |
| May | 2784 | 2959 | 3140 |
| June | 2971 | 3228 | 3385 |
| July | 3070 | 3326 | 3556 |
| August | 3148 | 3346 | 3693 |
| September | 3190 | 3358 | 3674 |
| October | 3126 | 3240 | 3503 |
| November | 2894 | 3028 | 3329 |
| December | 2583 | 2715 | 3092 |

Find a seasonal index for these data using the trend equation

$$y' = 2673.0 + 15.5x$$

(*origin, January 1952; x units, 1 month;*
*y, monthly activity in millions of dollars*)

2. Use the trend equation given in Exercise 1 and the seasonal index obtained in that exercise, to forecast the December 1961 construction activity in the United States.

3. The following are the 1951 through 1954 values of the index of prices received by farmers (base period 1910–1914):

|           | 1951 | 1952 | 1953 | 1954 |
|-----------|------|------|------|------|
| January   | 301  | 299  | 267  | 258  |
| February  | 313  | 293  | 263  | 257  |
| March     | 311  | 291  | 263  | 255  |
| April     | 312  | 292  | 260  | 257  |
| May       | 306  | 291  | 263  | 255  |
| June      | 300  | 290  | 257  | 247  |
| July      | 294  | 292  | 258  | 245  |
| August    | 291  | 294  | 255  | 249  |
| September | 292  | 288  | 256  | 246  |
| October   | 297  | 281  | 249  | 242  |
| November  | 303  | 275  | 249  | 242  |
| December  | 306  | 269  | 255  | 239  |

Find a seasonal index for these data using the trend equation

$$y' = 311.23 - 1.57x$$

(*origin, January 1951; x units, 1 month;*
*y, index of prices received by farmers*)

4. Use the trend equation given in Exercise 3 and the seasonal index obtained in that exercise to forecast the January 1961 value of the index of prices received by farmers.

5. Construct a seasonal index for the factory production of cheese in the United States, using the trend equation found in Exercise 7 on page 364 and the following data (in millions of pounds):

|           | 1952  | 1953  | 1954  |
|-----------|-------|-------|-------|
| January   | 69.1  | 87.0  | 101.3 |
| February  | 70.0  | 86.3  | 100.4 |
| March     | 85.0  | 110.1 | 120.3 |
| April     | 100.3 | 124.7 | 131.8 |
| May       | 136.2 | 156.5 | 158.5 |
| June      | 137.9 | 156.0 | 155.0 |
| July      | 117.7 | 132.4 | 127.2 |
| August    | 110.1 | 119.3 | 109.6 |
| September | 96.9  | 100.1 | 91.8  |
| October   | 87.8  | 91.2  | 85.7  |
| November  | 76.6  | 85.8  | 82.5  |
| December  | 82.6  | 95.3  | 89.4  |

6. Use the trend equation obtained in Exercise 7 on page 364 and the seasonal index obtained in Exercise 5 above to forecast the factory production of cheese in the United States for August 1962.

7. Use the seasonal index obtained in Exercise 1 to deseasonalize the given 1953 data on construction activity in the United States.

8. Use the seasonal index obtained in Exercise 5 to deseasonalize the given 1954 data on the factory production of cheese.

## 17.6 / Further Problems of Time Series Analysis

Looking upon the values of a time series as products of $T$, $S$, $C$, and $I$, that is, factors attributed to trend, seasonal variation, cyclical variation, and irregular variation, we have so far learned how to calculate $T$ and $S$. ($T$ is a trend value obtained with an equation like the ones we got in Section 17.3 and $S$ is a value of a seasonal index.) The product of $T$ and $S$ is sometimes called the *normal* and it represents, hypothetically, what the time series would have been like if trend and seasonal variation had been the only sources of variation present. The practical value of calculating the normal of a time series is that if we divide each value of the series by the corresponding value of the normal, we arrive at

$$\frac{T \cdot S \cdot C \cdot I}{T \cdot S} = C \cdot I$$

namely, another hypothetical time series in which only cyclical and irregular variations are at play. If we then eliminate irregular variations in some fashion, perhaps, by means of a moving average, we arrive at $C$, that is, a measure of whatever cyclical forces there are in the given series. We shall not go into the actual calculation of *cyclical irregulars* and *cyclical relatives* as $C \cdot I$ and $C$ are called, but references to their determination are given below.

Since our treatment of time series analysis has been very brief, we had to omit quite a few topics. For example, we did not go into the problem of *preliminary adjustments*, such as adjustments to account for the fact that months are of different lengths, adjustments for holidays, and adjustments for changes in prices and the size of populations. We also did not go into the problem of *graphing* time series on various kinds of special graph paper, a subject which should not be underestimated in importance as it can often bring out essential features of time series. Needless to say, we did not go into some of the more modern and more advanced methods, for example, the econometric approach, which requires considerably more mathematics than we assumed for this book.

## BIBLIOGRAPHY

A general discussion of the rational basis of time series analysis, together with a short history of trend analysis, may be found in

> Smith, J. G., and Duncan, A. J., *Elementary Statistics and Applications*. New York: McGraw-Hill, 1944, Chap. 20.

Some of the more modern methods of time series analysis are presented in

> Davis, H. T., *The Analysis of Economic Time Series*. Bloomington, Indiana: Principia Press, 1941.

> Tintner, G., *Econometrics*. New York: John Wiley, 1952.

Various alternate methods of fitting trend lines, fitting other kinds of trend curves, and calculating seasonal indexes are given in most texts on business statistics, for example, in

> Croxton, F. E., and Cowden, D. J., *Practical Business Statistics*, 3rd ed. Englewood Cliffs, N. J.: Prentice-Hall, 1960.

> Mills, F. C., *Statistical Methods*, 2nd ed. New York: Henry Holt, 1955.

> Neiswanger, W. A., *Elementary Statistical Methods*, rev. ed. New York: Macmillan, 1956.

These three books also give methods of evaluating *cyclical irregulars* and *cyclical relatives*.

# Rules of Summations

In order to follow some of the derivations in Chapters 3 and 4 and in later chapters, it will be helpful to study the following rules concerning summations:

RULE A: *The summation of the sum (or difference) of two or more terms equals the sum (or difference) of the individual summations.*

In the case of three terms we can write this rule symbolically as

$$I \qquad \sum_{i=1}^{n} (x_i + y_i + z_i) = \sum_{i=1}^{n} x_i + \sum_{i=1}^{n} y_i + \sum_{i=1}^{n} z_i$$

and if we had wanted to use minus signs instead of plus signs, we could have done so on both sides of the equation. The proof of this rule consists very simply of showing that the two sides of the equation are equal when written in full, that is, without summation signs.

RULE B: *The summation of a constant, k, times a variable, $x_i$, equals the constant times the summation of the variable.*

Symbolically, this rule states that

$$II \qquad \sum_{i=1}^{n} k \cdot x_i = k \cdot \sum_{i=1}^{n} x_i$$

and it may be proved as follows:

$$\sum_{i=1}^{n} k \cdot x_i = k \cdot x_1 + k \cdot x_2 + k \cdot x_3 + \ldots + k \cdot x_n$$
$$= k(x_1 + x_2 + x_3 + \ldots + x_n)$$
$$= k \cdot \sum_{i=1}^{n} x_i$$

The third rule is

RULE C: *The summation of a constant, k, from 1 to n, equals the product $k \cdot n$.*

Symbolically, this rule states that

$$\sum_{i=1}^{n} k = k \cdot n$$

and to prove it, let us write as in the proof of Rule B

$$\sum_{i=1}^{n} k \cdot x_i = k \cdot x_1 + k \cdot x_2 + k \cdot x_3 + \ldots + k \cdot x_n$$

If we then put all the $x$'s equal to 1, we obtain

$$\sum_{i=1}^{n} k \cdot 1 = k \cdot 1 + k \cdot 1 + k \cdot 1 + \ldots + k \cdot 1$$
$$= k(1 + 1 + 1 + \ldots + 1)$$
$$= k \cdot n$$

We could also have argued that since the constant $k$ does not depend on the subscript $i$, we can write directly

$$\sum_{i=1}^{n} k = k + k + k + \ldots + k = k \cdot n$$

*Appendix* **II**

# Calculations with Rounded Numbers

When facing the problem of rounding numbers, we find that there are essentially two kinds of questions. First, there is the mechanics of rounding quantities, say, to the nearest dollar, the nearest pound, the nearest 1000 persons, the nearest mile, and then there is the question of deciding in each case how far to round off.

If we want to round $249.28, which lies between $249 and $250, *to the nearest dollar*, we simply substitute whichever of the two values is closer, namely, $249. Similarly, if we wanted to round the number of physicians in the United States in 1953 to the nearest thousand, we would write 209 thousand instead of 209,211, and if we wanted to round the 1950 population of New York City to the nearest million, we would write 8 million instead of 7,891,957. In the first case we rounded *down* since 209,211 is closer to 209 thousand than it is to 210, and in the second case we rounded *up* since 7,891,957 is closer to 8 million than it is to 7. *Generally speaking, when rounding a number lying between two chosen units (pounds, dollars, 1000 houses, etc.) we substitute whichever of the two is closer.*

The only time that the above rule can lead to difficulties is when a number lies exactly half-way between two units. This would happen, for example, if we wanted to round $27.50 to the nearest dollar, 8.75 pounds to the nearest tenth of a pound, or 36.5 cents to the nearest cent. *The rule to follow here is always to round off in such a way that the last digit remaining on the right is even, namely, 0, 2, 4, 6, or 8.* Accordingly, we shall round the above quantities to $28, 8.8 pounds, and 36 cents. By following this rule we will sometimes round up, sometimes down, and in the long run the error due to rounding should more or less average out. If we consistently rounded up or down, we would be introducing what is called a *systematic error* or a *systematic bias.*

Although the above rule is obeyed in most scientific work, it is often ignored in practice. For instance, a grocer who sells 2 cans of vegetables for 49 cents does not round $49/2 = 24.5$ to 24; he sells single cans for 25 cents. Similarly, a bank which pays 1 per cent on savings accounts every 6 months will credit an account of $27.50 with 27 cents, rounding 27.5 to 27 instead of 28. These examples go to show that methods used in rounding numbers can be dictated by practical considerations.

The question of how far to round a number can actually be decided only on an individual basis. There is always the danger of *not rounding enough* and the equally important, and sometimes more serious, danger of *rounding too much.* The trouble with not rounding enough is that a number can thus give an impression of spurious accuracy. For instance, an insurance commissioner would probably be more impressed if a company reported the average cost of claims as $179.425791 than if it reported this figure as $179.43. If it so happened that this average is based on very few claims, the extra digits could easily create the unwarranted impression that the average represents more than it does.

The danger of rounding too much is best explained by means of an example. Let us suppose, for instance, that the accounting department of a firm finds that the over-all manufacturing cost of an item is 82.67 cents and that it reports this figure as 83 cents. If this value were used to estimate manufacturing cost of, say, 1,000,000 of these items, the error due to rounding off would be $830,000 - 826,700 = \$3,300$. To avoid this kind of error, it would have been better to report the cost as being $82.67 per 100 items. *The rule to follow here is never to round a figure too much if it is subsequently to be multiplied by a large number.*

When adding or subtracting rounded numbers we must keep in mind that a chain is only as strong as its weakest link. For instance,

if we want to add 25.8743, 3.45, 1005.2, and 16.8, all rounded to
the indicated numbers of decimals, we cannot give the result as
1051.3234. After all, 1005.2 stands for a number between 1005.15
and 1005.25, 16.8 stands for a number between 16.75 and 16.85, . . . ,
and we will therefore have to round the sum to 1051.3, or perhaps
to 1051, since we cannot be sure even of the .3. A relatively safe rule
to follow in the addition and subtraction of rounded numbers is
*never to carry a digit to the right of the last digit carried in any one of
the numbers which we add or subtract*. (Sometimes, when adding
a great many numbers, it is permissible to carry extra digits in view
of the fact that the rounding error can be expected to average out.)

When multiplying or dividing rounded numbers we must always
watch the so-called *number of significant digits*. By this we mean
the number of digits that remain after we have discarded all zeros
to the left of the first non-zero digit, and possibly also some of the
zeros to the right of the last non-zero digit. For example, 17.6,
rounded to the nearest tenth, has *three* significant digits; 0.019,
rounded to the nearest thousandth, has *two* significant digits; 212.53,
rounded to the nearest hundredth, has *five* significant digits; and
0.0000064, rounded to the nearest ten millionth, has *two* significant
digits. If we round 25,167 to the nearest thousand, we write 25
thousand or 25,000, and there would be only *two* significant digits.
If we round this number to the nearest hundred, we could write
252 hundred, 25.2 thousand, or 25,200, and there would be *three*
significant digits. This goes to show that if there are zeros on the
right we must be careful to investigate which ones are significant
and which ones are not.

The rule to be followed in the multiplication and division of
rounded numbers is very simple: *the result must not have more
significant digits than any one of the numbers which we multiply or
divide*. For instance, the product of 7.6 and 3.8445, both of which
are rounded numbers, should be given as 29 and not as 29.21820.
There are *two* significant digits in 7.6, *five* in 3.8445, and there should
be only *two* significant digits in the product. (Of course, when
multiplying or dividing a rounded number by an *exact* number,
the above does not apply. If we divide a rounded number, say,
46.74 by 2, we can write the result as 23.37.)

*Appendix* **III**

# The Use of Square Root

# Tables

Although square root tables are relatively easy to use, most beginners seem to have some difficulty in choosing the right column and in placing the decimal point correctly in the answer. Table VIII, in addition to containing the *squares* of the numbers from 1.00 to 9.99 spaced at intervals of 0.01, gives the *square roots* of these numbers rounded to 5 decimals. To find the square root of any positive number rounded to 3 significant digits, we have only to use the following rule in deciding whether to take the entry of the $\sqrt{n}$ or the $\sqrt{10n}$ column:

*Move the decimal point an even number of places to the right or to the left until a number greater than or equal to 1 but less than 100 is reached. If the resulting number is less than 10 go to the $\sqrt{n}$ column; if it is 10 or more go to the $\sqrt{10n}$ column.*

Thus, to find the square roots of 14,600, 459, and 0.0315 we go to the $\sqrt{n}$ column since the decimal point has to be moved, respectively, 4 places to the left, 2 places to the left, and 2 places to the right, to give 1.46, 4.59, and 3.15. Similarly, to find the square roots of 2163, 0.192, and 0.0000158 we go to the $\sqrt{10n}$ column since the decimal point has to be moved, respectively, 2 places to the left,

2 places to the right, and 6 places to the right, to give 21.63, 19.2, and 15.8.

Having found the entry in the appropriate column of Table VIII, the only thing that remains to be done is to put the decimal point in the right position in the answer. Here it will help to use the following rule:

*Having previously moved the decimal point an even number of places to the left or right to get a number greater than or equal to 1 but less than 100, the decimal point of the entry of the appropriate column in Table VIII is moved half as many places in the opposite direction.*

For example, to determine the square root of 14,600 we first note that the decimal point has to be moved *four places to the left* to give 1.46. We thus take the entry of the $\sqrt{n}$ column corresponding to 1.46, move its decimal point *two places to the right*, and get $\sqrt{14{,}600} = 120.830$. Similarly, to find the square root of 0.0000158, we note that the decimal point has to be moved *six places to the right* to give 15.8. We thus take the entry of the $\sqrt{10n}$ column corresponding to 1.58, move the decimal point *three places to the left*, and get $\sqrt{0.0000158} = 0.00397492$. In actual practice, if a number whose square root we want to find is *rounded*, the square root will have to be rounded to as many significant digits as the original number.

# Statistical Tables

## TABLE I

### Normal Curve Areas*

| z | .00 | .01 | .02 | .03 | .04 | .05 | .06 | .07 | .08 | .09 |
|---|-----|-----|-----|-----|-----|-----|-----|-----|-----|-----|
| 0.0 | .0000 | .0040 | .0080 | .0120 | .0160 | .0199 | .0239 | .0279 | .0319 | .0359 |
| 0.1 | .0398 | .0438 | .0478 | .0517 | .0557 | .0596 | .0636 | .0675 | .0714 | .0753 |
| 0.2 | .0793 | .0832 | .0871 | .0910 | .0948 | .0987 | .1026 | .1064 | .1103 | .1141 |
| 0.3 | .1179 | .1217 | .1255 | .1293 | .1331 | .1368 | .1406 | .1443 | .1480 | .1517 |
| 0.4 | .1554 | .1591 | .1628 | .1664 | .1700 | .1736 | .1772 | .1808 | .1844 | .1879 |
| 0.5 | .1915 | .1950 | .1985 | .2019 | .2054 | .2088 | .2123 | .2157 | .2190 | .2224 |
| 0.6 | .2257 | .2291 | .2324 | .2357 | .2389 | .2422 | .2454 | .2486 | .2517 | .2549 |
| 0.7 | .2580 | .2611 | .2642 | .2673 | .2704 | .2734 | .2764 | .2794 | .2823 | .2852 |
| 0.8 | .2881 | .2910 | .2939 | .2967 | .2995 | .3023 | .3051 | .3078 | .3106 | .3133 |
| 0.9 | .3159 | .3186 | .3212 | .3238 | .3264 | .3289 | .3315 | .3340 | .3365 | .3389 |
| 1.0 | .3413 | .3438 | .3461 | .3485 | .3508 | .3531 | .3554 | .3577 | .3599 | .3621 |
| 1.1 | .3643 | .3665 | .3686 | .3708 | .3729 | .3749 | .3770 | .3790 | .3810 | .3830 |
| 1.2 | .3849 | .3869 | .3888 | .3907 | .3925 | .3944 | .3962 | .3980 | .3997 | .4015 |
| 1.3 | .4032 | .4049 | .4066 | .4082 | .4099 | .4115 | .4131 | .4147 | .4162 | .4177 |
| 1.4 | .4192 | .4207 | .4222 | .4236 | .4251 | .4265 | .4279 | .4292 | .4306 | .4319 |
| 1.5 | .4332 | .4345 | .4357 | .4370 | .4382 | .4394 | .4406 | .4418 | .4429 | .4441 |
| 1.6 | .4452 | .4463 | .4474 | .4484 | .4495 | .4505 | .4515 | .4525 | .4535 | .4545 |
| 1.7 | .4554 | .4564 | .4573 | .4582 | .4591 | .4599 | .4608 | .4616 | .4625 | .4633 |
| 1.8 | .4641 | .4649 | .4656 | .4664 | .4671 | .4678 | .4686 | .4693 | .4699 | .4706 |
| 1.9 | .4713 | .4719 | .4726 | .4732 | .4738 | .4744 | .4750 | .4756 | .4761 | .4767 |
| 2.0 | .4772 | .4778 | .4783 | .4788 | .4793 | .4798 | .4803 | .4808 | .4812 | .4817 |
| 2.1 | .4821 | .4826 | .4830 | .4834 | .4838 | .4842 | .4846 | .4850 | .4854 | .4857 |
| 2.2 | .4861 | .4864 | .4868 | .4871 | .4875 | .4878 | .4881 | .4884 | .4887 | .4890 |
| 2.3 | .4893 | .4896 | .4898 | .4901 | .4904 | .4906 | .4909 | .4911 | .4913 | .4916 |
| 2.4 | .4918 | .4920 | .4922 | .4925 | .4927 | .4929 | .4931 | .4932 | .4934 | .4936 |
| 2.5 | .4938 | .4940 | .4941 | .4943 | .4945 | .4946 | .4948 | .4949 | .4951 | .4952 |
| 2.6 | .4953 | .4955 | .4956 | .4957 | .4959 | .4960 | .4961 | .4962 | .4963 | .4964 |
| 2.7 | .4965 | .4966 | .4967 | .4968 | .4969 | .4970 | .4971 | .4972 | .4973 | .4974 |
| 2.8 | .4974 | .4975 | .4976 | .4977 | .4977 | .4978 | .4979 | .4979 | .4980 | .4981 |
| 2.9 | .4981 | .4982 | .4982 | .4983 | .4984 | .4984 | .4985 | .4985 | .4986 | .4986 |
| 3.0 | .4987 | .4987 | .4987 | .4988 | .4988 | .4989 | .4989 | .4989 | .4990 | .4990 |

*This table is reproduced from J. Neyman, *First Course in Probability and Statistics*, Henry Holt and Co., Inc., New York, with the permission of the author and publishers.

## TABLE II

### Values of t*

| d.f. | $t_{.100}$ | $t_{.050}$ | $t_{.025}$ | $t_{.010}$ | $t_{.005}$ | d.f. |
|------|-----------|-----------|-----------|-----------|-----------|------|
| 1 | 3.078 | 6.314 | 12.706 | 31.821 | 63.657 | 1 |
| 2 | 1.886 | 2.920 | 4.303 | 6.965 | 9.925 | 2 |
| 3 | 1.638 | 2.353 | 3.182 | 4.541 | 5.841 | 3 |
| 4 | 1.533 | 2.132 | 2.776 | 3.747 | 4.604 | 4 |
| 5 | 1.476 | 2.015 | 2.571 | 3.365 | 4.032 | 5 |
| 6 | 1.440 | 1.943 | 2.447 | 3.143 | 3.707 | 6 |
| 7 | 1.415 | 1.895 | 2.365 | 2.998 | 3.499 | 7 |
| 8 | 1.397 | 1.860 | 2.306 | 2.896 | 3.355 | 8 |
| 9 | 1.383 | 1.833 | 2.262 | 2.821 | 3.250 | 9 |
| 10 | 1.372 | 1.812 | 2.228 | 2.764 | 3.169 | 10 |
| 11 | 1.363 | 1.796 | 2.201 | 2.718 | 3.106 | 11 |
| 12 | 1.356 | 1.782 | 2.179 | 2.681 | 3.055 | 12 |
| 13 | 1.350 | 1.771 | 2.160 | 2.650 | 3.012 | 13 |
| 14 | 1.345 | 1.761 | 2.145 | 2.624 | 2.977 | 14 |
| 15 | 1.341 | 1.753 | 2.131 | 2.602 | 2.947 | 15 |
| 16 | 1.337 | 1.746 | 2.120 | 2.583 | 2.921 | 16 |
| 17 | 1.333 | 1.740 | 2.110 | 2.567 | 2.898 | 17 |
| 18 | 1.330 | 1.734 | 2.101 | 2.552 | 2.878 | 18 |
| 19 | 1.328 | 1.729 | 2.093 | 2.539 | 2.861 | 19 |
| 20 | 1.325 | 1.725 | 2.086 | 2.528 | 2.845 | 20 |
| 21 | 1.323 | 1.721 | 2.080 | 2.518 | 2.831 | 21 |
| 22 | 1.321 | 1.717 | 2.074 | 2.508 | 2.819 | 22 |
| 23 | 1.319 | 1.714 | 2.069 | 2.500 | 2.807 | 23 |
| 24 | 1.318 | 1.711 | 2.064 | 2.492 | 2.797 | 24 |
| 25 | 1.316 | 1.708 | 2.060 | 2.485 | 2.787 | 25 |
| 26 | 1.315 | 1.706 | 2.056 | 2.479 | 2.779 | 26 |
| 27 | 1.314 | 1.703 | 2.052 | 2.473 | 2.771 | 27 |
| 28 | 1.313 | 1.701 | 2.048 | 2.467 | 2.763 | 28 |
| 29 | 1.311 | 1.699 | 2.045 | 2.462 | 2.756 | 29 |
| inf. | 1.282 | 1.645 | 1.960 | 2.326 | 2.576 | inf. |

*This table is abridged from Table IV of R. A. Fisher, *Statistical Methods for Research Workers*, published by Oliver and Boyd, Ltd., Edinburgh, by permission of the author and publishers.

## TABLE III

### Values of $\chi^2*$

| d.f. | $\chi^2_{.99}$ | $\chi^2_{.98}$ | $\chi^2_{.95}$ | $\chi^2_{.05}$ | $\chi^2_{.02}$ | $\chi^2_{.01}$ | d.f. |
|---|---|---|---|---|---|---|---|
| 1 | .000157 | .000628 | .00393 | 3.841 | 5.412 | 6.635 | 1 |
| 2 | .0201 | .0404 | .103 | 5.991 | 7.824 | 9.210 | 2 |
| 3 | .115 | .185 | .352 | 7.815 | 9.837 | 11.341 | 3 |
| 4 | .297 | .429 | .711 | 9.488 | 11.668 | 13.277 | 4 |
| 5 | .554 | .752 | 1.145 | 11.070 | 13.388 | 15.086 | 5 |
| 6 | .872 | 1.134 | 1.635 | 12.592 | 15.033 | 16.812 | 6 |
| 7 | 1.239 | 1.564 | 2.167 | 14.067 | 16.622 | 18.475 | 7 |
| 8 | 1.646 | 2.032 | 2.733 | 15.507 | 18.168 | 20.090 | 8 |
| 9 | 2.088 | 2.532 | 3.325 | 16.919 | 19.679 | 21.666 | 9 |
| 10 | 2.558 | 3.059 | 3.940 | 18.307 | 21.161 | 23.209 | 10 |
| 11 | 3.053 | 3.609 | 4.575 | 19.675 | 22.618 | 24.725 | 11 |
| 12 | 3.571 | 4.178 | 5.226 | 21.026 | 24.054 | 26.217 | 12 |
| 13 | 4.107 | 4.765 | 5.892 | 22.362 | 25.472 | 27.688 | 13 |
| 14 | 4.660 | 5.368 | 6.571 | 23.685 | 26.873 | 29.141 | 14 |
| 15 | 5.229 | 5.985 | 7.261 | 24.996 | 28.259 | 30.578 | 15 |
| 16 | 5.812 | 6.614 | 7.962 | 26.296 | 29.633 | 32.000 | 16 |
| 17 | 6.408 | 7.255 | 8.672 | 27.587 | 30.995 | 33.409 | 17 |
| 18 | 7.015 | 7.906 | 9.390 | 28.869 | 32.346 | 34.805 | 18 |
| 19 | 7.633 | 8.567 | 10.117 | 30.144 | 33.687 | 36.191 | 19 |
| 20 | 8.260 | 9.237 | 10.851 | 31.410 | 35.020 | 37.566 | 20 |
| 21 | 8.897 | 9.915 | 11.591 | 32.671 | 36.343 | 38.932 | 21 |
| 22 | 9.542 | 10.600 | 12.338 | 33.924 | 37.659 | 40.289 | 22 |
| 23 | 10.196 | 11.293 | 13.091 | 35.172 | 38.968 | 41.638 | 23 |
| 24 | 10.856 | 11.992 | 13.848 | 36.415 | 40.270 | 42.980 | 24 |
| 25 | 11.524 | 12.697 | 14.611 | 37.652 | 41.566 | 44.314 | 25 |
| 26 | 12.198 | 13.409 | 15.379 | 38.885 | 42.856 | 45.642 | 26 |
| 27 | 12.879 | 14.125 | 16.151 | 40.113 | 44.140 | 46.963 | 27 |
| 28 | 13.565 | 14.847 | 16.928 | 41.337 | 45.419 | 48.278 | 28 |
| 29 | 14.256 | 15.574 | 17.708 | 42.557 | 46.693 | 49.588 | 29 |
| 30 | 14.953 | 16.306 | 18.493 | 43.773 | 47.962 | 50.892 | 30 |

*This table is abridged from Table III of R. A. Fisher, *Statistical Methods for Research Workers*, published by Oliver & Boyd Ltd., Edinburgh, by permission of the author and publishers.

TABLE IVa   Values of F.05*

| Degrees of freedom for denominator | Degrees of freedom for numerator | | | | | | | | | | | | | | | | | | |
|---|---|---|---|---|---|---|---|---|---|---|---|---|---|---|---|---|---|---|---|
| | **1** | **2** | **3** | **4** | **5** | **6** | **7** | **8** | **9** | **10** | **12** | **15** | **20** | **24** | **30** | **40** | **60** | **120** | **∞** |
| 1 | 161 | 200 | 216 | 225 | 230 | 234 | 237 | 239 | 241 | 242 | 244 | 246 | 248 | 249 | 250 | 251 | 252 | 253 | 254 |
| 2 | 18.5 | 19.0 | 19.2 | 19.2 | 19.3 | 19.3 | 19.4 | 19.4 | 19.4 | 19.4 | 19.4 | 19.4 | 19.4 | 19.4 | 19.5 | 19.5 | 19.5 | 19.5 | 19.5 |
| 3 | 10.1 | 9.55 | 9.28 | 9.12 | 9.01 | 8.94 | 8.89 | 8.85 | 8.81 | 8.79 | 8.74 | 8.70 | 8.66 | 8.64 | 8.62 | 8.59 | 8.57 | 8.55 | 8.53 |
| 4 | 7.71 | 6.94 | 6.59 | 6.39 | 6.26 | 6.16 | 6.09 | 6.04 | 6.00 | 5.96 | 5.91 | 5.86 | 5.80 | 5.77 | 5.75 | 5.72 | 5.69 | 5.66 | 5.63 |
| 5 | 6.61 | 5.79 | 5.41 | 5.19 | 5.05 | 4.95 | 4.88 | 4.82 | 4.77 | 4.74 | 4.68 | 4.62 | 4.56 | 4.53 | 4.50 | 4.46 | 4.43 | 4.40 | 4.37 |
| 6 | 5.99 | 5.14 | 4.76 | 4.53 | 4.39 | 4.28 | 4.21 | 4.15 | 4.10 | 4.06 | 4.00 | 3.94 | 3.87 | 3.84 | 3.81 | 3.77 | 3.74 | 3.70 | 3.67 |
| 7 | 5.59 | 4.74 | 4.35 | 4.12 | 3.97 | 3.87 | 3.79 | 3.73 | 3.68 | 3.64 | 3.57 | 3.51 | 3.44 | 3.41 | 3.38 | 3.34 | 3.30 | 3.27 | 3.23 |
| 8 | 5.32 | 4.46 | 4.07 | 3.84 | 3.69 | 3.58 | 3.50 | 3.44 | 3.39 | 3.35 | 3.28 | 3.22 | 3.15 | 3.12 | 3.08 | 3.04 | 3.01 | 2.97 | 2.93 |
| 9 | 5.12 | 4.26 | 3.86 | 3.63 | 3.48 | 3.37 | 3.29 | 3.23 | 3.18 | 3.14 | 3.07 | 3.01 | 2.94 | 2.90 | 2.86 | 2.83 | 2.79 | 2.75 | 2.71 |
| 10 | 4.96 | 4.10 | 3.71 | 3.48 | 3.33 | 3.22 | 3.14 | 3.07 | 3.02 | 2.98 | 2.91 | 2.85 | 2.77 | 2.74 | 2.70 | 2.66 | 2.62 | 2.58 | 2.54 |
| 11 | 4.84 | 3.98 | 3.59 | 3.36 | 3.20 | 3.09 | 3.01 | 2.95 | 2.90 | 2.85 | 2.79 | 2.72 | 2.65 | 2.61 | 2.57 | 2.53 | 2.49 | 2.45 | 2.40 |
| 12 | 4.75 | 3.89 | 3.49 | 3.26 | 3.11 | 3.00 | 2.91 | 2.85 | 2.80 | 2.75 | 2.69 | 2.62 | 2.54 | 2.51 | 2.47 | 2.43 | 2.38 | 2.34 | 2.30 |
| 13 | 4.67 | 3.81 | 3.41 | 3.18 | 3.03 | 2.92 | 2.83 | 2.77 | 2.71 | 2.67 | 2.60 | 2.53 | 2.46 | 2.42 | 2.38 | 2.34 | 2.30 | 2.25 | 2.21 |
| 14 | 4.60 | 3.74 | 3.34 | 3.11 | 2.96 | 2.85 | 2.76 | 2.70 | 2.65 | 2.60 | 2.53 | 2.46 | 2.39 | 2.35 | 2.31 | 2.27 | 2.22 | 2.18 | 2.13 |
| 15 | 4.54 | 3.68 | 3.29 | 3.06 | 2.90 | 2.79 | 2.71 | 2.64 | 2.59 | 2.54 | 2.48 | 2.40 | 2.33 | 2.29 | 2.25 | 2.20 | 2.16 | 2.11 | 2.07 |
| 16 | 4.49 | 3.63 | 3.24 | 3.01 | 2.85 | 2.74 | 2.66 | 2.59 | 2.54 | 2.49 | 2.42 | 2.35 | 2.28 | 2.24 | 2.19 | 2.15 | 2.11 | 2.06 | 2.01 |
| 17 | 4.45 | 3.59 | 3.20 | 2.96 | 2.81 | 2.70 | 2.61 | 2.55 | 2.49 | 2.45 | 2.38 | 2.31 | 2.23 | 2.19 | 2.15 | 2.10 | 2.06 | 2.01 | 1.96 |
| 18 | 4.41 | 3.55 | 3.16 | 2.93 | 2.77 | 2.66 | 2.58 | 2.51 | 2.46 | 2.41 | 2.34 | 2.27 | 2.19 | 2.15 | 2.11 | 2.06 | 2.02 | 1.97 | 1.92 |
| 19 | 4.38 | 3.52 | 3.13 | 2.90 | 2.74 | 2.63 | 2.54 | 2.48 | 2.42 | 2.38 | 2.31 | 2.23 | 2.16 | 2.11 | 2.07 | 2.03 | 1.98 | 1.93 | 1.88 |
| 20 | 4.35 | 3.49 | 3.10 | 2.87 | 2.71 | 2.60 | 2.51 | 2.45 | 2.39 | 2.35 | 2.28 | 2.20 | 2.12 | 2.08 | 2.04 | 1.99 | 1.95 | 1.90 | 1.84 |
| 21 | 4.32 | 3.47 | 3.07 | 2.84 | 2.68 | 2.57 | 2.49 | 2.42 | 2.37 | 2.32 | 2.25 | 2.18 | 2.10 | 2.05 | 2.01 | 1.96 | 1.92 | 1.87 | 1.81 |
| 22 | 4.30 | 3.44 | 3.05 | 2.82 | 2.66 | 2.55 | 2.46 | 2.40 | 2.34 | 2.30 | 2.23 | 2.15 | 2.07 | 2.03 | 1.98 | 1.94 | 1.89 | 1.84 | 1.78 |
| 23 | 4.28 | 3.42 | 3.03 | 2.80 | 2.64 | 2.53 | 2.44 | 2.37 | 2.32 | 2.27 | 2.20 | 2.13 | 2.05 | 2.01 | 1.96 | 1.91 | 1.86 | 1.81 | 1.76 |
| 24 | 4.26 | 3.40 | 3.01 | 2.78 | 2.62 | 2.51 | 2.42 | 2.36 | 2.30 | 2.25 | 2.18 | 2.11 | 2.03 | 1.98 | 1.94 | 1.89 | 1.84 | 1.79 | 1.73 |
| 25 | 4.24 | 3.39 | 2.99 | 2.76 | 2.60 | 2.49 | 2.40 | 2.34 | 2.28 | 2.24 | 2.16 | 2.09 | 2.01 | 1.96 | 1.92 | 1.87 | 1.82 | 1.77 | 1.71 |
| 30 | 4.17 | 3.32 | 2.92 | 2.69 | 2.53 | 2.42 | 2.33 | 2.27 | 2.21 | 2.16 | 2.09 | 2.01 | 1.93 | 1.89 | 1.84 | 1.79 | 1.74 | 1.68 | 1.62 |
| 40 | 4.08 | 3.23 | 2.84 | 2.61 | 2.45 | 2.34 | 2.25 | 2.18 | 2.12 | 2.08 | 2.00 | 1.92 | 1.84 | 1.79 | 1.74 | 1.69 | 1.64 | 1.58 | 1.51 |
| 60 | 4.00 | 3.15 | 2.76 | 2.53 | 2.37 | 2.25 | 2.17 | 2.10 | 2.04 | 1.99 | 1.92 | 1.84 | 1.75 | 1.70 | 1.65 | 1.59 | 1.53 | 1.47 | 1.39 |
| 120 | 3.92 | 3.07 | 2.68 | 2.45 | 2.29 | 2.18 | 2.09 | 2.02 | 1.96 | 1.91 | 1.83 | 1.75 | 1.66 | 1.61 | 1.55 | 1.50 | 1.43 | 1.35 | 1.25 |
| ∞ | 3.84 | 3.00 | 2.60 | 2.37 | 2.21 | 2.10 | 2.01 | 1.94 | 1.88 | 1.83 | 1.75 | 1.67 | 1.57 | 1.52 | 1.46 | 1.39 | 1.32 | 1.22 | 1.00 |

## TABLE IVb  Values of $F_{.01}$

Degrees of freedom for numerator

| | 1 | 2 | 3 | 4 | 5 | 6 | 7 | 8 | 9 | 10 | 12 | 15 | 20 | 24 | 30 | 40 | 60 | 120 | ∞ |
|---|---|---|---|---|---|---|---|---|---|---|---|---|---|---|---|---|---|---|---|
| 1 | 4,052 | 5,000 | 5,403 | 5,625 | 5,764 | 5,859 | 5,928 | 5,982 | 6,023 | 6,056 | 6,106 | 6,157 | 6,209 | 6,235 | 6,261 | 6,287 | 6,313 | 6,339 | 6,366 |
| 2 | 98.5 | 99.0 | 99.2 | 99.2 | 99.3 | 99.3 | 99.4 | 99.4 | 99.4 | 99.4 | 99.4 | 99.4 | 99.4 | 99.5 | 99.5 | 99.5 | 99.5 | 99.5 | 99.5 |
| 3 | 34.1 | 30.8 | 29.5 | 28.7 | 28.2 | 27.9 | 27.7 | 27.5 | 27.3 | 27.2 | 27.1 | 26.9 | 26.7 | 26.6 | 26.5 | 26.4 | 26.3 | 26.2 | 26.1 |
| 4 | 21.2 | 18.0 | 16.7 | 16.0 | 15.5 | 15.2 | 15.0 | 14.8 | 14.7 | 14.5 | 14.4 | 14.2 | 14.0 | 13.9 | 13.8 | 13.7 | 13.7 | 13.6 | 13.5 |
| 5 | 16.3 | 13.3 | 12.1 | 11.4 | 11.0 | 10.7 | 10.5 | 10.3 | 10.2 | 10.1 | 9.89 | 9.72 | 9.55 | 9.47 | 9.38 | 9.29 | 9.20 | 9.11 | 9.02 |
| 6 | 13.7 | 10.9 | 9.78 | 9.15 | 8.75 | 8.47 | 8.26 | 8.10 | 7.98 | 7.87 | 7.72 | 7.56 | 7.40 | 7.31 | 7.23 | 7.14 | 7.06 | 6.97 | 6.88 |
| 7 | 12.2 | 9.55 | 8.45 | 7.85 | 7.46 | 7.19 | 6.99 | 6.84 | 6.72 | 6.62 | 6.47 | 6.31 | 6.16 | 6.07 | 5.99 | 5.91 | 5.82 | 5.74 | 5.65 |
| 8 | 11.3 | 8.65 | 7.59 | 7.01 | 6.63 | 6.37 | 6.18 | 6.03 | 5.91 | 5.81 | 5.67 | 5.52 | 5.36 | 5.28 | 5.20 | 5.12 | 5.03 | 4.95 | 4.86 |
| 9 | 10.6 | 8.02 | 6.99 | 6.42 | 6.06 | 5.80 | 5.61 | 5.47 | 5.35 | 5.26 | 5.11 | 4.96 | 4.81 | 4.73 | 4.65 | 4.57 | 4.48 | 4.40 | 4.31 |
| 10 | 10.0 | 7.56 | 6.55 | 5.99 | 5.64 | 5.39 | 5.20 | 5.06 | 4.94 | 4.85 | 4.71 | 4.56 | 4.41 | 4.33 | 4.25 | 4.17 | 4.08 | 4.00 | 3.91 |
| 11 | 9.65 | 7.21 | 6.22 | 5.67 | 5.32 | 5.07 | 4.89 | 4.74 | 4.63 | 4.54 | 4.40 | 4.25 | 4.10 | 4.02 | 3.94 | 3.86 | 3.78 | 3.69 | 3.60 |
| 12 | 9.33 | 6.93 | 5.95 | 5.41 | 5.06 | 4.82 | 4.64 | 4.50 | 4.39 | 4.30 | 4.16 | 4.01 | 3.86 | 3.78 | 3.70 | 3.62 | 3.54 | 3.45 | 3.36 |
| 13 | 9.07 | 6.70 | 5.74 | 5.21 | 4.86 | 4.62 | 4.44 | 4.30 | 4.19 | 4.10 | 3.96 | 3.82 | 3.66 | 3.59 | 3.51 | 3.43 | 3.34 | 3.25 | 3.17 |
| 14 | 8.86 | 6.51 | 5.56 | 5.04 | 4.70 | 4.46 | 4.28 | 4.14 | 4.03 | 3.94 | 3.80 | 3.66 | 3.51 | 3.43 | 3.35 | 3.27 | 3.18 | 3.09 | 3.00 |
| 15 | 8.68 | 6.36 | 5.42 | 4.89 | 4.56 | 4.32 | 4.14 | 4.00 | 3.89 | 3.80 | 3.67 | 3.52 | 3.37 | 3.29 | 3.21 | 3.13 | 3.05 | 2.96 | 2.87 |
| 16 | 8.53 | 6.23 | 5.29 | 4.77 | 4.44 | 4.20 | 4.03 | 3.89 | 3.78 | 3.69 | 3.55 | 3.41 | 3.26 | 3.18 | 3.10 | 3.02 | 2.93 | 2.84 | 2.75 |
| 17 | 8.40 | 6.11 | 5.19 | 4.67 | 4.34 | 4.10 | 3.93 | 3.79 | 3.68 | 3.59 | 3.46 | 3.31 | 3.16 | 3.08 | 3.00 | 2.92 | 2.83 | 2.75 | 2.65 |
| 18 | 8.29 | 6.01 | 5.09 | 4.58 | 4.25 | 4.01 | 3.84 | 3.71 | 3.60 | 3.51 | 3.37 | 3.23 | 3.08 | 3.00 | 2.92 | 2.84 | 2.75 | 2.66 | 2.57 |
| 19 | 8.19 | 5.93 | 5.01 | 4.50 | 4.17 | 3.94 | 3.77 | 3.63 | 3.52 | 3.43 | 3.30 | 3.15 | 3.00 | 2.92 | 2.84 | 2.76 | 2.67 | 2.58 | 2.49 |
| 20 | 8.10 | 5.85 | 4.94 | 4.43 | 4.10 | 3.87 | 3.70 | 3.56 | 3.46 | 3.37 | 3.23 | 3.09 | 2.94 | 2.86 | 2.78 | 2.69 | 2.61 | 2.52 | 2.42 |
| 21 | 8.02 | 5.78 | 4.87 | 4.37 | 4.04 | 3.81 | 3.64 | 3.51 | 3.40 | 3.31 | 3.17 | 3.03 | 2.88 | 2.80 | 2.72 | 2.64 | 2.55 | 2.46 | 2.36 |
| 22 | 7.95 | 5.72 | 4.82 | 4.31 | 3.99 | 3.76 | 3.59 | 3.45 | 3.35 | 3.26 | 3.12 | 2.98 | 2.83 | 2.75 | 2.67 | 2.58 | 2.50 | 2.40 | 2.31 |
| 23 | 7.88 | 5.66 | 4.76 | 4.26 | 3.94 | 3.71 | 3.54 | 3.41 | 3.30 | 3.21 | 3.07 | 2.93 | 2.78 | 2.70 | 2.62 | 2.54 | 2.45 | 2.35 | 2.26 |
| 24 | 7.82 | 5.61 | 4.72 | 4.22 | 3.90 | 3.67 | 3.50 | 3.36 | 3.26 | 3.17 | 3.03 | 2.89 | 2.74 | 2.66 | 2.58 | 2.49 | 2.40 | 2.31 | 2.21 |
| 25 | 7.77 | 5.57 | 4.68 | 4.18 | 3.86 | 3.63 | 3.46 | 3.32 | 3.22 | 3.13 | 2.99 | 2.85 | 2.70 | 2.62 | 2.53 | 2.45 | 2.36 | 2.27 | 2.17 |
| 30 | 7.56 | 5.39 | 4.51 | 4.02 | 3.70 | 3.47 | 3.30 | 3.17 | 3.07 | 2.98 | 2.84 | 2.70 | 2.55 | 2.47 | 2.39 | 2.30 | 2.21 | 2.11 | 2.01 |
| 40 | 7.31 | 5.18 | 4.31 | 3.83 | 3.51 | 3.29 | 3.12 | 2.99 | 2.89 | 2.80 | 2.66 | 2.52 | 2.37 | 2.29 | 2.20 | 2.11 | 2.02 | 1.92 | 1.80 |
| 60 | 7.08 | 4.98 | 4.13 | 3.65 | 3.34 | 3.12 | 2.95 | 2.82 | 2.72 | 2.63 | 2.50 | 2.35 | 2.20 | 2.12 | 2.03 | 1.94 | 1.84 | 1.73 | 1.60 |
| 120 | 6.85 | 4.79 | 3.95 | 3.48 | 3.17 | 2.96 | 2.79 | 2.66 | 2.56 | 2.47 | 2.34 | 2.19 | 2.03 | 1.95 | 1.86 | 1.76 | 1.66 | 1.53 | 1.38 |
| ∞ | 6.63 | 4.61 | 3.78 | 3.32 | 3.02 | 2.80 | 2.64 | 2.51 | 2.41 | 2.32 | 2.18 | 2.04 | 1.88 | 1.79 | 1.70 | 1.59 | 1.47 | 1.32 | 1.00 |

Degrees of freedom for denominator

*This table is reproduced from M. Merrington and C. M. Thompson, "Tables of percentage points of the inverted beta (F) distribution," *Biometrika*, vol. 33 (1943), by permission of the *Biometrika* trustees.

## TABLE V

### 95 Per Cent Confidence Intervals for Proportions*

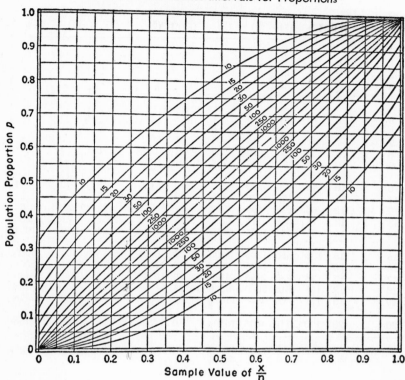

*This table is reproduced from C. J. Clopper and E. S. Pearson, "The use of confidence or fiducial limits illustrated in the case of the binomial," *Biometrika*, vol. 26 (1934), by permission of the *Biometrika* trustees.

eg. n=250
X=60
Y=190

Problem: estimate true
proportion of smokers
preferring Brand X

.24

STATISTICAL TABLES

## TABLE VI

### Binomial Coefficients

| $n$ | $\binom{n}{0}$ | $\binom{n}{1}$ | $\binom{n}{2}$ | $\binom{n}{3}$ | $\binom{n}{4}$ | $\binom{n}{5}$ | $\binom{n}{6}$ | $\binom{n}{7}$ | $\binom{n}{8}$ | $\binom{n}{9}$ | $\binom{n}{10}$ |
|---|---|---|---|---|---|---|---|---|---|---|---|
| 0 | 1 | | | | | | | | | | |
| 1 | 1 | 1 | | | | | | | | | |
| 2 | 1 | 2 | 1 | | | | | | | | |
| 3 | 1 | 3 | 3 | 1 | | | | | | | |
| 4 | 1 | 4 | 6 | 4 | 1 | | | | | | |
| 5 | 1 | 5 | 10 | 10 | 5 | 1 | | | | | |
| 6 | 1 | 6 | 15 | 20 | 15 | 6 | 1 | | | | |
| 7 | 1 | 7 | 21 | 35 | 35 | 21 | 7 | 1 | | | |
| 8 | 1 | 8 | 28 | 56 | 70 | 56 | 28 | 8 | 1 | | |
| 9 | 1 | 9 | 36 | 84 | 126 | 126 | 84 | 36 | 9 | 1 | |
| 10 | 1 | 10 | 45 | 120 | 210 | 252 | 210 | 120 | 45 | 10 | 1 |
| 11 | 1 | 11 | 55 | 165 | 330 | 462 | 462 | 330 | 165 | 55 | 11 |
| 12 | 1 | 12 | 66 | 220 | 495 | 792 | 924 | 792 | 495 | 220 | 66 |
| 13 | 1 | 13 | 78 | 286 | 715 | 1287 | 1716 | 1716 | 1287 | 715 | 286 |
| 14 | 1 | 14 | 91 | 364 | 1001 | 2002 | 3003 | 3432 | 3003 | 2002 | 1001 |
| 15 | 1 | 15 | 105 | 455 | 1365 | 3003 | 5005 | 6435 | 6435 | 5005 | 3003 |
| 16 | 1 | 16 | 120 | 560 | 1820 | 4368 | 8008 | 11440 | 12870 | 11440 | 8008 |
| 17 | 1 | 17 | 136 | 680 | 2380 | 6188 | 12376 | 19448 | 24310 | 24310 | 19448 |
| 18 | 1 | 18 | 153 | 816 | 3060 | 8568 | 18564 | 31824 | 43758 | 48620 | 43758 |
| 19 | 1 | 19 | 171 | 969 | 3876 | 11628 | 27132 | 50388 | 75582 | 92378 | 92378 |
| 20 | 1 | 20 | 190 | 1140 | 4845 | 15504 | 38760 | 77520 | 125970 | 167960 | 184756 |

# TABLE VII
## Sample Page of Random Numbers*

### Thirty-first Thousand

| | 1–4 | 5–8 | 9–12 | 13–16 | 17–20 | 21–24 | 25–28 | 29–32 | 33–36 | 37–40 |
|---|---|---|---|---|---|---|---|---|---|---|
| 1 | 87 35 | 67 44 | 51 49 | 18 98 | 97 84 | 75 22 | 53 29 | 10 52 | 26 87 | 54 92 |
| 2 | 25 52 | 29 67 | 35 99 | 48 88 | 40 68 | 63 68 | 82 39 | 38 47 | 91 39 | 11 00 |
| 3 | 87 17 | 83 31 | 25 59 | 87 48 | 25 80 | 24 08 | 81 45 | 21 32 | 90 08 | 44 31 |
| 4 | 05 04 | 40 35 | 72 95 | 48 56 | 77 57 | 63 19 | 80 19 | 48 52 | 06 47 | 64 98 |
| 5 | 81 16 | 09 24 | 91 71 | 29 76 | 54 01 | 53 47 | 30 67 | 62 95 | 56 58 | 10 91 |
| 6 | 54 85 | 79 88 | 57 91 | 11 69 | 10 22 | 71 87 | 24 92 | 52 64 | 42 82 | 78 95 |
| 7 | 44 78 | 19 18 | 35 40 | 27 66 | 89 72 | 21 17 | 71 69 | 95 17 | 97 17 | 62 60 |
| 8 | 97 20 | 98 97 | 37 33 | 93 75 | 18 88 | 35 85 | 46 05 | 07 20 | 08 17 | 66 24 |
| 9 | 98 77 | 57 51 | 40 41 | 76 24 | 18 54 | 60 61 | 79 13 | 94 57 | 50 73 | 89 68 |
| 10 | 78 12 | 77 30 | 83 30 | 59 28 | 73 33 | 47 07 | 60 07 | 45 38 | 82 10 | 73 19 |
| 11 | 41 19 | 70 62 | 43 46 | 06 13 | 22 38 | 31 18 | 64 60 | 07 14 | 49 16 | 28 16 |
| 12 | 70 64 | 30 55 | 67 46 | 95 79 | 63 66 | 82 56 | 67 10 | 76 77 | 03 22 | 42 18 |
| 13 | 06 56 | 09 89 | 68 87 | 79 19 | 35 94 | 66 18 | 17 94 | 72 81 | 72 77 | 92 39 |
| 14 | 29 46 | 18 28 | 08 88 | 48 56 | 49 44 | 67 82 | 72 67 | 28 83 | 10 26 | 58 13 |
| 15 | 42 14 | 55 51 | 72 95 | 29 25 | 15 18 | 25 68 | 48 92 | 87 16 | 78 43 | 17 47 |
| 16 | 33 75 | 87 15 | 15 23 | 13 79 | 62 73 | 76 69 | 09 77 | 82 65 | 72 47 | 59 56 |
| 17 | 09 80 | 99 61 | 98 08 | 34 11 | 88 79 | 08 32 | 46 78 | 33 58 | 44 16 | 12 23 |
| 18 | 98 31 | 57 50 | 85 80 | 53 39 | 05 92 | 54 42 | 29 01 | 35 23 | 09 84 | 96 64 |
| 19 | 51 70 | 52 55 | 83 12 | 95 02 | 79 11 | 49 79 | 87 95 | 98 48 | 88 68 | 64 77 |
| 20 | 27 83 | 61 07 | 49 05 | 46 20 | 35 78 | 31 34 | 42 50 | 68 11 | 42 14 | 29 77 |
| 21 | 78 84 | 69 15 | 64 42 | 92 39 | 36 08 | 56 39 | 35 02 | 92 78 | 46 63 | 82 98 |
| 22 | 22 12 | 89 66 | 49 09 | 99 10 | 62 53 | 19 31 | 81 83 | 50 43 | 37 42 | 10 00 |
| 23 | 69 41 | 59 54 | 82 72 | 44 66 | 64 03 | 76 59 | 12 12 | 41 56 | 34 90 | 26 06 |
| 24 | 54 99 | 46 54 | 51 38 | 59 07 | 64 21 | 81 17 | 88 47 | 23 05 | 63 43 | 08 67 |
| 25 | 99 91 | 82 79 | 92 62 | 44 24 | 01 34 | 45 16 | 33 56 | 17 78 | 42 86 | 70 94 |

### Thirty-second Thousand

| | 1–4 | 5–8 | 9–12 | 13–16 | 17–20 | 21–24 | 25–28 | 29–32 | 33–36 | 37–40 |
|---|---|---|---|---|---|---|---|---|---|---|
| 1 | 54 96 | 58 70 | 68 38 | 49 37 | 08 25 | 51 28 | 42 09 | 45 96 | 78 84 | 34 59 |
| 2 | 88 37 | 31 01 | 58 97 | 65 10 | 96 97 | 32 75 | 65 73 | 06 01 | 60 19 | 68 10 |
| 3 | 49 40 | 84 90 | 19 91 | 75 41 | 55 63 | 98 25 | 01 69 | 29 57 | 72 77 | 75 95 |
| 4 | 21 18 | 87 99 | 98 48 | 38 12 | 64 18 | 78 50 | 43 97 | 04 07 | 85 18 | 98 87 |
| 5 | 06 31 | 99 51 | 27 13 | 43 21 | 07 55 | 90 35 | 29 84 | 08 70 | 66 03 | 18 96 |
| 6 | 58 56 | 75 14 | 19 32 | 35 15 | 47 05 | 38 54 | 92 08 | 08 72 | 79 66 | 65 20 |
| 7 | 83 00 | 61 74 | 76 68 | 58 67 | 31 58 | 77 93 | 92 44 | 94 16 | 01 29 | 32 19 |
| 8 | 51 45 | 05 35 | 16 73 | 80 43 | 44 64 | 19 14 | 52 22 | 81 62 | 79 68 | 13 37 |
| 9 | 90 55 | 27 93 | 33 06 | 76 42 | 16 08 | 16 81 | 86 15 | 09 79 | 30 86 | 74 77 |
| 10 | 68 65 | 05 79 | 82 57 | 78 22 | 37 41 | 82 44 | 07 43 | 98 89 | 78 23 | 96 04 |
| 11 | 51 84 | 34 98 | 03 38 | 87 12 | 79 88 | 57 88 | 46 81 | 62 56 | 94 91 | 06 59 |
| 12 | 85 23 | 92 01 | 84 05 | 83 64 | 12 95 | 51 44 | 00 64 | 68 86 | 53 05 | 26 16 |
| 13 | 31 95 | 14 27 | 80 20 | 36 96 | 81 84 | 88 55 | 60 47 | 22 39 | 70 56 | 66 41 |
| 14 | 91 55 | 02 31 | 42 31 | 54 72 | 45 32 | 43 76 | 89 95 | 74 04 | 79 33 | 46 91 |
| 15 | 46 80 | 10 25 | 92 61 | 83 83 | 58 58 | 71 46 | 29 95 | 72 38 | 89 05 | 26 05 |
| 16 | 07 78 | 66 31 | 63 37 | 30 38 | 95 57 | 84 99 | 85 32 | 91 28 | 06 85 | 67 13 |
| 17 | 48 69 | 61 99 | 15 93 | 98 43 | 38 84 | 46 49 | 84 89 | 44 51 | 75 42 | 45 17 |
| 18 | 70 69 | 68 47 | 02 10 | 60 99 | 02 84 | 41 36 | 81 65 | 44 08 | 49 93 | 49 62 |
| 19 | 98 63 | 62 58 | 95 62 | 61 53 | 28 49 | 20 20 | 21 49 | 45 35 | 01 57 | 45 65 |
| 20 | 76 50 | 34 97 | 87 14 | 65 07 | 59 45 | 02 56 | 89 50 | 85 03 | 42 65 | 07 35 |
| 21 | 23 47 | 83 35 | 73 08 | 83 52 | 47 19 | 79 85 | 26 07 | 53 80 | 00 33 | 18 07 |
| 22 | 18 38 | 27 88 | 50 09 | 58 11 | 96 83 | 05 86 | 49 61 | 35 03 | 46 63 | 88 48 |
| 23 | 93 93 | 51 63 | 96 33 | 82 81 | 58 02 | 19 36 | 55 80 | 74 84 | 14 63 | 79 22 |
| 24 | 65 23 | 13 22 | 01 10 | 20 01 | 11 15 | 36 43 | 39 49 | 19 24 | 77 70 | 95 08 |
| 25 | 77 19 | 27 34 | 65 55 | 62 52 | 47 73 | 09 34 | 58 38 | 28 28 | 18 15 | 82 65 |

*Reproduced from page 20 of *Tracts for Computers* XXIV, Cambridge University Press, 1939, by permission of Professor E. S. Pearson.

## TABLE VIII

### Squares and Square Roots*

| $n$ | $n^2$ | $\sqrt{n}$ | $\sqrt{10n}$ | $n$ | $n^2$ | $\sqrt{n}$ | $\sqrt{10n}$ |
|---|---|---|---|---|---|---|---|
| **1.00** | 1.0000 | 1.00000 | 3.16228 | **1.50** | 2.2500 | 1.22474 | 3.87298 |
| 1.01 | 1.0201 | 1.00499 | 3.17805 | 1.51 | 2.2801 | 1.22882 | 3.88587 |
| 1.02 | 1.0404 | 1.00995 | 3.19374 | 1.52 | 2.3104 | 1.23288 | 3.89872 |
| 1.03 | 1.0609 | 1.01489 | 3.20936 | 1.53 | 2.3409 | 1.23693 | 3.91152 |
| 1.04 | 1.0816 | 1.01980 | 3.22490 | 1.54 | 2.3716 | 1.24097 | 3.92428 |
| 1.05 | 1.1025 | 1.02470 | 3.24037 | 1.55 | 2.4025 | 1.24499 | 3.93700 |
| 1.06 | 1.1236 | 1.02956 | 3.25576 | 1.56 | 2.4336 | 1.24900 | 3.94968 |
| 1.07 | 1.1449 | 1.03441 | 3.27109 | 1.57 | 2.4649 | 1.25300 | 3.96232 |
| 1.08 | 1.1664 | 1.03923 | 3.28634 | 1.58 | 2.4964 | 1.25698 | 3.97492 |
| 1.09 | 1.1881 | 1.04403 | 3.30151 | 1.59 | 2.5281 | 1.26095 | 3.98748 |
| **1.10** | 1.2100 | 1.04881 | 3.31662 | **1.60** | 2.5600 | 1.26491 | 4.00000 |
| 1.11 | 1.2321 | 1.05357 | 3.33167 | 1.61 | 2.5921 | 1.26886 | 4.01248 |
| 1.12 | 1.2544 | 1.05830 | 3.34664 | 1.62 | 2.6244 | 1.27279 | 4.02492 |
| 1.13 | 1.2769 | 1.06301 | 3.36155 | 1.63 | 2.6569 | 1.27671 | 4.03733 |
| 1.14 | 1.2996 | 1.06771 | 3.37639 | 1.64 | 2.6896 | 1.28062 | 4.04969 |
| 1.15 | 1.3225 | 1.07238 | 3.39116 | 1.65 | 2.7225 | 1.28452 | 4.06202 |
| 1.16 | 1.3456 | 1.07703 | 3.40588 | 1.66 | 2.7556 | 1.28841 | 4.07431 |
| 1.17 | 1.3689 | 1.08167 | 3.42053 | 1.67 | 2.7889 | 1.29228 | 4.08656 |
| 1.18 | 1.3924 | 1.08628 | 3.43511 | 1.68 | 2.8224 | 1.29615 | 4.09878 |
| 1.19 | 1.4161 | 1.09087 | 3.44964 | 1.69 | 2.8561 | 1.30000 | 4.11096 |
| **1.20** | 1.4400 | 1.09545 | 3.46410 | **1.70** | 2.8900 | 1.30384 | 4.12311 |
| 1.21 | 1.4641 | 1.10000 | 3.47851 | 1.71 | 2.9241 | 1.30767 | 4.13521 |
| 1.22 | 1.4884 | 1.10454 | 3.49285 | 1.72 | 2.9584 | 1.31149 | 4.14729 |
| 1.23 | 1.5129 | 1.10905 | 3.50714 | 1.73 | 2.9929 | 1.31529 | 4.15933 |
| 1.24 | 1.5376 | 1.11355 | 3.52136 | 1.74 | 3.0276 | 1.31909 | 4.17133 |
| 1.25 | 1.5625 | 1.11803 | 3.53553 | 1.75 | 3.0625 | 1.32288 | 4.18330 |
| 1.26 | 1.5876 | 1.12250 | 3.54965 | 1.76 | 3.0976 | 1.32665 | 4.19524 |
| 1.27 | 1.6129 | 1.12694 | 3.56371 | 1.77 | 3.1329 | 1.33041 | 4.20714 |
| 1.28 | 1.6384 | 1.13137 | 3.57771 | 1.78 | 3.1684 | 1.33417 | 4.21900 |
| 1.29 | 1.6641 | 1.13578 | 3.59166 | 1.79 | 3.2041 | 1.33791 | 4.23084 |
| **1.30** | 1.6900 | 1.14018 | 3.60555 | **1.80** | 3.2400 | 1.34164 | 4.24264 |
| 1.31 | 1.7161 | 1.14455 | 3.61939 | 1.81 | 3.2761 | 1.34536 | 4.25441 |
| 1.32 | 1.7424 | 1.14891 | 3.63318 | 1.82 | 3.3124 | 1.34907 | 4.26615 |
| 1.33 | 1.7689 | 1.15326 | 3.64692 | 1.83 | 3.3489 | 1.35277 | 4.27785 |
| 1.34 | 1.7956 | 1.15758 | 3.66060 | 1.84 | 3.3856 | 1.35647 | 4.28952 |
| 1.35 | 1.8225 | 1.16190 | 3.67423 | 1.85 | 3.4225 | 1.36015 | 4.30116 |
| 1.36 | 1.8496 | 1.16619 | 3.68782 | 1.86 | 3.4596 | 1.36382 | 4.31277 |
| 1.37 | 1.8769 | 1.17047 | 3.70135 | 1.87 | 3.4969 | 1.36748 | 4.32435 |
| 1.38 | 1.9044 | 1.17473 | 3.71484 | 1.88 | 3.5344 | 1.37113 | 4.33590 |
| 1.39 | 1.9321 | 1.17898 | 3.72827 | 1.89 | 3.5721 | 1.37477 | 4.34741 |
| **1.40** | 1.9600 | 1.18322 | 3.74166 | **1.90** | 3.6100 | 1.37840 | 4.35890 |
| 1.41 | 1.9881 | 1.18743 | 3.75500 | 1.91 | 3.6481 | 1.38203 | 4.37035 |
| 1.42 | 2.0164 | 1.19164 | 3.76829 | 1.92 | 3.6864 | 1.38564 | 4.38178 |
| 1.43 | 2.0449 | 1.19583 | 3.78153 | 1.93 | 3.7249 | 1.38924 | 4.39318 |
| 1.44 | 2.0736 | 1.20000 | 3.79473 | 1.94 | 3.7636 | 1.39284 | 4.40454 |
| 1.45 | 2.1025 | 1.20416 | 3.80789 | 1.95 | 3.8025 | 1.39642 | 4.41588 |
| 1.46 | 2.1316 | 1.20830 | 3.82099 | 1.96 | 3.8416 | 1.40000 | 4.42719 |
| 1.47 | 2.1609 | 1.21244 | 3.83406 | 1.97 | 3.8809 | 1.40357 | 4.43847 |
| 1.48 | 2.1904 | 1.21655 | 3.84708 | 1.98 | 3.9204 | 1.40712 | 4.44972 |
| 1.49 | 2.2201 | 1.22066 | 3.86005 | 1.99 | 3.9601 | 1.41067 | 4.46094 |

*This Table is reproduced, by permission, from the *Macmillan Tables*, The Macmillan Company, New York.

## TABLE VIII (Cont'd)

### Squares and Square Roots

| $n$ | $n^2$ | $\sqrt{n}$ | $\sqrt{10n}$ | $n$ | $n^2$ | $\sqrt{n}$ | $\sqrt{10n}$ |
|---|---|---|---|---|---|---|---|
| **2.00** | 4.0000 | 1.41421 | 4.47214 | **2.50** | 6.2500 | 1.58114 | 5.00000 |
| 2.01 | 4.0401 | 1.41774 | 4.48330 | 2.51 | 6.3001 | 1.58430 | 5.00999 |
| 2.02 | 4.0804 | 1.42127 | 4.49444 | 2.52 | 6.3504 | 1.58745 | 5.01996 |
| 2.03 | 4.1209 | 1.42478 | 4.50555 | 2.53 | 6.4009 | 1.59060 | 5.02991 |
| 2.04 | 4.1616 | 1.42829 | 4.51664 | 2.54 | 6.4516 | 1.59374 | 5.03984 |
| 2.05 | 4.2025 | 1.43178 | 4.52769 | 2.55 | 6.5025 | 1.59687 | 5.04975 |
| 2.06 | 4.2436 | 1.43527 | 4.53872 | 2.56 | 6.5536 | 1.60000 | 5.05964 |
| 2.07 | 4.2849 | 1.43875 | 4.54973 | 2.57 | 6.6049 | 1.60312 | 5.06952 |
| 2.08 | 4.3264 | 1.44222 | 4.56070 | 2.58 | 6.6564 | 1.60624 | 5.07937 |
| 2.09 | 4.3681 | 1.44568 | 4.57165 | 2.59 | 6.7081 | 1.60935 | 5.08920 |
| **2.10** | 4.4100 | 1.44914 | 4.58258 | **2.60** | 6.7600 | 1.61245 | 5.09902 |
| 2.11 | 4.4521 | 1.45258 | 4.59347 | 2.61 | 6.8121 | 1.61555 | 5.10882 |
| 2.12 | 4.4944 | 1.45602 | 4.60435 | 2.62 | 6.8644 | 1.61864 | 5.11859 |
| 2.13 | 4.5369 | 1.45945 | 4.61519 | 2.63 | 6.9169 | 1.62173 | 5.12835 |
| 2.14 | 4.5796 | 1.46287 | 4.62601 | 2.64 | 6.9696 | 1.62481 | 5.13809 |
| 2.15 | 4.6225 | 1.46629 | 4.63681 | 2.65 | 7.0225 | 1.62788 | 5.14782 |
| 2.16 | 4.6656 | 1.46969 | 4.64758 | 2.66 | 7.0756 | 1.63095 | 5.15752 |
| 2.17 | 4.7089 | 1.47309 | 4.65833 | 2.67 | 7.1289 | 1.63401 | 5.16720 |
| 2.18 | 4.7524 | 1.47648 | 4.66905 | 2.68 | 7.1824 | 1.63707 | 5.17687 |
| 2.19 | 4.7961 | 1.47986 | 4.67974 | 2.69 | 7.2361 | 1.64012 | 5.18652 |
| **2.20** | 4.8400 | 1.48324 | 4.69042 | **2.70** | 7.2900 | 1.64317 | 5.19615 |
| 2.21 | 4.8841 | 1.48661 | 4.70106 | 2.71 | 7.3441 | 1.64621 | 5.20577 |
| 2.22 | 4.9284 | 1.48997 | 4.71169 | 2.72 | 7.3984 | 1.64924 | 5.21536 |
| 2.23 | 4.9729 | 1.49332 | 4.72229 | 2.73 | 7.4529 | 1.65227 | 5.22494 |
| 2.24 | 5.0176 | 1.49666 | 4.73286 | 2.74 | 7.5076 | 1.65529 | 5.23450 |
| 2.25 | 5.0625 | 1.50000 | 4.74342 | 2.75 | 7.5625 | 1.65831 | 5.24404 |
| 2.26 | 5.1076 | 1.50333 | 4.75395 | 2.76 | 7.6176 | 1.66132 | 5.25357 |
| 2.27 | 5.1529 | 1.50665 | 4.76445 | 2.77 | 7.6729 | 1.66433 | 5.26308 |
| 2.28 | 5.1984 | 1.50997 | 4.77493 | 2.78 | 7.7284 | 1.66733 | 5.27257 |
| 2.29 | 5.2441 | 1.51327 | 4.78539 | 2.79 | 7.7841 | 1.67033 | 5.28205 |
| **2.30** | 5.2900 | 1.51658 | 4.79583 | **2.80** | 7.8400 | 1.67332 | 5.29150 |
| 2.31 | 5.3361 | 1.51987 | 4.80625 | 2.81 | 7.8961 | 1.67631 | 5.30094 |
| 2.32 | 5.3824 | 1.52315 | 4.81664 | 2.82 | 7.9524 | 1.67929 | 5.31037 |
| 2.33 | 5.4289 | 1.52643 | 4.82701 | 2.83 | 8.0089 | 1.68226 | 5.31977 |
| 2.34 | 5.4756 | 1.52971 | 4.83735 | 2.84 | 8.0656 | 1.68523 | 5.32917 |
| 2.35 | 5.5225 | 1.53297 | 4.84768 | 2.85 | 8.1225 | 1.68819 | 5.33854 |
| 2.36 | 5.5696 | 1.53623 | 4.85798 | 2.86 | 8.1796 | 1.69115 | 5.34790 |
| 2.37 | 5.6169 | 1.53948 | 4.86826 | 2.87 | 8.2369 | 1.69411 | 5.35724 |
| 2.38 | 5.6644 | 1.54272 | 4.87852 | 2.88 | 8.2944 | 1.69706 | 5.36656 |
| 2.39 | 5.7121 | 1.54596 | 4.88876 | 2.89 | 8.3521 | 1.70000 | 5.37587 |
| **2.40** | 5.7600 | 1.54919 | 4.89898 | **2.90** | 8.4100 | 1.70294 | 5.38516 |
| 2.41 | 5.8081 | 1.55242 | 4.90918 | 2.91 | 8.4681 | 1.70587 | 5.39444 |
| 2.42 | 5.8564 | 1.55563 | 4.91935 | 2.92 | 8.5264 | 1.70880 | 5.40370 |
| 2.43 | 5.9049 | 1.55885 | 4.92950 | 2.93 | 8.5849 | 1.71172 | 5.41295 |
| 2.44 | 5.9536 | 1.56205 | 4.93964 | 2.94 | 8.6436 | 1.71464 | 5.42218 |
| 2.45 | 6.0025 | 1.56525 | 4.94975 | 2.95 | 8.7025 | 1.71756 | 5.43139 |
| 2.46 | 6.0516 | 1.56844 | 4.95984 | 2.96 | 8.7616 | 1.72047 | 5.44059 |
| 2.47 | 6.1009 | 1.57162 | 4.96991 | 2.97 | 8.8209 | 1.72337 | 5.44977 |
| 2.48 | 6.1504 | 1.57480 | 4.97996 | 2.98 | 8.8804 | 1.72627 | 5.45894 |
| 2.49 | 6.2001 | 1.57797 | 4.98999 | 2.99 | 8.9401 | 1.72916 | 5.46809 |

## TABLE VIII (Cont'd)

### Squares and Square Roots

| $n$ | $n^2$ | $\sqrt{n}$ | $\sqrt{10n}$ | $n$ | $n^2$ | $\sqrt{n}$ | $\sqrt{10n}$ |
|---|---|---|---|---|---|---|---|
| **3.00** | 9.0000 | 1.73205 | 5.47723 | **3.50** | 12.2500 | 1.87083 | 5.91608 |
| 3.01 | 9.0601 | 1.73494 | 5.48635 | 3.51 | 12.3201 | 1.87350 | 5.92453 |
| 3.02 | 9.1204 | 1.73781 | 5.49545 | 3.52 | 12.3904 | 1.87617 | 5.93296 |
| 3.03 | 9.1809 | 1.74069 | 5.50454 | 3.53 | 12.4609 | 1.87883 | 5.94138 |
| 3.04 | 9.2416 | 1.74356 | 5.51362 | 3.54 | 12.5316 | 1.88149 | 5.94979 |
| 3.05 | 9.3025 | 1.74642 | 5.52268 | 3.55 | 12.6025 | 1.88414 | 5.95819 |
| 3.06 | 9.3636 | 1.74929 | 5.53173 | 3.56 | 12.6736 | 1.88680 | 5.96657 |
| 3.07 | 9.4249 | 1.75214 | 5.54076 | 3.57 | 12.7449 | 1.88944 | 5.97495 |
| 3.08 | 9.4864 | 1.75499 | 5.54977 | 3.58 | 12.8164 | 1.89209 | 5.98331 |
| 3.09 | 9.5481 | 1.75784 | 5.55878 | 3.59 | 12.8881 | 1.89473 | 5.99166 |
| **3.10** | 9.6100 | 1.76068 | 5.56776 | **3.60** | 12.9600 | 1.89737 | 6.00000 |
| 3.11 | 9.6721 | 1.76352 | 5.57674 | 3.61 | 13.0321 | 1.90000 | 6.00833 |
| 3.12 | 9.7344 | 1.76635 | 5.58570 | 3.62 | 13.1044 | 1.90263 | 6.01664 |
| 3.13 | 9.7969 | 1.76918 | 5.59464 | 3.63 | 13.1769 | 1.90526 | 6.02495 |
| 3.14 | 9.8596 | 1.77200 | 5.60357 | 3.64 | 13.2496 | 1.90788 | 6.03324 |
| 3.15 | 9.9225 | 1.77482 | 5.61249 | 3.65 | 13.3225 | 1.91050 | 6.04152 |
| 3.16 | 9.9856 | 1.77764 | 5.62139 | 3.66 | 13.3956 | 1.91311 | 6.04979 |
| 3.17 | 10.0489 | 1.78045 | 5.63028 | 3.67 | 13.4689 | 1.91572 | 6.05805 |
| 3.18 | 10.1124 | 1.78326 | 5.63915 | 3.68 | 13.5424 | 1.91833 | 6.06630 |
| 3.19 | 10.1761 | 1.78606 | 5.64801 | 3.69 | 13.6161 | 1.92094 | 6.07454 |
| **3.20** | 10.2400 | 1.78885 | 5.65685 | **3.70** | 13.6900 | 1.92354 | 6.08276 |
| 3.21 | 10.3041 | 1.79165 | 5.66569 | 3.71 | 13.7641 | 1.92614 | 6.09098 |
| 3.22 | 10.3684 | 1.79444 | 5.67450 | 3.72 | 13.8384 | 1.92873 | 6.09918 |
| 3.23 | 10.4329 | 1.79722 | 5.68331 | 3.73 | 13.9129 | 1.93132 | 6.10737 |
| 3.24 | 10.4976 | 1.80000 | 5.69210 | 3.74 | 13.9876 | 1.93391 | 6.11555 |
| 3.25 | 10.5625 | 1.80278 | 5.70088 | 3.75 | 14.0625 | 1.93649 | 6.12372 |
| 3.26 | 10.6276 | 1.80555 | 5.70964 | 3.76 | 14.1376 | 1.93907 | 6.13188 |
| 3.27 | 10.6929 | 1.80831 | 5.71839 | 3.77 | 14.2129 | 1.94165 | 6.14003 |
| 3.28 | 10.7584 | 1.81108 | 5.72713 | 3.78 | 14.2884 | 1.94422 | 6.14817 |
| 3.29 | 10.8241 | 1.81384 | 5.73585 | 3.79 | 14.3641 | 1.94679 | 6.15630 |
| **3.30** | 10.8900 | 1.81659 | 5.74456 | **3.80** | 14.4400 | 1.94936 | 6.16441 |
| 3.31 | 10.9561 | 1.81934 | 5.75326 | 3.81 | 14.5161 | 1.95192 | 6.17252 |
| 3.32 | 11.0224 | 1.82209 | 5.76194 | 3.82 | 14.5924 | 1.95448 | 6.18061 |
| 3.33 | 11.0889 | 1.82483 | 5.77062 | 3.83 | 14.6689 | 1.95704 | 6.18870 |
| 3.34 | 11.1556 | 1.82757 | 5.77927 | 3.84 | 14.7456 | 1.95959 | 6.19677 |
| 3.35 | 11.2225 | 1.83030 | 5.78792 | 3.85 | 14.8225 | 1.96214 | 6.20484 |
| 3.36 | 11.2896 | 1.83303 | 5.79655 | 3.86 | 14.8996 | 1.96469 | 6.21289 |
| 3.37 | 11.3569 | 1.83576 | 5.80517 | 3.87 | 14.9769 | 1.96723 | 6.22093 |
| 3.38 | 11.4244 | 1.83848 | 5.81378 | 3.88 | 15.0544 | 1.96977 | 6.22896 |
| 3.39 | 11.4921 | 1.84120 | 5.82237 | 3.89 | 15.1321 | 1.97231 | 6.23699 |
| **3.40** | 11.5600 | 1.84391 | 5.83095 | **3.90** | 15.2100 | 1.97484 | 6.24500 |
| 3.41 | 11.6281 | 1.84662 | 5.83952 | 3.91 | 15.2881 | 1.97737 | 6.25300 |
| 3.42 | 11.6964 | 1.84932 | 5.84808 | 3.92 | 15.3664 | 1.97990 | 6.26099 |
| 3.43 | 11.7649 | 1.85203 | 5.85662 | 3.93 | 15.4449 | 1.98242 | 6.26897 |
| 3.44 | 11.8336 | 1.85472 | 5.86515 | 3.94 | 15.5236 | 1.98494 | 6.27694 |
| 3.45 | 11.9025 | 1.85742 | 5.87367 | 3.95 | 15.6025 | 1.98746 | 6.28490 |
| 3.46 | 11.9716 | 1.86011 | 5.88218 | 3.96 | 15.6816 | 1.98997 | 6.29285 |
| 3.47 | 12.0409 | 1.86279 | 5.89067 | 3.97 | 15.7609 | 1.99249 | 6.30079 |
| 3.48 | 12.1104 | 1.86548 | 5.89915 | 3.98 | 15.8404 | 1.99499 | 6.30872 |
| 3.49 | 12.1801 | 1.86815 | 5.90762 | **3.99** | 15.9201 | 1.99750 | 6.31664 |

## TABLE VIII (Cont'd)

### Squares and Square Roots

| $n$ | $n^2$ | $\sqrt{n}$ | $\sqrt{10n}$ | $n$ | $n^2$ | $\sqrt{n}$ | $\sqrt{10n}$ |
|------|---------|-----------|-----------|------|---------|-----------|-----------|
| **4.00** | 16.0000 | 2.00000 | 6.32456 | **4.50** | 20.2500 | 2.12132 | 6.70820 |
| 4.01 | 16.0801 | 2.00250 | 6.33246 | 4.51 | 20.3401 | 2.12368 | 6.71565 |
| 4.02 | 16.1604 | 2.00499 | 6.34035 | 4.52 | 20.4304 | 2.12603 | 6.72309 |
| 4.03 | 16.2409 | 2.00749 | 6.34823 | 4.53 | 20.5209 | 2.12838 | 6.73053 |
| 4.04 | 16.3216 | 2.00998 | 6.35610 | 4.54 | 20.6116 | 2.13073 | 6.73795 |
| 4.05 | 16.4025 | 2.01246 | 6.36396 | 4.55 | 20.7025 | 2.13307 | 6.74537 |
| 4.06 | 16.4836 | 2.01494 | 6.37181 | 4.56 | 20.7936 | 2.13542 | 6.75278 |
| 4.07 | 16.5649 | 2.01742 | 6.37966 | 4.57 | 20.8849 | 2.13776 | 6.76018 |
| 4.08 | 16.6464 | 2.01990 | 6.38749 | 4.58 | 20.9764 | 2.14009 | 6.76757 |
| 4.09 | 16.7281 | 2.02237 | 6.39531 | 4.59 | 21.0681 | 2.14243 | 6.77495 |
| **4.10** | 16.8100 | 2.02485 | 6.40312 | **4.60** | 21.1600 | 2.14476 | 6.78233 |
| 4.11 | 16.8921 | 2.02731 | 6.41093 | 4.61 | 21.2521 | 2.14709 | 6.78970 |
| 4.12 | 16.9744 | 2.02978 | 6.41872 | 4.62 | 21.3444 | 2.14942 | 6.79706 |
| 4.13 | 17.0569 | 2.03224 | 6.42651 | 4.63 | 21.4369 | 2.15174 | 6.80441 |
| 4.14 | 17.1396 | 2.03470 | 6.43428 | 4.64 | 21.5296 | 2.15407 | 6.81175 |
| 4.15 | 17.2225 | 2.03715 | 6.44205 | 4.65 | 21.6225 | 2.15639 | 6.81909 |
| 4.16 | 17.3056 | 2.03961 | 6.44981 | 4.66 | 21.7156 | 2.15870 | 6.82642 |
| 4.17 | 17.3889 | 2.04206 | 6.45755 | 4.67 | 21.8089 | 2.16102 | 6.83374 |
| 4.18 | 17.4724 | 2.04450 | 6.46529 | 4.68 | 21.9024 | 2.16333 | 6.84105 |
| 4.19 | 17.5561 | 2.04695 | 6.47302 | 4.69 | 21.9961 | 2.16564 | 6.84836 |
| **4.20** | 17.6400 | 2.04939 | 6.48074 | **4.70** | 22.0900 | 2.16795 | 6.85565 |
| 4.21 | 17.7241 | 2.05183 | 6.48845 | 4.71 | 22.1841 | 2.17025 | 6.86294 |
| 4.22 | 17.8084 | 2.05426 | 6.49615 | 4.72 | 22.2784 | 2.17256 | 6.87023 |
| 4.23 | 17.8929 | 2.05670 | 6.50384 | 4.73 | 22.3729 | 2.17486 | 6.87750 |
| 4.24 | 17.9776 | 2.05913 | 6.51153 | 4.74 | 22.4676 | 2.17715 | 6.88477 |
| 4.25 | 18.0625 | 2.06155 | 6.51920 | 4.75 | 22.5625 | 2.17945 | 6.89202 |
| 4.26 | 18.1476 | 2.06398 | 6.52687 | 4.76 | 22.6576 | 2.18174 | 6.89928 |
| 4.27 | 18.2329 | 2.06640 | 6.53452 | 4.77 | 22.7529 | 2.18403 | 6.90652 |
| 4.28 | 18.3184 | 2.06882 | 6.54217 | 4.78 | 22.8484 | 2.18632 | 6.91375 |
| 4.29 | 18.4041 | 2.07123 | 6.54981 | 4.79 | 22.9441 | 2.18861 | 6.92098 |
| **4.30** | 18.4900 | 2.07364 | 6.55744 | **4.80** | 23.0400 | 2.19089 | 6.92820 |
| 4.31 | 18.5761 | 2.07605 | 6.56506 | 4.81 | 23.1361 | 2.19317 | 6.93542 |
| 4.32 | 18.6624 | 2.07846 | 6.57267 | 4.82 | 23.2324 | 2.19545 | 6.94262 |
| 4.33 | 18.7489 | 2.08087 | 6.58027 | 4.83 | 23.3289 | 2.19773 | 6.94982 |
| 4.34 | 18.8356 | 2.08327 | 6.58787 | 4.84 | 23.4256 | 2.20000 | 6.95701 |
| 4.35 | 18.9225 | 2.08567 | 6.59545 | 4.85 | 23.5225 | 2.20227 | 6.96419 |
| 4.36 | 19.0096 | 2.08806 | 6.60303 | 4.86 | 23.6196 | 2.20454 | 6.97137 |
| 4.37 | 19.0969 | 2.09045 | 6.61060 | 4.87 | 23.7169 | 2.20681 | 6.97854 |
| 4.38 | 19.1844 | 2.09284 | 6.61816 | 4.88 | 23.8144 | 2.20907 | 6.98570 |
| 4.39 | 19.2721 | 2.09523 | 6.62571 | 4.89 | 23.9121 | 2.21133 | 6.99285 |
| **4.40** | 19.3600 | 2.09762 | 6.63325 | **4.90** | 24.0100 | 2.21359 | 7.00000 |
| 4.41 | 19.4481 | 2.10000 | 6.64078 | 4.91 | 24.1081 | 2.21585 | 7.00714 |
| 4.42 | 19.5364 | 2.10238 | 6.64831 | 4.92 | 24.2064 | 2.21811 | 7.01427 |
| 4.43 | 19.6249 | 2.10476 | 6.65582 | 4.93 | 24.3049 | 2.22036 | 7.02140 |
| 4.44 | 19.7136 | 2.10713 | 6.66333 | 4.94 | 24.4036 | 2.22261 | 7.02851 |
| 4.45 | 19.8025 | 2.10950 | 6.67083 | 4.95 | 24.5025 | 2.22486 | 7.03562 |
| 4.46 | 19.8916 | 2.11187 | 6.67832 | 4.96 | 24.6016 | 2.22711 | 7.04273 |
| 4.47 | 19.9809 | 2.11424 | 6.68581 | 4.97 | 24.7009 | 2.22935 | 7.04982 |
| 4.48 | 20.0704 | 2.11660 | 6.69328 | 4.98 | 24.8004 | 2.23159 | 7.05691 |
| 4.49 | 20.1601 | 2.11896 | 6.70075 | 4.99 | 24.9001 | 2.23383 | 7.06399 |

## TABLE VIII (Cont'd)

### Squares and Square Roots

| $n$ | $n^2$ | $\sqrt{n}$ | $\sqrt{10n}$ | $n$ | $n^2$ | $\sqrt{n}$ | $\sqrt{10n}$ |
|---|---|---|---|---|---|---|---|
| **5.00** | 25.0000 | 2.23607 | 7.07107 | **5.50** | 30.2500 | 2.34521 | 7.41620 |
| 5.01 | 25.1001 | 2.23830 | 7.07814 | 5.51 | 30.3601 | 2.34734 | 7.42294 |
| 5.02 | 25.2004 | 2.24054 | 7.08520 | 5.52 | 30.4704 | 2.34947 | 7.42967 |
| 5.03 | 25.3009 | 2.24277 | 7.09225 | 5.53 | 30.5809 | 2.35160 | 7.43640 |
| 5.04 | 25.4016 | 2.24499 | 7.09930 | 5.54 | 30.6916 | 2.35372 | 7.44312 |
| 5.05 | 25.5025 | 2.24722 | 7.10634 | 5.55 | 30.8025 | 2.35584 | 7.44983 |
| 5.06 | 25.6036 | 2.24944 | 7.11337 | 5.56 | 30.9136 | 2.35797 | 7.45654 |
| 5.07 | 25.7049 | 2.25167 | 7.12039 | 5.57 | 31.0249 | 2.36008 | 7.46324 |
| 5.08 | 25.8064 | 2.25389 | 7.12741 | 5.58 | 31.1364 | 2.36220 | 7.46994 |
| 5.09 | 25.9081 | 2.25610 | 7.13442 | 5.59 | 31.2481 | 2.36432 | 7.47663 |
| **5.10** | 26.0100 | 2.25832 | 7.14143 | **5.60** | 31.3600 | 2.36643 | 7.48331 |
| 5.11 | 26.1121 | 2.26053 | 7.14843 | 5.61 | 31.4721 | 2.36854 | 7.48999 |
| 5.12 | 26.2144 | 2.26274 | 7.15542 | 5.62 | 31.5844 | 2.37065 | 7.49667 |
| 5.13 | 26.3169 | 2.26495 | 7.16240 | 5.63 | 31.6969 | 2.37276 | 7.50333 |
| 5.14 | 26.4196 | 2.26716 | 7.16938 | 5.64 | 31.8096 | 2.37487 | 7.50999 |
| 5.15 | 26.5225 | 2.26936 | 7.17635 | 5.65 | 31.9225 | 2.37697 | 7.51665 |
| 5.16 | 26.6256 | 2.27156 | 7.18331 | 5.66 | 32.0356 | 2.37908 | 7.52330 |
| 5.17 | 26.7289 | 2.27376 | 7.19027 | 5.67 | 32.1489 | 2.38118 | 7.52994 |
| 5.18 | 26.8324 | 2.27596 | 7.19722 | 5.68 | 32.2624 | 2.38238 | 7.53658 |
| 5.19 | 26.9361 | 2.27816 | 7.20417 | 5.69 | 32.3761 | 2.38537 | 7.54321 |
| **5.20** | 27.0400 | 2.28035 | 7.21110 | **5.70** | 32.4900 | 2.38747 | 7.54983 |
| 5.21 | 27.1441 | 2.28254 | 7.21803 | 5.71 | 32.6041 | 2.38956 | 7.55645 |
| 5.22 | 27.2484 | 2.28473 | 7.22496 | 5.72 | 32.7184 | 2.39165 | 7.56307 |
| 5.23 | 27.3529 | 2.28692 | 7.23187 | 5.73 | 32.8329 | 2.39374 | 7.56968 |
| 5.24 | 27.4576 | 2.28910 | 7.23878 | 5.74 | 32.9476 | 2.39583 | 7.57628 |
| 5.25 | 27.5625 | 2.29129 | 7.24569 | 5.75 | 33.0625 | 2.39792 | 7.58288 |
| 5.26 | 27.6676 | 2.29347 | 7.25259 | 5.76 | 33.1776 | 2.40000 | 7.58947 |
| 5.27 | 27.7729 | 2.29565 | 7.25948 | 5.77 | 33.2929 | 2.40208 | 7.59605 |
| 5.28 | 27.8784 | 2.29783 | 7.26636 | 5.78 | 33.4084 | 2.40416 | 7.60263 |
| 5.29 | 27.9841 | 2.30000 | 7.27324 | 5.79 | 33.5241 | 2.40624 | 7.60920 |
| **5.30** | 28.0900 | 2.30217 | 7.28011 | **5.80** | 33.6400 | 2.40832 | 7.61577 |
| 5.31 | 28.1961 | 2.30434 | 7.28697 | 5.81 | 33.7561 | 2.41039 | 7.62234 |
| 5.32 | 28.3024 | 2.30651 | 7.29383 | 5.82 | 33.8724 | 2.41247 | 7.62889 |
| 5.33 | 28.4089 | 2.30868 | 7.30068 | 5.83 | 33.9889 | 2.41454 | 7.63544 |
| 5.34 | 28.5156 | 2.31084 | 7.30753 | 5.84 | 34.1056 | 2.41661 | 7.64199 |
| 5.35 | 28.6225 | 2.31301 | 7.31437 | 5.85 | 34.2225 | 2.41868 | 7.64853 |
| 5.36 | 28.7296 | 2.31517 | 7.32120 | 5.86 | 34.3396 | 2.42074 | 7.65506 |
| 5.37 | 28.8369 | 2.31733 | 7.32803 | 5.87 | 34.4569 | 2.42281 | 7.66159 |
| 5.38 | 28.9444 | 2.31948 | 7.33485 | 5.88 | 34.5744 | 2.42487 | 7.66812 |
| 5.39 | 29.0521 | 2.32164 | 7.34166 | 5.89 | 34.6921 | 2.42693 | 7.67463 |
| **5.40** | 29.1600 | 2.32379 | 7.34847 | **5.90** | 34.8100 | 2.42899 | 7.68115 |
| 5.41 | 29.2681 | 2.32594 | 7.35527 | 5.91 | 34.9281 | 2.43105 | 7.68765 |
| 5.42 | 29.3764 | 2.32809 | 7.36206 | 5.92 | 35.0464 | 2.43311 | 7.69415 |
| 5.43 | 29.4849 | 2.33024 | 7.36885 | 5.93 | 35.1649 | 2.43516 | 7.70065 |
| 5.44 | 29.5936 | 2.33238 | 7.37564 | 5.94 | 35.2836 | 2.43721 | 7.70714 |
| 5.45 | 29.7025 | 2.33452 | 7.38241 | 5.95 | 35.4025 | 2.43926 | 7.71362 |
| 5.46 | 29.8116 | 2.33666 | 7.38918 | 5.96 | 35.5216 | 2.44131 | 7.72010 |
| 5.47 | 29.9209 | 2.33880 | 7.39594 | 5.97 | 35.6409 | 2.44336 | 7.72658 |
| 5.48 | 30.0304 | 2.34094 | 7.40270 | 5.98 | 35.7604 | 2.44540 | 7.73305 |
| 5.49 | 30.1401 | 2.34307 | 7.40945 | 5.99 | 35.8801 | 2.44745 | 7.73951 |

## TABLE VIII (Cont'd)

### Squares and Square Roots

| $n$ | $n^2$ | $\sqrt{n}$ | $\sqrt{10n}$ | $n$ | $n^2$ | $\sqrt{n}$ | $\sqrt{10n}$ |
|------|---------|---------|---------|------|---------|---------|---------|
| **6.00** | 36.0000 | 2.44949 | 7.74597 | **6.50** | 42.2500 | 2.54951 | 8.06226 |
| 6.01 | 36.1201 | 2.45153 | 7.75242 | 6.51 | 42.3801 | 2.55147 | 8.06846 |
| 6.02 | 36.2404 | 2.45357 | 7.75887 | 6.52 | 42.5104 | 2.55343 | 8.07465 |
| 6.03 | 36.3609 | 2.45561 | 7.76531 | 6.53 | 42.6409 | 2.55539 | 8.08084 |
| 6.04 | 36.4816 | 2.45764 | 7.77174 | 6.54 | 42.7716 | 2.55734 | 8.08703 |
| 6.05 | 36.6025 | 2.45967 | 7.77817 | 6.55 | 42.9025 | 2.55930 | 8.09321 |
| 6.06 | 36.7236 | 2.46171 | 7.78460 | 6.56 | 43.0336 | 2.56125 | 8.09938 |
| 6.07 | 36.8449 | 2.46374 | 7.79102 | 6.57 | 43.1649 | 2.56320 | 8.10555 |
| 6.08 | 36.9664 | 2.46577 | 7.79744 | 6.58 | 43.2964 | 2.56515 | 8.11172 |
| 6.09 | 37.0881 | 2.46779 | 7.80385 | 6.59 | 43.4281 | 2.56710 | 8.11788 |
| **6.10** | 37.2100 | 2.46982 | 7.81025 | **6.60** | 43.5600 | 2.56905 | 8.12404 |
| 6.11 | 37.3321 | 2.47184 | 7.81665 | 6.61 | 43.6921 | 2.57099 | 8.13019 |
| 6.12 | 37.4544 | 2.47386 | 7.82304 | 6.62 | 43.8244 | 2.57294 | 8.13634 |
| 6.13 | 37.5769 | 2.47588 | 7.82943 | 6.63 | 43.9569 | 2.57488 | 8.14248 |
| 6.14 | 37.6996 | 2.47790 | 7.83582 | 6.64 | 44.0896 | 2.57682 | 8.14862 |
| 6.15 | 37.8225 | 2.47992 | 7.84219 | 6.65 | 44.2225 | 2.57876 | 8.15475 |
| 6.16 | 37.9456 | 2.48193 | 7.84857 | 6.66 | 44.3556 | 2.58070 | 8.16088 |
| 6.17 | 38.0689 | 2.48395 | 7.85493 | 6.67 | 44.4889 | 2.58263 | 8.16701 |
| 6.18 | 38.1924 | 2.48596 | 7.86130 | 6.68 | 44.6224 | 2.58457 | 8.17313 |
| 6.19 | 38.3161 | 2.48797 | 7.86766 | 6.69 | 44.7561 | 2.58650 | 8.17924 |
| **6.20** | 38.4400 | 2.48998 | 7.87401 | **6.70** | 44.8900 | 2.58844 | 8.18535 |
| 6.21 | 38.5641 | 2.49199 | 7.88036 | 6.71 | 45.0241 | 2.59037 | 8.19146 |
| 6.22 | 38.6884 | 2.49399 | 7.88670 | 6.72 | 45.1584 | 2.59230 | 8.19756 |
| 6.23 | 38.8129 | 2.49600 | 7.89303 | 6.73 | 45.2929 | 2.59422 | 8.20366 |
| 6.24 | 38.9376 | 2.49800 | 7.89937 | 6.74 | 45.4276 | 2.59615 | 8.20975 |
| 6.25 | 39.0625 | 2.50000 | 7.90569 | 6.75 | 45.5625 | 2.59808 | 8.21584 |
| 6.26 | 39.1876 | 2.50200 | 7.91202 | 6.76 | 45.6976 | 2.60000 | 8.22192 |
| 6.27 | 39.3129 | 2.50400 | 7.91833 | 6.77 | 45.8329 | 2.60192 | 8.22800 |
| 6.28 | 39.4384 | 2.50599 | 7.92465 | 6.78 | 45.9684 | 2.60384 | 8.23408 |
| 6.29 | 39.5641 | 2.50799 | 7.93095 | 6.79 | 46.1041 | 2.60576 | 8.24015 |
| **6.30** | 39.6900 | 2.50998 | 7.93725 | **6.80** | 46.2400 | 2.60768 | 8.24621 |
| 6.31 | 39.8161 | 2.51197 | 7.94355 | 6.81 | 46.3761 | 2.60960 | 8.25227 |
| 6.32 | 39.9424 | 2.51396 | 7.94984 | 6.82 | 46.5124 | 2.61151 | 8.25833 |
| 6.33 | 40.0689 | 2.51595 | 7.95613 | 6.83 | 46.6489 | 2.61343 | 8.26438 |
| 6.34 | 40.1956 | 2.51794 | 7.96241 | 6.84 | 46.7856 | 2.61534 | 8.27043 |
| 6.35 | 40.3225 | 2.51992 | 7.96869 | 6.85 | 46.9225 | 2.61725 | 8.27647 |
| 6.36 | 40.4496 | 2.52190 | 7.97496 | 6.86 | 47.0596 | 2.61916 | 8.28251 |
| 6.37 | 40.5769 | 2.52389 | 7.98123 | 6.87 | 47.1969 | 2.62107 | 8.28855 |
| 6.38 | 40.7044 | 2.52587 | 7.98749 | 6.88 | 47.3344 | 2.62298 | 8.29458 |
| 6.39 | 40.8321 | 2.52784 | 7.99375 | 6.89 | 47.4721 | 2.62488 | 8.30060 |
| **6.40** | 40.9600 | 2.52982 | 8.00000 | **6.90** | 47.6100 | 2.62679 | 8.30662 |
| 6.41 | 41.0881 | 2.53180 | 8.00625 | 6.91 | 47.7481 | 2.62869 | 8.31264 |
| 6.42 | 41.2164 | 2.53377 | 8.01249 | 6.92 | 47.8864 | 2.63059 | 8.31865 |
| 6.43 | 41.3449 | 2.53574 | 8.01873 | 6.93 | 48.0249 | 2.63249 | 8.32466 |
| 6.44 | 41.4736 | 2.53772 | 8.02496 | 6.94 | 48.1636 | 2.63439 | 8.33067 |
| 6.45 | 41.6025 | 2.53969 | 8.03119 | 6.95 | 48.3025 | 2.63629 | 8.33667 |
| 6.46 | 41.7316 | 2.54165 | 8.03741 | 6.96 | 48.4416 | 2.63818 | 8.34266 |
| 6.47 | 41.8609 | 2.54362 | 8.04363 | 6.97 | 48.5809 | 2.64008 | 8.34865 |
| 6.48 | 41.9904 | 2.54558 | 8.04984 | 6.98 | 48.7204 | 2.64197 | 8.35464 |
| 6.49 | 42.1201 | 2.54755 | 8.05605 | 6.99 | 48.8601 | 2.64386 | 8.36062 |

## TABLE VIII (Cont'd)

### Squares and Square Roots

| $n$ | $n^2$ | $\sqrt{n}$ | $\sqrt{10n}$ | $n$ | $n^2$ | $\sqrt{n}$ | $\sqrt{10n}$ |
|---|---|---|---|---|---|---|---|
| **7.00** | 49.0000 | 2.64575 | 8.36660 | **7.50** | 56.2500 | 2.73861 | 8.66025 |
| 7.01 | 49.1401 | 2.64764 | 8.37257 | 7.51 | 56.4001 | 2.74044 | 8.66603 |
| 7.02 | 49.2804 | 2.64953 | 8.37854 | 7.52 | 56.5504 | 2.74226 | 8.67179 |
| 7.03 | 49.4209 | 2.65141 | 8.38451 | 7.53 | 56.7009 | 2.74408 | 8.67756 |
| 7.04 | 49.5616 | 2.65330 | 8.39047 | 7.54 | 56.8516 | 2.74591 | 8.68332 |
| 7.05 | 49.7025 | 2.65518 | 8.39643 | 7.55 | 57.0025 | 2.74773 | 8.68907 |
| 7.06 | 49.8436 | 2.65707 | 8.40238 | 7.56 | 57.1536 | 2.74955 | 8.69483 |
| 7.07 | 49.9849 | 2.65895 | 8.40833 | 7.57 | 57.3049 | 2.75136 | 8.70057 |
| 7.08 | 50.1264 | 2.66083 | 8.41427 | 7.58 | 57.4564 | 2.75318 | 8.70632 |
| 7.09 | 50.2681 | 2.66271 | 8.42021 | 7.59 | 57.6081 | 2.75500 | 8.71206 |
| **7.10** | 50.4100 | 2.66458 | 8.42615 | **7.60** | 57.7600 | 2.75681 | 8.71780 |
| 7.11 | 50.5521 | 2.66646 | 8.43208 | 7.61 | 57.9121 | 2.75862 | 8.72353 |
| 7.12 | 50.6944 | 2.66833 | 8.43801 | 7.62 | 58.0644 | 2.76043 | 8.72926 |
| 7.13 | 50.8369 | 2.67021 | 8.44393 | 7.63 | 58.2169 | 2.76225 | 8.73499 |
| 7.14 | 50.9796 | 2.67208 | 8.44985 | 7.64 | 58.3696 | 2.76405 | 8.74071 |
| 7.15 | 51.1225 | 2.67395 | 8.45577 | 7.65 | 58.5225 | 2.76586 | 8.74643 |
| 7.16 | 51.2656 | 2.67582 | 8.46168 | 7.66 | 58.6756 | 2.76767 | 8.75214 |
| 7.17 | 51.4089 | 2.67769 | 8.46759 | 7.67 | 58.8289 | 2.76948 | 8,75785 |
| 7.18 | 51.5524 | 2.67955 | 8.47349 | 7.68 | 58.9824 | 2.77128 | 8.76356 |
| 7.19 | 51.6961 | 2.68142 | 8.47939 | 7.69 | 59.1361 | 2.77308 | 8.76926 |
| **7.20** | 51.8400 | 2.68328 | 8.48528 | **7.70** | 59.2900 | 2.77489 | 8.77496 |
| 7.21 | 51.9841 | 2.68514 | 8.49117 | 7.71 | 59.4441 | 2.77669 | 8.78066 |
| 7.22 | 52.1284 | 2.68701 | 8.49706 | 7.72 | 59.5984 | 2.77849 | 8.78635 |
| 7.23 | 52.2729 | 2.68887 | 8.50294 | 7.73 | 59.7529 | 2.78029 | 8.79204 |
| 7.24 | 52.4176 | 2.69072 | 8.50882 | 7.74 | 59.9076 | 2.78209 | 8.79773 |
| 7.25 | 52.5625 | 2.69258 | 8.51469 | 7.75 | 60.0625 | 2.78388 | 8.80341 |
| 7.26 | 52.7076 | 2.69444 | 8.52056 | 7.76 | 60.2176 | 2.78568 | 8.80909 |
| 7.27 | 52.8529 | 2.69629 | 8.52643 | 7.77 | 60.3729 | 2.78747 | 8.81476 |
| 7.28 | 52.9984 | 2.69815 | 8.53229 | 7.78 | 60.5284 | 2.78927 | 8.82043 |
| 7.29 | 53.1441 | 2.70000 | 8.53815 | 7.79 | 60.6841 | 2.79106 | 8.82610 |
| **7.30** | 53.2900 | 2.70185 | 8.54400 | **7.80** | 60.8400 | 2.79285 | 8.83176 |
| 7.31 | 53.4361 | 2.70370 | 8.54985 | 7.81 | 60.9961 | 2.79464 | 8.83742 |
| 7.32 | 53.5824 | 2.70555 | 8.55570 | 7.82 | 61.1524 | 2.79643 | 8.84308 |
| 7.33 | 53.7289 | 2.70740 | 8.56154 | 7.83 | 61.3089 | 2.79821 | 8.84873 |
| 7.34 | 53.8756 | 2.70924 | 8.56738 | 7.84 | 61.4656 | 2.80000 | 8.85438 |
| 7.35 | 54.0225 | 2.71109 | 8.57321 | 7.85 | 61.6225 | 2.80179 | 8.86002 |
| 7.36 | 54.1696 | 2.71293 | 8.57904 | 7.86 | 61.7796 | 2.80357 | 8.86566 |
| 7.37 | 54.3169 | 2.71477 | 8.58487 | 7.87 | 61.9369 | 2.80535 | 8.87130 |
| 7.38 | 54.4644 | 2.71662 | 8.59069 | 7.88 | 62.0944 | 2.80713 | 8.87694 |
| 7.39 | 54.6121 | 2.71846 | 8.59651 | 7.89 | 62.2521 | 2.80891 | 8.88257 |
| **7.40** | 54.7600 | 2.72029 | 8.60233 | **7.90** | 62.4100 | 2.81069 | 8.88819 |
| 7.41 | 54.9081 | 2.72213 | 8.60814 | 7.91 | 62.5681 | 2.81247 | 8.89382 |
| 7.42 | 55.0564 | 2.72397 | 8.61394 | 7.92 | 62.7264 | 2.81425 | 8.89944 |
| 7.43 | 55.2049 | 2.72580 | 8.61974 | 7.93 | 62.8849 | 2.81603 | 8.90505 |
| 7.44 | 55.3536 | 2.72764 | 8.62554 | 7.94 | 63.0436 | 2.81780 | 8.91067 |
| 7.45 | 55.5025 | 2.72947 | 8.63134 | 7.95 | 63.2025 | 2.81957 | 8.91628 |
| 7.46 | 55.6516 | 2.73130 | 8.63713 | 7.96 | 63.3616 | 2.82135 | 8.92188 |
| 7.47 | 55.8009 | 2.73313 | 8.64292 | 7.97 | 63.5209 | 2.82312 | 8.92749 |
| 7.48 | 55.9504 | 2.73496 | 8.64870 | 7.98 | 63.6804 | 2.82489 | 8.93308 |
| 7.49 | 56.1001 | 2.73679 | 8.65448 | 7.99 | 63.8401 | 2.82666 | 8.93868 |

## TABLE VIII (Cont'd)

### Squares and Square Roots

| $n$ | $n^2$ | $\sqrt{n}$ | $\sqrt{10n}$ | $n$ | $n^2$ | $\sqrt{n}$ | $\sqrt{10n}$ |
|---|---|---|---|---|---|---|---|
| **8.00** | 64.0000 | 2.82843 | 8.94427 | **8.50** | 72.2500 | 2.91548 | 9.21954 |
| 8.01 | 64.1601 | 2.83019 | 8.94986 | 8.51 | 72.4201 | 2.91719 | 9.22497 |
| 8.02 | 64.3204 | 2.83196 | 8.95545 | 8.52 | 72.5904 | 2.91890 | 9.23038 |
| 8.03 | 64.4809 | 2.83373 | 8.96103 | 8.53 | 72.7609 | 2.92062 | 9.23580 |
| 8.04 | 64.6416 | 2.83549 | 8.96660 | 8.54 | 72.9316 | 2.92233 | 9.24121 |
| 8.05 | 64.8025 | 2.83725 | 8.97218 | 8.55 | 73.1025 | 2.92404 | 9.24662 |
| 8.06 | 64.9636 | 2.83901 | 8.97775 | 8.56 | 73.2736 | 2.92575 | 9.25203 |
| 8.07 | 65.1249 | 2.84077 | 8.98332 | 8.57 | 73.4449 | 2.92746 | 9.25743 |
| 8.08 | 65.2864 | 2.84253 | 8.98888 | 8.58 | 73.6164 | 2.92916 | 9.26283 |
| 8.09 | 65.4481 | 2.84429 | 8.99444 | 8.59 | 73.7881 | 2.93087 | 9.26823 |
| **8.10** | 65.6100 | 2.84605 | 9.00000 | **8.60** | 73.9600 | 2.93258 | 9.27362 |
| 8.11 | 65.7721 | 2.84781 | 9.00555 | 8.61 | 74.1321 | 2.93428 | 9.27901 |
| 8.12 | 65.9344 | 2.84956 | 9.01110 | 8.62 | 74.3044 | 2.93598 | 9.28440 |
| 8.13 | 66.0969 | 2.85132 | 9.01665 | 8.63 | 74.4769 | 2.93769 | 9.28978 |
| 8.14 | 66.2596 | 2.85307 | 9.02219 | 8.64 | 74.6496 | 2.93939 | 9.29516 |
| 8.15 | 66.4225 | 2.85482 | 9.02774 | 8.65 | 74.8225 | 2.94109 | 9.30054 |
| 8.16 | 66.5856 | 2.85657 | 9.03327 | 8.66 | 74.9956 | 2.94279 | 9.30591 |
| 8.17 | 66.7489 | 2.85832 | 9.03881 | 8.67 | 75.1689 | 2.94449 | 9.31128 |
| 8.18 | 66.9124 | 2.86007 | 9.04434 | 8.68 | 75.3424 | 2.94618 | 9.31665 |
| 8.19 | 67.0761 | 2.86182 | 9.04986 | 8.69 | 75.5161 | 2.94788 | 9.32202 |
| **8.20** | 67.2400 | 2.86356 | 9.05539 | **8.70** | 75.6900 | 2.94958 | 9.32738 |
| 8.21 | 67.4041 | 2.86531 | 9.06091 | 8.71 | 75.8641 | 2.95127 | 9.33274 |
| 8.22 | 67.5684 | 2.86705 | 9.06642 | 8.72 | 76.0384 | 2.95296 | 9.33809 |
| 8.23 | 67.7329 | 2.86880 | 9.07193 | 8.73 | 76.2129 | 2.95466 | 9.34345 |
| 8.24 | 67.8976 | 2.87054 | 9.07744 | 8.74 | 76.3876 | 2.95635 | 9.34880 |
| 8.25 | 68.0625 | 2.87228 | 9.08295 | 8.75 | 76.5625 | 2.95804 | 9.35414 |
| 8.26 | 68.2276 | 2.87402 | 9.08845 | 8.76 | 76.7376 | 2.95973 | 9.35949 |
| 8.27 | 68.3929 | 2.87576 | 9.09395 | 8.77 | 76.9129 | 2.96142 | 9.36483 |
| 8.28 | 68.5584 | 2.87750 | 9.09945 | 8.78 | 77.0884 | 2.96311 | 9.37017 |
| 8.29 | 68.7241 | 2.87924 | 9.10494 | 8.79 | 77.2641 | 2.96479 | 9.37550 |
| **8.30** | 68.8900 | 2.88097 | 9.11043 | **8.80** | 77.4400 | 2.96648 | 9.38083 |
| 8.31 | 69.0561 | 2.88271 | 9.11592 | 8.81 | 77.6161 | 2.96816 | 9.38616 |
| 8.32 | 69.2224 | 2.88444 | 9.12140 | 8.82 | 77.7924 | 2.96985 | 9.39149 |
| 8.33 | 69.3889 | 2.88617 | 9.12688 | 8.83 | 77.9689 | 2.97153 | 9.39681 |
| 8.34 | 69.5556 | 2.88791 | 9.13236 | 8.84 | 78.1456 | 2.97321 | 9.40213 |
| 8.35 | 69.7225 | 2.88964 | 9.13783 | 8.85 | 78.3225 | 2.97489 | 9.40744 |
| 8.36 | 69.8896 | 2.89137 | 9.14330 | 8.86 | 78.4996 | 2.97658 | 9.41276 |
| 8.37 | 70.0569 | 2.89310 | 9.14877 | 8.87 | 78.6769 | 2.97825 | 9.41807 |
| 8.38 | 70.2244 | 2.89482 | 9.15423 | 8.88 | 78.8544 | 2.97993 | 9.42338 |
| 8.39 | 70.3921 | 2.89655 | 9.15969 | 8.89 | 79.0321 | 2.98161 | 9.42868 |
| **8.40** | 70.5600 | 2.89828 | 9.16515 | **8.90** | 79.2100 | 2.98329 | 9.43398 |
| 8.41 | 70.7281 | 2.90000 | 9.17061 | 8.91 | 79.3881 | 2.98496 | 9.43928 |
| 8.42 | 70.8964 | 2.90172 | 9.17606 | 8.92 | 79.5664 | 2.98664 | 9.44458 |
| 8.43 | 71.0649 | 2.90345 | 9.18150 | 8.93 | 79.7449 | 2.98831 | 9.44987 |
| 8.44 | 71.2336 | 2.90517 | 9.18695 | 8.94 | 79.9236 | 2.98998 | 9.45516 |
| 8.45 | 71.4025 | 2.90689 | 9.19239 | 8.95 | 80.1025 | 2.99166 | 9.46044 |
| 8.46 | 71.5716 | 2.90861 | 9.19783 | 8.96 | 80.2816 | 2.99333 | 9.46573 |
| 8.47 | 71.7409 | 2.91033 | 9.20326 | 8.97 | 80.4609 | 2.99500 | 9.47101 |
| 8.48 | 71.9104 | 2.91204 | 9.20869 | 8.98 | 80.6404 | 2.99666 | 9.47629 |
| 8.49 | 72.0801 | 2.91376 | 9.21412 | 8.99 | 80.8201 | 2.99833 | 9.48156 |

## TABLE VIII (Cont'd)

### Squares and Square Roots

| $n$ | $n^2$ | $\sqrt{n}$ | $\sqrt{10n}$ | $n$ | $n^2$ | $\sqrt{n}$ | $\sqrt{10n}$ |
|---|---|---|---|---|---|---|---|
| **9.00** | 81.0000 | 3.00000 | 9.48683 | **9.50** | 90.2500 | 3.08221 | 9.74679 |
| 9.01 | 81.1801 | 3.00167 | 9.49210 | 9.51 | 90.4401 | 3.08383 | 9.75192 |
| 9.02 | 81.3604 | 3.00333 | 9.49737 | 9.52 | 90.6304 | 3.08545 | 9.75705 |
| 9.03 | 81.5409 | 3.00500 | 9.50263 | 9.53 | 90.8209 | 3.08707 | 9.76217 |
| 9.04 | 81.7216 | 3.00666 | 9.50789 | 9.54 | 91.0116 | 3.08869 | 9.76729 |
| 9.05 | 81.9025 | 3.00832 | 9.51315 | 9.55 | 91.2025 | 3.09031 | 9.77241 |
| 9.06 | 82.0836 | 3.00998 | 9.51840 | 9.56 | 91.3936 | 3.09192 | 9.77753 |
| 9.07 | 82.2649 | 3.01164 | 9.52365 | 9.57 | 91.5849 | 3.09354 | 9.78264 |
| 9.08 | 82.4464 | 3.01330 | 9.52890 | 9.58 | 91.7764 | 3.09516 | 9.78775 |
| 9.09 | 82.6281 | 3.01496 | 9.53415 | 9.59 | 91.9681 | 3.09677 | 9.79285 |
| **9.10** | 82.8100 | 3.01662 | 9.53939 | **9.60** | 92.1600 | 3.09839 | 9.79796 |
| 9.11 | 82.9921 | 3.01828 | 9.54463 | 9.61 | 92.3521 | 3.10000 | 9.80306 |
| 9.12 | 83.1744 | 3.01993 | 9.54987 | 9.62 | 92.5444 | 3.10161 | 9.80816 |
| 9.13 | 83.3569 | 3.02159 | 9.55510 | 9.63 | 92.7369 | 3.10322 | 9.81326 |
| 9.14 | 83.5396 | 3.02324 | 9.56033 | 9.64 | 92.9296 | 3.10483 | 9.81835 |
| 9.15 | 83.7225 | 3.02490 | 9.56556 | 9.65 | 93.1225 | 3.10644 | 9.82344 |
| 9.16 | 83.9056 | 3.02655 | 9.57079 | 9.66 | 93.3156 | 3.10805 | 9.82853 |
| 9.17 | 84.0889 | 3.02820 | 9.57601 | 9.67 | 93.5089 | 3.10966 | 9.83362 |
| 9.18 | 84.2724 | 3.02985 | 9.58123 | 9.68 | 93.7024 | 3.11127 | 9.83870 |
| 9.19 | 84.4561 | 3.03150 | 9.58645 | 9.69 | 93.8961 | 3.11288 | 9.84378 |
| **9.20** | 84.6400 | 3.03315 | 9.59166 | **9.70** | 94.0900 | 3.11448 | 9.84886 |
| 9.21 | 84.8241 | 3.03480 | 9.59687 | 9.71 | 94.2841 | 3.11609 | 9.85393 |
| 9.22 | 85.0084 | 3.03645 | 9.60208 | 9.72 | 94.4784 | 3.11769 | 9.85901 |
| 9.23 | 85.1929 | 3.03809 | 9.60729 | 9.73 | 94.6729 | 3.11929 | 9.86408 |
| 9.24 | 85.3776 | 3.03974 | 9.61249 | 9.74 | 94.8676 | 3.12090 | 9.86914 |
| 9.25 | 85.5625 | 3.04138 | 9.61769 | 9.75 | 95.0625 | 3.12250 | 9.87421 |
| 9.26 | 85.7476 | 3.04302 | 9.62289 | 9.76 | 95.2576 | 3.12410 | 9.87927 |
| 9.27 | 85.9329 | 3.04467 | 9.62808 | 9.77 | 95.4529 | 3.12570 | 9.88433 |
| 9.28 | 86.1184 | 3.04631 | 9.63328 | 9.78 | 95.6484 | 3.12730 | 9.88939 |
| 9.29 | 86.3041 | 3.04795 | 9.63846 | 9.79 | 95.8441 | 3.12890 | 9.89444 |
| **9.30** | 86.4900 | 3.04959 | 9.64365 | **9.80** | 96.0400 | 3.13050 | 9.89949 |
| 9.31 | 86.6761 | 3.05123 | 9.64883 | 9.81 | 96.2361 | 3.13209 | 9.90454 |
| 9.32 | 86.8624 | 3.05287 | 9.65401 | 9.82 | 96.4324 | 3.13369 | 9.90959 |
| 9.33 | 87.0489 | 3.05450 | 9.65919 | 9.83 | 96.6289 | 3.13528 | 9.91464 |
| 9.34 | 87.2356 | 3.05614 | 9.66437 | 9.84 | 96.8256 | 3.13688 | 9.91968 |
| 9.35 | 87.4225 | 3.05778 | 9.66954 | 9.85 | 97.0225 | 3.13847 | 9.92472 |
| 9.36 | 87.6096 | 3.05941 | 9.67471 | 9.86 | 97.2196 | 3.14006 | 9.92975 |
| 9.37 | 87.7969 | 3.06105 | 9.67988 | 9.87 | 97.4169 | 3.14166 | 9.93479 |
| 9.38 | 87.9844 | 3.06268 | 9.68504 | 9.88 | 97.6144 | 3.14325 | 9.93982 |
| 9.39 | 88.1721 | 3.06431 | 9.69020 | 9.89 | 97.8121 | 3.14484 | 9.94485 |
| **9.40** | 88.3600 | 3.06594 | 9.69536 | **9.90** | 98.0100 | 3.14643 | 9.94987 |
| 9.41 | 88.5481 | 3.06757 | 9.70052 | 9.91 | 98.2081 | 3.14802 | 9.95490 |
| 9.42 | 88.7364 | 3.06920 | 9.70567 | 9.92 | 98.4064 | 3.14960 | 9.95992 |
| 9.43 | 88.9249 | 3.07083 | 9.71082 | 9.93 | 98.6049 | 3.15119 | 9.96494 |
| 9.44 | 89.1136 | 3.07246 | 9.71597 | 9.94 | 98.8036 | 3.15278 | 9.96995 |
| 9.45 | 89.3025 | 3.07409 | 9.72111 | 9.95 | 99.0025 | 3.15436 | 9.97497 |
| 9.46 | 89.4916 | 3.07571 | 9.72625 | 9.96 | 99.2016 | 3.15595 | 9.97998 |
| 9.47 | 89.6809 | 3.07734 | 9.73139 | 9.97 | 99.4009 | 3.15753 | 9.98499 |
| 9.48 | 89.8704 | 3.07896 | 9.73653 | 9.98 | 99.6004 | 3.15911 | 9.98999 |
| 9.49 | 90.0601 | 3.08058 | 9.74166 | 9.99 | 99.8001 | 3.16070 | 9.99500 |

# Answers

1. (a) $x_1 + x_2 + x_3 + x_4 + x_5 + x_6$.
   (b) $x_2^2 + x_3^2 + x_4^2$.
   (c) $(x_1 + y_1) + (x_2 + y_2) + (x_3 + y_3)$.
   (d) $(x_1 - 3) + (x_2 - 3) + (x_3 - 3) + (x_4 - 3)$.
   (e) $x_3 y_3 z_3 + x_4 y_4 z_4 + x_5 y_5 z_5 + x_6 y_6 z_6 + x_7 y_7 z_7$.
   (f) $x_i^2 f_1 + x_2^2 f_2 + x_3^2 f_3 + x_4^2 f_4 + x_5^2 f_5$.

3. (a) 8.  (b) 10.  (c) 47.  (d) 8.  (e) 23.  (f) $-3$.

1. For example, 80–89, 90–99, 100–109, 110–119, 120–129, 130–139, 140–149, 150–159, 160–169, 170–179; the corresponding class marks are 84.5, 94.5, 104.5, 114.5, 124.5, 134.5, 144.5, 154.5, 164.5, and 174.5.

3. (a) \$9.5, \$19.5, \$29.5, \$39.5, \$49.5.
   (b) \$14.5, \$24.5, \$34.5, \$44.5.
   (c) \$10.

5. (a) 5–9, 10–14, 15–19, 20–24, 25–29, 30–34.
   (b) 7, 12, 17, 22, 27, 32.
   (c) 5.

7. 10–24, 25–39, 40–54, 55–69, 70–84, 85–99.

9. Using the class limits 10–19, 20–29, ..., 110–119, the respective frequencies are 1, 1, 4, 21, 38, 43, 41, 20, 12, 0, and 2.

11. The class frequencies are 2, 6, 12, 38, 26, 13, 7, 8, 5, and 3; less than .50 there are 0, less than .60 there are 2, less than .70 there are 8, less than .80 there are 20, less than .90 there are 58, less than 1.00 there are 84, less than 1.10 there are 97, less than 1.20 there are 104, less than 1.30 there are 112, less than 1.40 there are 117, and less than 1.50 there are 120.

13: The class frequencies are 1, 0, 7, 15, 31, 46, 27, 14, 9, and 0; the "or more" percentages are 100.0, 99.3, 99.3, 94.7, 84.7, 64.0, 33.3, 15.3, 6.0, and 0.0.

**15.** Using the class intervals 16.0–16.9, 17.0–17.9, ..., 25.0–25.9, the frequencies are 1, 2, 15, 38, 26, 9, 5, 3, 0, and 1. Less than 16.0 there are 0, less than 17.0 there is 1, less than 18.0 there are 3, less than 19.0 there are 18, less than 20.0 there are 56, less than 21.0 there are 82, less than 22.0 there are 91, less than 23.0 there are 96, less than 24.0 there are 99, less than 25.0 there are 99, and less than 26.0 there are 100.

**17:** The class frequencies are 4, 1, 3, 12, 25, 36, 20, 4, and 1; beginning with 39, the "or less" frequencies are 0, 4, 5, 8, 20, 45, 81, 101, 105, and 106.

### Page 44

**1.** (a) The data constitute a sample if inferences are to be drawn about male freshmen entering other universities that fall, about male freshmen entering that university in other years, about female freshmen entering that university, etc.

(b) The data constitute a population if one is interested, say, in calculating the average score obtained by male freshmen entering the particular university in the fall of 1958.

**3.** (a) The data constitute a sample if one is interested, for example, in the salaries paid to elevator operators in New York City throughout 1958.

(b) The data constitute a population if one is interested, for example, to calculate the average salary paid to elevator operators in New York City in April, 1958.

### Page 53

**1.** The mean of the daily high temperature readings is 69.7, that of the daily low readings is 46.4.

**3.** The mean of the weights is 199.5 pounds.

**5.** $13.76.      **7.** 69.66.      **9.** 52.9 mph.

**11.** (a) 0.941. (b) 0.943.      **13.** (a) $30.98. (b) $30.98.

**15.** (a) 3.05. (b) 3.06.      **17.** 64.6 and 64.2.

### Page 62

**1.** 68.      **3.** 8.      **5.** 197 pounds.      **7.** 81.13.

**9.** 0.903.      **11.** $31.43.      **13.** 65.6.

### Page 65

**1.** 53.

**3.** The mode of the high temperatures is 65, the modes of the low temperatures are 43, 46, and 51.

**5.** Apple pie.

## Page 70

**1.** (a) 8. (b) 10. (c) 2.　　　　　 **3.** (a) 144. (b) 4.　　　　　 **5.** 0.264.

**7.** 196.6 pounds.　　　　　 **9.** 9.58 pounds.

## Page 74

**1.** $Q_1 = 58.26$ and $Q_3 = 118.97$.　　 **3.** $Q_1 = 47.16$ and $Q_3 = 89.42$.

**7.** $D_2 = 42.5$ and $D_8 = 96.12$.　　 **9.** $P_{15} = 1.06$ and $P_{85} = 17.0$.

## Page 84

**1.** 100.　　　　 **3.** 2.8.　　　　 **5.** 1.95.　　　　 **7.** 7.3.

## Page 93

**1.** $s = 4$.　　　 **3.** $s = 4.53$.　　　 **5.** $s = 2.28$.　　　 **7.** $s = 6.53$.

**9.** $S = 16.06$ and $\sigma = 16.01$.　　 **13.** $\sigma = 31.2$.

**15.** Brown is 2.33 standard deviations above average for his age group and Green is 1.67 standard deviations above average for his age group; Brown is thus relatively more overweight.

## Page 96

**1.** 60.71 and 30.36.　　 **3.** 47.6%.　　 **5.** 8.2%.　　 **7.** 30.9%.

## Page 105

**1.** $SK = -0.09$.　　　　 **3.** $SK = 0.61$.

## Page 114

**1.** (a) 119.2 and 123.7.　　　 (b) 1.038 and 1.037.

**3.** 83.6.

## Page 117

**3.** 224.9.　　　　 **5.** 167.8.

## Page 120

**1.** The Ideal Index satisfies the time reversal test.

**3.** 124.3.

## Page 133

**1.** (a) $P(B \mid A)$. (b) $P(A \mid B)$. (c) $1 - P(B)$.

**3.** (a) 0. (b) 0. (c) 0.70. (d) 0. (e) 0.30.

**5.** Only (a) and (c) are mutually exclusive.

**7.** 0.70 and 0.30. **9.** 0.10.

**11.** 35/36. **13.** (a) 0.75. (b) 0.65.

## Page 138

**1.** 2/13. **3.** 2/3. **5.** 7/50. **7.** 1/16.

**9.** 2/169. **11.** (a) 1/2197. (b) 1/5525. **13.** 247/1700.

## Page 140

**1.** $0.50. **3.** 0.61 bases. **5.** $0.28.

## Page 147

**1.** In the second location.

**3.** Pessimists: first location; optimists; second location.

**5.** 19, the mid-range.

## Page 153

**1.** The expected frequencies for 0, 1, 2, 3, and 4 heads are 10, 40, 60, 40, and 10, respectively.

**3.** The expected frequencies for 0, 1, 2, 3, 4, and 5 heads are 5, 25, 50, 50, 25, and 5, respectively.

**5.** The expected frequencies for the four suits are 10, 10, 10, and 10.

**7.** The probabilities of being ahead 0, 1, 2, 3, or 4 times are 6/16, 3/16, 2/16, 2/16, and 3/16, respectively.

## Page 160

**1.** 231/1024. **3:** 5103/16384; No.

**5.** 1701/8192. **7.** 63/256.

**9.** The probabilities that 0, 1, 2, or 3 of the patients recover are 1/64, 9/64, 27/64, and 27/64, respectively.

## Page 163

**1.** $\mu = 1.5$ and $\sigma = 0.866$.

**3.** (a) $\mu = 5/3$ and $\sigma = 1.054$. (b) $\mu = 2/5$ and $\sigma = 3/5$.

## Page 175

1. (a) 1.07.  (b) −1.50.  (c) 6.50  (d) −2.18.

3. (a) $z = 1.66$.  (b) $z = 0.49$.  (c) $z = -0.85$.  (d) $z = -0.11$.
   (e) $z = 1.13$.

5. (a) 0.2119.  (b) 0.7357.  (c) 0.0463.

## Page 179

1. (a) 4.55%.  (b) 46.49%.  (c) 2.37 inches.

3. (a) 84.48%.  (b) 0.1738.  (c) $Q_1 = 24.4$ and $Q_3 = 28.8$.

5. 1.65 million.

## Page 183

1. (a) 0.205. (b) 0.2034.  3. 0.1469.

5. 0.064.  7. 0.066.  9. 0.56.

## Page 208

1. $s = 0.73$ and $\sigma_{\bar{x}} = 0.69$.  5. It is divided by 3.

7. 0.83.  9. 0.13.

## Page 220

1. 2057.1–2170.9 vehicles.  3. 105.28–108.72.

5. 2.680–2.706.  7. $53.21–$71.15.

9. 0.004.  11. 327 (rounded up).

## Page 225

1. 80.937–81.363.  3. $229.74–$247.26.

5. It will not exceed $7.26.  7. It will not exceed 0.52 inches.

## Page 232

1. 0.08–0.23.

3. 0.075–0.39.

5. (a) 0.55–0.65.  (b) it will not exceed 0.048.

7. (a) 0.435–0.465.  (b) it will not exceed 0.02.

9. 0.06–0.66.

11. 4161.

13. 136.

## Page 236

**1.** 11.29–13.75.

**3.** 0.19–4.09.

## Page 243

**1.** (a) 0.042. (b) 0.063.

**3.** 0.174.

## Page 246

**1.** *Type I error:* if the average price charged for 3-bedroom homes in the Phoenix area is \$13,000, but this figure is rejected; *Type II error:* if the \$13,000, figure is accepted, whereas actually it is false.

**3.** (a) *Type I error:* if it is decided that Mr. Smith is not competent, whereas actually he is; *Type II error:* if it is decided that Mr. Smith is competent, whereas actually he is not.

(b) *Type I error:* if it is decided that Mr. Smith is competent, whereas actually he is not; *Type II error:* if it is decided that Mr. Smith is not competent, whereas actually he is.

## Page 256

**1.** $z = 2.77$, reject the claim.

**3.** $z = -0.75$, accept the hypothesis or reserve judgment.

**5.** The difference between 311, the observed frequency, and 325, the expected frequency, may reasonably be attributed to chance.

**7.** $z = 1.87$, cannot reject the hypothesis.

**9.** Reject the hypothesis.

## Page 260

**1.** $z = -2.77$, difference is significant.

**3.** $z = 4.56$, difference is significant and the test item is good.

## Page 265

**1.** $z = 5$, reject the hypothesis.

**3.** $z = 2.5$, accept the hypothesis or reserve judgment.

**5.** $z = -2.53$, yes.

**7.** $t = 1.60$, accept the claim or reserve judgment.

## Page 269

1. $z = 1.22$, difference is not significant.

3. $z = 3.21$, difference is significant.

5. $t = 2.15$, difference is not significant.

7. $t = -2.85$, the diet is effective.

## Page 281

1. $\chi^2 = 8.70$, differences are significant.

3. $\chi^2 = 10.73$, reject hypothesis that the proportions are the same for all three materials.

5. $\chi^2 = 27.51$, reject the hypothesis of independence.

## Page 286

1. $\chi^2 = 3.891$, there is a good fit.

3. $\chi^2 = 7.841$, there is a good fit.

7. $\chi^2 = 4.2$, accept the hypothesis that the die is balanced or reserve judgment.

## Page 292

1. $F = 5.95$, differences are significant.

3. $F = 0.59$, differences are not significant.

## Page 300

1. No significant difference.

3. $z = 4.8$; reject hypothesis.

5. $z = 2.23$; reject hypothesis.

## Page 305

1. $z = -0.32$; no significant deviation from randomness.

5. $z = -1.25$; no significant deviation from randomness.

7. $z = 3.46$; significantly non-random.

## Page 318

1. (a) $a = 122.16$ and $b = -1.02$.     (c) 66.06.

3. (a) $y' = 1.52 + 7.03x$.     (c) 5.75

5. $a = -4.58$ and $b = 0.989$.

## Page 331

**1.** $r = -0.94$.    **3.** $r = 0.90$.    **7.** $r = 0.99$.    **9.** $r = 0.78$.

## Page 338

**1.** (a) significant.    (b) significant.    (c) significant.    (d) significant.
(e) not significant.

**3.** $z = 2.35$; significant.

**5.** $z = 2.97$; significant.

## Page 344

**1.** $r = 0.75$.    **3.** $r = 0.60$.

## Page 348

**1.** $r' = 0.79$.    **3.** $r' = 1$.

**5.** $r' = 1$; significant.    **7.** $r' = 0.75$.

## Page 351

**1.** $C = 0.38$.    **3.** (a) $\chi^2 = 85.2$; significant. (b) $C = 0.34$.

## Page 364

**1.** $y' = 92.64 - 2.00x$.

**3.** $y' = 137.22 + 2.33x$; the 1946 and 1954 trend values are 127.90 and 146.54, respectively.

**5.** $y' = 160.05 + 1.39x$.

**7.** $y' = 103.42 + 0.165x$.

## Page 366

**1.** The 1931 through 1953 values of the three-year moving average are 2.4, 1.9, 2.0, 2.9, 3.7, 4.4, 3.9, 3.6, 3.5, 4.3, 3.4, 2.2, 0.8, 0.7, 1.5, 2.9, 4.4, 5.5, 6.5, 7.0, 6.8, 6.5, 6.5.

**3.** The 1930 through 1953 values of the three-year moving average are 19.1, 14.5, 12.1, 10.9, 10.9, 11.2, 11.7, 11.7, 11.9, 11.2, 12.3, 14.2, 18.2, 22.4, 22.6, 31.8, 39.4, 49.2, 58.2, 71.8, 90.3, 106.4, 116.9, 120.3.

## Page 371

**1.** 82.4, 79.1, 86.8, 94.0, 101.7, 109.1, 112.6, 114.7, 114.5, 110.0, 102.6, 92.4.

**3.** 99.5, 100.0, 100.0, 100.7, 100.8, 99.4, 99.6, 100.2, 100.1, 99.4, 100.0, 100.5; apparently there is no annual cyclical pattern.

**5.** 80.4, 80.1, 98.2, 111.0, 140.2, 139.4, 117.0, 105.0, 89.3, 81.8, 75.4, 82.2.

**7.** 2,908, 2,937, 2,953, 2,967, 2,910, 2,959, 2,954, 2,917, 2,933, 2,945, 2,951, 2,938.

# Index